Section Four — Geometry and Measures

Section Five — Pythagoras and Trigonometry

Section Six — Statistics and Probability

Published by CGP

From original material by Richard Parsons.

Updated by: Sammy El-Bahrawy and Tom Miles

With thanks to Dawn Wright for the proofreading.

ISBN: 978 1 78908 071 1

Printed by Elanders Ltd, Newcastle upon Tyne.
Clipart from Corel®

Edexcel International GCSE

Mathematics

It's no secret — International GCSE Maths is *seriously* tricky. But with this brilliant all-in-one CGP book, you'll have everything you need for exam success.

It's packed with straightforward study notes and examples, plus plenty of exam-style questions on each topic. There's even a full set of realistic practice exams!

On top of all that, we've included fully worked answers for every question, plus helpful grade info throughout the book. All your revision-related dreams have come true.

How to access your free Online Edition

This book includes a free Online Edition to read on your PC, Mac or tablet.
You'll just need to go to **cgpbooks.co.uk/extras** and enter this code:

0423 4344 4556 6345

By the way, this code only works for one person. If somebody else has used this book before you, they might have already claimed the Online Edition.

Complete
Revision & Practice

Everything you need to pass the exams!

Contents

Throughout this book you'll see grade stamps like these:
You can use these to focus your revision on easier or harder work.
But remember — to get a top grade you have to know **everything**, not just the hardest topics.

Order of Operations

Welcome to the wonderful world of maths. It may not always be fun, but sadly you've got to learn it all. We'll start off with some nice straightforward stuff on the <u>order of operations</u> — also known as <u>BODMAS</u>.

BODMAS	<u>B</u>rackets, <u>O</u>ther, <u>D</u>ivision & <u>M</u>ultiplication, <u>A</u>ddition & <u>S</u>ubtraction

<u>BODMAS</u> tells you the <u>ORDER</u> in which these operations should be done:

> Work out <u>Brackets</u> first, then <u>Other</u> things like squaring, then
> <u>Divide</u> / <u>Multiply</u> groups of numbers before <u>Adding</u> / <u>Subtracting</u>.
>
> To decide between dividing and multiplying, or between adding
> and subtracting, just work <u>from left to right</u>.

This set of rules works really well, so remember the word BODMAS.

EXAMPLES:

1. **Work out 7 + 9 ÷ 3**

1) Follow BODMAS — do the <u>division</u> first... $7 + 9 \div 3$

2) ...then the <u>addition</u>: $= 7 + 3$

$= 10$

If you don't follow BODMAS, you get:
$7 + 9 \div 3 = 16 \div 3$
$= 5.333... ✗$

2. **Calculate 15 − 7²**

1) The square is an 'other' so that's first: $15 - 7^2$

2) Then do the <u>subtraction</u>: $= 15 - 49$

$= -34$

3. **Find (5 + 3) × (12 − 3)**

1) Start by working out the <u>brackets</u>: $(5 + 3) \times (12 - 3)$

2) And now the <u>multiplication</u>: $= 8 \times 9$

$= 72$

4. $e = (f - 7)^2 + \dfrac{4g}{h+1}$, **where f = 4, g = 3, h = −2.**
Work out the value of e.

1) Write down the formula: $e = (f - 7)^2 + \dfrac{4g}{h+1}$

2) Put the numbers in: $e = (4 - 7)^2 + \dfrac{4 \times 3}{-2+1}$

3) Then work it out <u>in stages</u>: $= (-3)^2 + \dfrac{12}{-1}$

$= 9 + \dfrac{12}{-1}$

$= 9 + -12$

$= -3$

Work <u>brackets</u> out first.

Around the top and bottom of a fraction there are '<u>invisible brackets</u>'. You just have to imagine they're there.

Then <u>other</u> stuff — in this case square the first bit.

Then <u>divide</u>.

Finally <u>add or subtract</u>.

Putting brackets round the negative number makes it clear that −3 is squared, not just 3.

Make sure you're confident with this before moving on

BODMAS comes up all the time (even if you don't realise it), so it's really important that you can do it without getting confused. The good thing is, you're going to get loads of practice at it during your revision.

Calculator Buttons

This page covers some really important stuff about using <u>calculators</u>.

Know Your **Buttons**

Look for these buttons on your calculator — they might be a bit different on yours.

 The <u>reciprocal</u> button. The reciprocal of a number is <u>1 divided by it</u>. So the reciprocal of 2 is ½.

 The <u>cube root</u> button. You might have to press <u>shift</u> first.

Ans This uses your <u>last answer</u> in your current calculation. Super useful.

 Flips your answer from a <u>fraction or surd</u> to a <u>decimal</u> and vice versa.

BODMAS on Your Calculator

BODMAS questions can be packed with <u>tricky decimals</u> and maybe a <u>square root</u> and <u>sin/cos/tan</u>. You <u>could</u> do it on your calculator in one go, but that runs the risk of losing precious marks.

Work out $\left(\dfrac{64\cos 80°}{0.48 + \sqrt{0.79}}\right)^3$.

Write down all the figures on your calculator display.

You <u>MUST</u> write down the numbers <u>as you go</u>. That way, even if you mess up at the end, you'll still get a mark.

$\left(\dfrac{64\cos 80°}{0.48 + \sqrt{0.79}}\right)^3$

$= \left(\dfrac{11.11348337}{1.368819442}\right)^3$

$= 8.119027997^3$

$= 535.1950858$

There are lots of <u>slightly different ways</u> of working out this type of calculation. Here's one:

1) Work out the <u>bottom</u> of the fraction: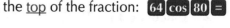

Write the answer down and store it in the <u>memory</u> by pressing: **STO** **M+**

2) Now work out the <u>top</u> of the fraction: **64** **cos** **80** **=**

3) Do the division: **Ans** **÷** **RCL** **M+** **=**

This gets the value of the <u>bottom</u> of the fraction out of the <u>memory</u>.

4) And cube: **Ans** **x◼** **3** **=**

NOTE:

1) On some calculators, a <u>bracket</u> opens when you use a <u>trig function</u> or the square/cube root function. So to enter something like tan 40° + 1, you have to <u>close the bracket</u>: **tan** **40** **)** **+** **1**

2) On some calculators, the cursor stays <u>under the square root bar</u> until you nudge it out by pressing the <u>right arrow</u>.

Check Your Answer Using **Brackets** **(** and **)**

<u>Check your answer</u> to a question like the one above by plugging it into your calculator <u>in fewer steps</u>.

1) To work out $\dfrac{64\cos 80°}{0.48 + \sqrt{0.79}}$ you <u>CAN'T</u> just press **64** **cos** **80** **÷** **0.48** **+** **√** **0.79** **=**

2) The calculator follows BODMAS, so it'll think you mean $\dfrac{64\cos 80°}{0.48} + \sqrt{0.79}$.

3) The secret is to <u>OVERRIDE</u> the automatic <u>BODMAS</u> using the <u>BRACKETS BUTTONS</u>.

4) The calculator will do the bits in brackets first. So you'd press:

(**64** **cos** **80** **)** **÷** **(** **0.48** **+** **√** **0.79** **)** **=** ← (Cube this to check the question above.)

Your calculator might need you to add an extra ")" here. See the note above.

And maybe an extra ")" or a right arrow nudge here.

Your calculator can save you precious minutes in the exam

Different kinds of calculator have different ways of doing things — for example, some have a fraction button, while on others you just have to divide. Make sure you're familiar with yours before the exam.

Types of Number

Before we go any further, there are a few different types of number that you need to know about.

Integers

You need to make sure you know the <u>meaning</u> of this word — it'll come up <u>all the time</u> in maths.
An <u>integer</u> is another name for a <u>whole number</u> — either a positive or negative number, or zero.

<u>Examples</u>

Integers:	−365, 0, 1, 17, 989, 1 234 567 890
Not integers:	0.5, $\frac{2}{3}$, $\sqrt{7}$, $13\frac{3}{4}$, −1000.1, 66.66, π

Rational and Irrational Numbers

All numbers fall into one of these two categories.

<u>Rational numbers</u> can be written as <u>fractions</u>. Most numbers you deal with are rational.

> Rational numbers come in 3 different forms:
> 1) <u>Integers</u> e.g. $4\left(=\frac{4}{1}\right)$, $-5\left(=\frac{-5}{1}\right)$, $-12\left(=\frac{-12}{1}\right)$
> 2) <u>Fractions</u> $\frac{p}{q}$, where p and q are (non-zero) integers, e.g. $\frac{1}{4}$, $-\frac{1}{2}$, $\frac{3}{4}$
> 3) <u>Terminating or recurring decimals</u> e.g. $0.125\left(=\frac{1}{8}\right)$, $0.33333333...\left(=\frac{1}{3}\right)$, $0.143143143...\left(=\frac{143}{999}\right)$

- <u>Irrational numbers</u> are messy. They <u>can't</u> be written as fractions
  — they're <u>never-ending</u>, <u>non-repeating decimals</u>.
- <u>Roots</u> of positive integers are either integers or irrational (e.g. $\sqrt{3}$ and $\sqrt[3]{2}$ are irrational, but $\sqrt{4} = 2$ isn't).
- <u>Surds</u> (see p.51) are numbers or expressions containing irrational roots. π is also irrational.

Square Numbers

1) When you <u>multiply</u> a whole number by <u>itself</u>, you get a <u>square number</u>.
2) You'll save lots of time if you know these <u>by heart</u>:

1^2	2^2	3^2	4^2	5^2	6^2	7^2	8^2	9^2	10^2	11^2	12^2	13^2	14^2	15^2
1	4	9	16	25	36	49	64	81	100	121	144	169	196	225
(1×1)	(2×2)	(3×3)	(4×4)	(5×5)	(6×6)	(7×7)	(8×8)	(9×9)	(10×10)	(11×11)	(12×12)	(13×13)	(14×14)	(15×15)

Cube Numbers

1) When you <u>multiply</u> a whole number by <u>itself</u>, then by itself <u>again</u>, you get a <u>cube number</u>.
2) It's handy to know some cubes <u>by heart</u> too — these are the ones that crop up a lot:

1^3	2^3	3^3	4^3	5^3	10^3
1	8	27	64	125	1000
(1×1×1)	(2×2×2)	(3×3×3)	(4×4×4)	(5×5×5)	(10×10×10)

An integer can be positive, negative or zero

Remember that <u>all</u> numbers are either rational or irrational. It's really important that you know these different types of number and understand what they are — otherwise you'll run into trouble further on.

Square Roots and Cube Roots

<u>Roots</u> are the opposite of powers. Knowing your square and cube numbers will be handy on this page.

Square Roots

'<u>Squared</u>' means '<u>multiplied by itself</u>': $8^2 = 8 \times 8 = 64$
<u>SQUARE ROOT</u> $\sqrt{}$ is the <u>reverse process</u>: $\sqrt{64} = 8$

The best way to think of it is:

'Square Root' means 'What Number <u>Times by Itself</u> gives...'

1. **What is $\sqrt{49}$?**

7 times by itself gives 49: $49 = 7 \times 7$
So $\sqrt{49} = 7$

> 49 is a <u>square number</u> — make sure you know all the <u>square numbers</u> on p.3 so you can answer questions like this <u>without a calculator</u>.

2. **What is $\sqrt{29.16}$?**

Press: $\boxed{\sqrt{}}$ $\boxed{29.16}$ $\boxed{=}$ 5.4

> If the number isn't a square number, use the $\boxed{\sqrt{}}$ button on your <u>calculator</u>.

> <u>All</u> numbers also have a <u>NEGATIVE SQUARE ROOT</u> — it's just the '–' version of the normal positive one.

3. **Find both square roots of 36.**

$6 \times 6 = 36$, so positive square root = 6

$-6 \times -6 = 36$, so negative square root = –6

Cube Roots

'<u>Cubed</u>' means '<u>multiplied by itself and then by itself again</u>': $2^3 = 2 \times 2 \times 2 = 8$
<u>CUBE ROOT</u> $\sqrt[3]{}$ is the <u>reverse process</u>: $\sqrt[3]{8} = 2$

'Cube Root' means 'What Number <u>Times by Itself and then by Itself Again</u> gives...'

Make sure you can write down the cube roots of the <u>cube numbers</u> given on p.3 <u>without</u> using a <u>calculator</u>.
To find the cube root of any other number you can use your calculator — press $\boxed{\sqrt[3]{}}$.

1. **What is $\sqrt[3]{27}$?**   27 is a cube number.

3 times by itself and then by itself again gives 27: $27 = 3 \times 3 \times 3$
So $\sqrt[3]{27} = 3$

2. **What is $\sqrt[3]{4913}$?**

Press: $\boxed{\sqrt[3]{}}$ $\boxed{4913}$ $\boxed{=}$ 17

Use your calculator to make these questions really easy

If you can spot that a number is a square or cube number, you can quickly work out the root in your head. Otherwise, you can just use your calculator — as long as you know where all the right buttons are.

Warm-Up and Worked Exam Questions

This stuff is pretty straightforward, but that doesn't mean you can get away without learning the facts and practising the questions. You should have learnt the facts already — try these to make sure.

Warm-Up Questions

1) Find the value of: a) $15 - 12 \div 3$ b) $5 \times 2 + 3 \times 9$ c) $(3 + 5) \div 2 - 1$

2) Work out $\dfrac{\sqrt{8.67 - 4.94}}{4 \tan 87°}$. Write down all the figures on your calculator display.

3) Choose from the numbers 1, 2.3, 3.2312, 10, −4, 7, $\sqrt{2}$, −5.1, $\frac{2}{7}$, 6π:
 Which numbers are: a) integers?
                 b) irrational?

4) The number n is an integer, and $3n$ is a square number between 10 and 50. What is the value of n?

5) Explain why −3 is not a cube root of 27.

Worked Exam Questions

Here are a couple of exam-style questions that have been worked out for you. Read them carefully, making sure you can follow them all the way through. Then have a go at the questions on the next page.

1   $d = \dfrac{3a^2 + 2b}{4(c + 3)}$, where $a = -2$, $b = 2$ and $c = -4$.   (3)

    Work out the value of d. Show all your working.

First, substitute the numbers in.

$$d = \frac{3(-2)^2 + 2 \times 2}{4(-4 + 3)}$$

Then follow BODMAS for the numerator and denominator separately — do the brackets and the squared number...

$$= \frac{3 \times 4 + 2 \times 2}{4 \times (-1)}$$

...then the multiplications...

$$= \frac{12 + 4}{-4}$$

...and finally, the addition.

$$= \frac{16}{-4} = -4$$

Then divide to get the answer.

$d = -4$

[2 marks]

2   Use your calculator to work out $\sqrt{\dfrac{12.71 + 137.936}{\cos 50° \times 13.2^2}}$ (4)

    Give your answer to 2 decimal places.

Use BODMAS.

$$\sqrt{\frac{12.71 + 137.936}{\cos 50° \times 13.2^2}} = \sqrt{\frac{150.646}{0.642787609... \times 174.24}}$$

$$= \sqrt{1.34506182...}$$

$$= 1.1597680...$$

1.16 (2 d.p.)

[2 marks]

Exam Questions

3   1 is the first odd number. It is also the first square number and the first cube number. **(3)**
     Which is greater:

    a)   the third odd number, the third square number or the third cube number?

....

[1 mark]

    b)   the sixth odd number, the fourth square number or the second cube number?

....

[2 marks]

4   Juliette thinks of a number between 1 and 10. The cube of the number is equal to **(3)**
     the square of double the number. What is the number Juliette is thinking of?

....

[2 marks]

5   Use your calculator to work out the value of $\sqrt{\dfrac{7}{4^3} - (53 \div 2^4)^2}$. **(4)**

     Write down all the figures on your calculator display.

....

[1 mark]

6   x and y are integers and $0 < x < y$.
     Write down two sets of values for x and y such that $6 = \sqrt{3x + 2y}$. **(5)**

$x =$ .... , $y =$ ....

or $x =$ .... , $y =$ ....

[2 marks]

Prime Numbers

There's one more type of number that you need to know about — and that's <u>prime numbers</u>.

PRIME Numbers **Don't Divide** by Anything

<u>Prime numbers</u> are all the numbers that <u>DON'T</u> come up in <u>times tables</u>:

| 2 | 3 | 5 | 7 | 11 | 13 | 17 | 19 | 23 | 29 | 31 | 37 | ... |

The <u>only way</u> to get <u>ANY PRIME NUMBER</u> is: 1 × ITSELF

E.g. The <u>only</u> numbers that multiply to give 7 are: 1 × 7
The <u>only</u> numbers that multiply to give 31 are: 1 × 31

> **EXAMPLE:**   **Show that 24 is not a prime number.**
>
> Just find another way to make 24 other than 1 × 24:   2 × 12 = 24
>
> 24 divides by other numbers apart from 1 and 24, so it isn't a prime number.

Five **Important Facts**

1) <u>1</u> is <u>NOT</u> a prime number.
2) <u>2</u> is the <u>ONLY</u> even prime number.
3) The first four prime numbers are <u>2, 3, 5 and 7</u>.
4) <u>Prime numbers</u> end in <u>1, 3, 7 or 9</u> (2 and 5 are the only exceptions to this rule).
5) But <u>NOT ALL</u> numbers ending in <u>1, 3, 7 or 9</u> are primes, as shown here:
(Only the <u>circled ones</u> are <u>primes</u>.)

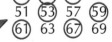

How to **FIND** Prime Numbers — a very simple method

> 1) <u>All primes</u> (above 5) <u>end in 1, 3, 7 or 9</u>. So ignore any numbers that don't end in one of those.
> 2) Now, to find which of them <u>ACTUALLY ARE</u> primes you only need to <u>divide each one by 3 and 7</u>.
> If it doesn't divide exactly by either 3 or 7 then it's a prime.

This simple rule using <u>just 3 and 7</u> works for checking numbers <u>up to 120</u>.

> **EXAMPLE:**   **Find all the prime numbers in this list:**   **71, 72, 73, 74, 75, 76, 77, 78**
>
> **1** First, get rid of anything that doesn't end in 1, 3, 7 or 9:   71, ~~72~~, 73, ~~74~~, ~~75~~, ~~76~~, 77, ~~78~~
>
> **2** Now try dividing 71, 73 and 77 by 3 and 7:
>
> 71 ÷ 3 = 23.667   71 ÷ 7 = 10.143   so 71 is a prime number
>
> 73 ÷ 3 = 24.333   73 ÷ 7 = 10.429   so 73 is a prime number
>
> 77 ÷ 3 = 25.667   BUT: 77 ÷ 7 = 11 — 11 is a whole number,
> so 77 is NOT a prime, because it divides by 7.
>
> So the prime numbers in the list are 71 and 73.

Learn those five facts — they're important for a reason

A really common mistake people make with prime numbers is saying that 1 is prime — it just isn't.
Don't forget that you can use your calculator to help you check if a number is divisible by 3 or 7.

Multiples, Factors and Prime Factors

You need to know what <u>multiples</u>, <u>factors</u>, <u>primes</u> and <u>prime factors</u> are — and how to find them.

Multiples and Factors

> The <u>MULTIPLES</u> of a number are just its <u>times table</u>.

EXAMPLE: **Find the first 8 multiples of 13.**
You just need to find the first 8 numbers in the 13 times table:

13 26 39 52 65 78 91 104

> The <u>FACTORS</u> of a number are all the numbers that <u>divide into it</u>.

There's a method that guarantees you'll find them all:

1) Start off with <u>1 × the number itself</u>, then try <u>2 ×</u>, then <u>3 ×</u> and so on, listing the pairs in <u>rows</u>.
2) Try each one in turn. <u>Cross out</u> the row if it doesn't divide <u>exactly</u>.
3) Eventually, when you get a number <u>repeated</u>, <u>stop</u>.
4) The numbers in the rows you <u>haven't</u> crossed out make up the list of factors.

EXAMPLE: **Find all the factors of 24.**

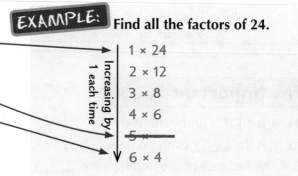

Increasing by 1 each time

1 × 24
2 × 12
3 × 8
4 × 6
5̶ ̶×̶
6 × 4

So the factors of 24 are: 1, 2, 3, 4, 6, 8, 12, 24

Finding Prime Factors — the Factor Tree

<u>Any number</u> can be broken down into a string of prime numbers all multiplied together — this is called '<u>expressing it as a product of prime factors</u>'.

EXAMPLE:

Express 280 as a product of powers of prime factors.

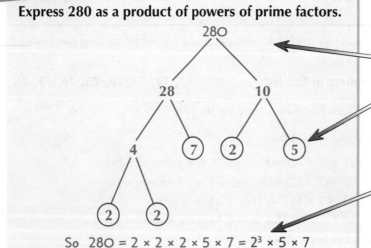

So 280 = 2 × 2 × 2 × 5 × 7 = 2^3 × 5 × 7

To write a number as a product of its prime factors, use the <u>Factor Tree</u> method:

1) Start with the number at the top, and <u>split</u> it into <u>factors</u> as shown.
2) Every time you get a prime, <u>ring it</u>.
3) Keep going until you can't go further (i.e. you're just left with primes), then write the primes out <u>in order</u>.
4) The question asks for <u>powers of prime factors</u>, so if a factor appears more than once you need to write it using <u>powers</u> (see p.45).

Factors and multiples are easy marks

Factor and multiple questions are simple multiplications and divisions so there's no reason to lose marks. Practise doing them quickly and accurately and make sure you know what all the words mean.

LCM and HCF

You'll need to know about <u>multiples</u> and <u>factors</u> from the previous page before you have a go at this one...

LCM — 'Lowest Common Multiple'

The <u>SMALLEST</u> number that will <u>DIVIDE BY ALL</u> the numbers in question.

If you're given two numbers and asked to find their LCM, just <u>LIST</u> the <u>MULTIPLES</u> of <u>BOTH</u> numbers and find the <u>SMALLEST</u> one that's in <u>BOTH</u> lists.

So, to find the LCM of <u>12</u> and <u>15</u>, list their multiples (multiples of 12 = 12, 24, 36, 48, 60, 72, ... and multiples of 15 = 15, 30, 45, 60, 75, ...) and find the smallest one that's in both lists — so <u>LCM = 60</u>.

However, if you already know the <u>prime factors</u> of the numbers, you can use this method instead:

1) List all the <u>PRIME FACTORS</u> that appear in <u>EITHER</u> number.
2) If a factor appears <u>MORE THAN ONCE</u> in one of the numbers, list it <u>THAT MANY TIMES</u>.
3) <u>MULTIPLY</u> these together to give the <u>LCM</u>.

EXAMPLE: $18 = 2 \times 3^2$ and $30 = 2 \times 3 \times 5$.
Find the LCM of 18 and 30.

$18 = 2 \times 3 \times 3$ $30 = 2 \times 3 \times 5$

So the prime factors that appear in either number are: 2, 3, 3, 5 —— List 3 twice as it appears twice in 18.
LCM = $2 \times 3 \times 3 \times 5 = 90$

HCF — 'Highest Common Factor'

The <u>BIGGEST</u> number that will <u>DIVIDE INTO ALL</u> the numbers in question.

If you're given two numbers and asked to find their HCF, just <u>LIST</u> the <u>FACTORS</u> of <u>BOTH</u> numbers and find the <u>BIGGEST</u> one that's in <u>BOTH</u> lists.

Take care listing the factors — make sure you use the proper method (as shown on the previous page).

So, to find the HCF of <u>36</u> and <u>54</u>, list their factors (factors of 36 = 1, 2, 3, 4, 6, 9, 12, 18 and 36 and factors of 54 = 1, 2, 3, 6, 9, 18, 27 and 54) and find the biggest one that's in both lists — so <u>HCF = 18</u>.

Again, there's a different method you can use if you already know the <u>prime factors</u> of the numbers:

1) List all the <u>PRIME FACTORS</u> that appear in <u>BOTH</u> numbers.
2) <u>MULTIPLY</u> these together to find the <u>HCF</u>.

EXAMPLE: $180 = 2^2 \times 3^2 \times 5$ and $84 = 2^2 \times 3 \times 7$.
Use this to find the HCF of 180 and 84.

$180 = ②\times②\times③\times 3 \times 5$ $84 = ②\times②\times③\times 7$

2, 2 and 3 are prime factors of both numbers, so HCF = $2 \times 2 \times 3 = 12$

Don't be put off by the fancy names

Lowest common multiple and highest common factor questions can be a bit intimidating in the exam — but they're easy enough if you take them step by step. It's just multiplication and division again.

Warm-Up and Worked Exam Questions

Time for a quick few warm-up questions to make sure all that has sunk in. If you're not sure about any of them, take a look back at the previous pages. Otherwise, you can move on to the exam questions.

Warm-Up Questions

1) Find all the factors of 40.
2) Write down the multiples of 17 between 20 and 70.
3) Explain why 231 is not a prime number.
4) Write 40 as a product of its prime factors.
5) a) Find the lowest common multiple (LCM) of 9 and 12.
   b) Find the highest common factor (HCF) of 18 and 42.

Worked Exam Questions

Take a look at these worked exam questions. They're not too hard, but they should give you a good idea of what to write. Make the most of the handy hints now — they won't be there in the exam.

1 Express:

a) 210 as a product of its prime factors.

Draw a factor tree.

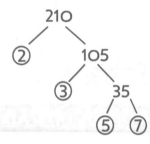

$210 = 2 \times 3 \times 5 \times 7$

[3 marks]

b) 105^2 as a product of its prime factors.

From part a), $105 = 3 \times 5 \times 7$, so:

$105^2 = (3 \times 5 \times 7) \times (3 \times 5 \times 7)$

You could also write this as $105^2 = 3^2 \times 5^2 \times 7^2$

$105^2 = 3 \times 3 \times 5 \times 5 \times 7 \times 7$

[3 marks]

2 Find the LCM of 6, 8 and 10.

Write each number as the product of prime factors.

$6 = 2 \times 3$

$8 = 2 \times 2 \times 2$ —— 2 appears three times, so write it three times here.

$10 = 2 \times 5$

Multiply the factors together to get the LCM.

So LCM $= 2 \times 2 \times 2 \times 3 \times 5$

120

[3 marks]

Exam Questions

3   a)   List all the factors of 30.   (3)

....
[2 marks]

b)   List all the factors of 48.   (3)

....
[2 marks]

c)   What is the HCF of 30 and 48?   (5)

....
[1 mark]

4   Two remote-control cars start at the same time from the start line on a track.   (5)
One car takes half a minute to complete a circuit.
The other car takes 1 minute 10 seconds to complete a circuit.

If they start side by side, how long will it be before they are next side by side on the start line?
State the units in your answer.

....
[2 marks]

5   Given that $25x^2 - 1$ factorises to give $(5x - 1)(5x + 1)$,   (7)
express 2499 as a product of its prime factors.

This uses the 'difference of two squares' rule — you'll see this on page 50.

....
[3 marks]

Fractions

These pages show you how to cope with fraction calculations without your <u>calculator</u> or if you're asked in the exam to <u>show all your working</u>.

1) Cancelling down

To <u>cancel down</u> or <u>simplify</u> a fraction, <u>divide top and bottom by the same number</u>, till they won't go further:

> **EXAMPLE:** **Simplify $\frac{18}{24}$.**
>
> Cancel down in a series of <u>easy steps</u> — keep going till the top and bottom don't have <u>any</u> common factors.
>
> $$\overset{\div 3 \quad \div 2}{\frac{18}{24} = \frac{6}{8} = \frac{3}{4}}$$
> $$\div 3 \quad \div 2$$

The number on the top of the fraction is the <u>numerator</u>, and the number on the bottom is the <u>denominator</u>.

2) Mixed numbers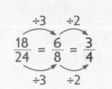

<u>Mixed numbers</u> are things like $3\frac{1}{3}$, with an integer part and a fraction part. <u>Improper fractions</u> are ones where the top number is larger than the bottom number (they're also sometimes called <u>vulgar fractions</u>). You need to be able to convert between the two.

> **EXAMPLES:** **1. Write $4\frac{2}{3}$ as an improper fraction.**
>
> 1) Think of the <u>mixed number</u> as an <u>addition</u>:
> $$4\frac{2}{3} = 4 + \frac{2}{3}$$
>
> 2) Turn the <u>integer</u> part into a <u>fraction</u>:
> $$4 + \frac{2}{3} = \frac{12}{3} + \frac{2}{3} = \frac{12+2}{3} = \frac{14}{3}$$

> **2. Write $\frac{31}{4}$ as a mixed number.**
>
> <u>Divide</u> the top number by the bottom.
> 1) The <u>answer</u> gives the <u>whole number part</u>.
> 2) The <u>remainder</u> goes <u>on top</u> of the fraction.
>
> $31 \div 4 = 7$ remainder 3, so $\frac{31}{4} = 7\frac{3}{4}$

3) Multiplying

Multiply top and bottom separately. It usually helps to cancel down first if you can.

> **EXAMPLE:** **Find $\frac{8}{15} \times \frac{5}{12}$.**
>
> 8 and 12 both divide by 4
>
> 1) <u>Cancel down</u> by dividing top and bottom by any common factors you find in <u>either</u> fraction:
> $$\frac{{}^2 8}{15} \times \frac{5}{{}_3 12} = \frac{2}{15} \times \frac{{}^1 5}{3}$$
> 15 and 5 both divide by 5
>
> 2) Now multiply the top and bottom numbers <u>separately</u>:
> $$= \frac{2}{3} \times \frac{1}{3} = \frac{2 \times 1}{3 \times 3} = \frac{2}{9}$$

Fractions

Here are some more tricks for dealing with fractions.

4) Dividing

To divide one fraction by another, turn the second fraction <u>upside down</u> and then <u>multiply</u>:

> **EXAMPLE:** Find $2\frac{1}{3} \div 3\frac{1}{2}$.
>
> 1) Rewrite the <u>mixed numbers</u> as <u>fractions</u>: $2\frac{1}{3} \div 3\frac{1}{2} = \frac{7}{3} \div \frac{7}{2}$
>
> 2) Turn $\frac{7}{2}$ <u>upside down</u> and <u>multiply</u>: $= \frac{7}{3} \times \frac{2}{7}$
>
> 3) <u>Simplify</u> by cancelling the 7s: $= \frac{1}{3} \times \frac{2}{1} = \frac{2}{3}$

> When you're multiplying or dividing with <u>mixed numbers</u>, <u>always</u> turn them into improper fractions first.

5) Common denominators

This comes in handy for <u>ordering fractions</u> by size, and for <u>adding</u> or <u>subtracting</u> fractions.

You need to find a number that <u>all</u> the denominators <u>divide into</u> — this will be your <u>common denominator</u>.

The simplest way is to find the <u>lowest common multiple</u> of the denominators:

> **EXAMPLE:** Put these fractions in ascending order of size:
>
> $$\frac{8}{3} \qquad \frac{5}{4} \qquad \frac{12}{5}$$
>
> The <u>LCM</u> of 3, 4 and 5 is 60,
> so make 60 the <u>common denominator</u>:
>
> $$\overset{\times 20}{\frac{8}{3} = \frac{160}{60}}_{\times 20} \qquad \overset{\times 15}{\frac{5}{4} = \frac{75}{60}}_{\times 15} \qquad \overset{\times 12}{\frac{12}{5} = \frac{144}{60}}_{\times 12}$$
>
> *Don't forget to use the original fractions in the final answer.*
>
> So the correct order is $\frac{75}{60}, \frac{144}{60}, \frac{160}{60}$ i.e. $\frac{5}{4}, \frac{12}{5}, \frac{8}{3}$

Don't be put off by mixed numbers

You can easily turn mixed numbers into improper fractions, like you did on the previous page. Finding a common denominator will often come in handy too — if you need a reminder on how to find the LCM, flick back to p.9. You don't have to use the LCM, but if you don't then you might have to simplify later.

Fractions

6) Adding, subtracting — sort the denominators first

You can use this method to add or subtract any two fractions.

> 1) Make sure the denominators are <u>the same</u> (see previous page).

> 2) Add (or subtract) the top lines (numerators) <u>only</u>.

If you're adding or subtracting <u>mixed numbers</u>, it usually helps to convert them to improper fractions first.

EXAMPLE: Calculate $2\frac{1}{5} - 1\frac{1}{2}$.

1) Rewrite the <u>mixed numbers</u> as <u>fractions</u>: $\qquad 2\frac{1}{5} - 1\frac{1}{2} = \frac{11}{5} - \frac{3}{2}$

2) Find a <u>common denominator</u>: $\qquad\qquad\qquad = \frac{22}{10} - \frac{15}{10}$

3) Combine the <u>top lines</u>: $\qquad\qquad\qquad\quad = \frac{22-15}{10} = \frac{7}{10}$

> People usually find <u>adding and subtracting fractions</u> harder than multiplying and dividing — but it's actually <u>pretty easy</u> as long as you <u>make sure the denominators are the same</u>.

7) Fractions of something

> **Multiply the 'something' by the <u>TOP</u> of the fraction and divide it by the <u>BOTTOM</u>.**

It <u>doesn't matter</u> which order you do those two steps in — just start with whatever's <u>easiest</u>.

EXAMPLE: What is $\frac{9}{20}$ of £360?

Start by dividing by 20, since that's easiest. $\qquad \frac{9}{20}$ of £360 = (£360 ÷ 20) × 9

$\qquad\qquad\qquad\qquad\qquad\qquad\qquad\qquad\qquad = £18 × 9 = £162$

8) Expressing as a Fraction

EXAMPLE: Write 180 as a fraction of 80.

Just write the first number over the second and <u>cancel down</u>. $\qquad \frac{180}{80} = \frac{9}{4}$

You have to learn to handle fractions in these 8 situations

If you've learnt how to find a common denominator (p.13), then adding and subtracting fractions should be pretty easy. To find a fraction of something, carry out the two steps whichever way's easiest.

Fractions, Decimals and Percentages

The one word that describes all these three is <u>PROPORTION</u>. Fractions, decimals and percentages are simply <u>three different ways</u> of expressing a <u>proportion</u> of something — and it's pretty important you should see them as <u>closely related and completely interchangeable</u> with each other.

This table shows the really common conversions which you should know straight off without having to work them out:

Fraction	Decimal	Percentage
$\frac{1}{2}$	0.5	50%
$\frac{1}{4}$	0.25	25%
$\frac{3}{4}$	0.75	75%
$\frac{1}{3}$	0.333333...	$33\frac{1}{3}\%$
$\frac{2}{3}$	0.666666...	$66\frac{2}{3}\%$
$\frac{1}{10}$	0.1	10%
$\frac{2}{10}$	0.2	20%
$\frac{1}{5}$	0.2	20%
$\frac{2}{5}$	0.4	40%

The more of those conversions you learn, the better — but for those that you <u>don't know</u>, you must <u>also learn</u> how to <u>convert</u> between the three types. These are the methods:

$$\textbf{Fraction} \xrightarrow{\text{Divide}} \textbf{Decimal} \xrightarrow{\times \text{ by } 100} \textbf{Percentage}$$

E.g. $\frac{7}{20}$ is $7 \div 20$ $\qquad = 0.35 \qquad$ e.g. $0.35 \times 100 \qquad = 35\%$

$$\textbf{Fraction} \xleftarrow[\text{The awkward one}]{} \textbf{Decimal} \xleftarrow[\div \text{ by } 100]{} \textbf{Percentage}$$

<u>Converting decimals to fractions</u> is awkward, because it's different for different types of decimal. There are two different methods you need to learn:

1) <u>Terminating decimals</u> to fractions — this is fairly easy. The digits after the decimal point go on the top, and a <u>power of 10</u> on the bottom — with the same number of zeros as there were decimal places.

$0.6 = \frac{6}{10}$	$0.3 = \frac{3}{10}$	$0.7 = \frac{7}{10}$	etc.
$0.12 = \frac{12}{100}$	$0.78 = \frac{78}{100}$	$0.05 = \frac{5}{100}$	etc.
$0.345 = \frac{345}{1000}$	$0.908 = \frac{908}{1000}$	$0.024 = \frac{24}{1000}$	etc.

These can often be <u>cancelled down</u> — see p.12.

2) <u>Recurring decimals</u> to fractions — this is trickier. See the next page...

Fractions, decimals and percentages are interchangeable

It's important you remember that a fraction, decimal or percentage can be converted into either of the other two forms. And it's even more important that you learn how to do it.

Fractions and Recurring Decimals

Recurring and terminating decimals can always be written as fractions.

Recurring or Terminating...

1) Recurring decimals have a pattern of numbers which repeats forever, e.g. $\frac{1}{3}$ is the decimal 0.333333...
   Note, it doesn't have to be a single digit that repeats. You could have, for instance: 0.143143143...

2) The repeating part is usually marked with dots or a bar on top of the number. If there's one dot, then only one digit is repeated. If there are two dots, then everything from the first dot to the second dot is the repeating bit. E.g. $0.2\dot{5} = 0.2555555...$, $0.\dot{2}\dot{5} = 0.25252525...$, $0.\dot{2}5\dot{5} = 0.255255255...$

3) Terminating decimals are finite (they come to an end), e.g $\frac{1}{20}$ is the decimal 0.05.

The denominator (bottom number) of a fraction in its simplest form tells you if it converts to a recurring or terminating decimal. Fractions where the denominator has prime factors of only 2 or 5 will give terminating decimals. All other fractions will give recurring decimals.

	Only prime factors: 2 and 5				Also other prime factors				
Fraction	$\frac{1}{5}$	$\frac{1}{125}$	$\frac{1}{2}$	$\frac{1}{20}$	$\frac{1}{7}$	$\frac{1}{35}$	$\frac{1}{3}$	$\frac{1}{6}$	For prime factors, see p.8.
Equivalent Decimal	0.2	0.008	0.5	0.05	$0.\dot{1}4285\dot{7}$	$0.0\dot{2}8571\dot{4}$	$0.\dot{3}$	$0.1\dot{6}$	
	Terminating decimals				Recurring decimals				

Converting terminating decimals into fractions was covered on the previous page.
Converting recurring decimals is quite a bit harder — but you'll be OK once you've learnt the method...

Recurring Decimals into Fractions

1) Basic Ones

Turning a recurring decimal into a fraction uses a really clever trick. Just watch this...

EXAMPLE: **Write $0.\dot{2}3\dot{4}$ as a fraction.**

1) Name your decimal — I've called it r.
   $\qquad$ Let $r = 0.\dot{2}3\dot{4}$

2) Multiply r by a power of ten to move it past the decimal point by one full repeated lump — here that's 1000:
   $\qquad$ $1000r = 234.\dot{2}3\dot{4}$

3) Now you can subtract to get rid of the decimal part:
   $\qquad$ $\begin{array}{r} 1000r = 234.\dot{2}3\dot{4} \\ -\quad r = 0.\dot{2}3\dot{4} \\ \hline 999r = 234 \end{array}$

4) Then just divide to leave r, and cancel if possible:
   $\qquad$ $r = \frac{234}{999} = \frac{26}{111}$

The 'Just Learning the Result' Method:

1) For converting recurring decimals to fractions, you could just learn the result that the fraction always has the repeating unit on the top and the same number of nines on the bottom...

2) BUT this only works if the repeating bit starts straight after the decimal point (see the next page for an example where it doesn't).

3) AND some exam questions will ask you to 'show that' or 'prove' that a fraction and a recurring decimal are equivalent — and that means you have to use the proper method.

Fractions and Recurring Decimals

If the recurring bit doesn't come right after the decimal point,
things are slightly trickier — but only slightly.

EXAMPLE: **Write 0.1$\dot{6}$ as a fraction.**

1) Name your decimal.   Let $r = 0.1\dot{6}$

2) Multiply r by a <u>power of ten</u> to move the
   <u>non-repeating part</u> past the decimal point. $10r = 1.\dot{6}$

3) Now multiply again to move <u>one full</u>
   <u>repeated lump</u> past the decimal point. $100r = 16.\dot{6}$

4) <u>Subtract</u> to <u>get rid</u> of the decimal part:

$$100r = 16.\dot{6}$$
$$-\quad 10r = 1.\dot{6}$$
$$\overline{90r = 15}$$

5) <u>Divide</u> to leave r, and <u>cancel</u> if possible: $r = \dfrac{15}{90} = \dfrac{1}{6}$

Fractions into Recurring Decimals

You might find this cropping up in your exam too. There are <u>two ways</u> you can do
these questions — make sure you know <u>both</u> in case you're told to use a particular one.

EXAMPLE: **Write $\dfrac{8}{33}$ as a recurring decimal.**

1 Find an equivalent fraction with <u>all nines</u> on the bottom.
   The number on the top will tell you the <u>recurring part</u>.

$$\dfrac{8}{33} \overset{\times 3}{\underset{\times 3}{=}} \dfrac{24}{99}$$

$$\dfrac{24}{99} = 0.\dot{2}\dot{4}$$

2 Remember, $\dfrac{8}{33}$ means $8 \div 33$, so you could just
   <u>do the division</u> on your calculator:

$$8 \div 33 = 0.24242424...$$
$$\dfrac{8}{33} = 0.\dot{2}\dot{4}$$

Watch out — the <u>number of nines</u> on the bottom tells you the <u>number of digits</u> in the recurring part.
For example, $\dfrac{24}{99} = 0.\dot{2}\dot{4}$, but $\dfrac{24}{999} = 0.\dot{0}2\dot{4}$

If you're in <u>any doubt</u>, just use your <u>calculator</u> to <u>check</u> that your answer is right.

You could be asked to convert either kind of decimal into a fraction

Make sure you get plenty of practice turning both terminating and recurring decimals into fractions,
and going the other way as well. Fortunately, your calculator will really help you out here.

Warm-Up and Worked Exam Questions

These warm-up questions will help to check that you've learnt the basics from the last few pages — if you're struggling with any of them, go and look back over that page before you go any further.

Warm-Up Questions

1) Work these out, then simplify your answers where possible:

   a) $\frac{2}{5} \times \frac{2}{3}$ b) $\frac{2}{5} \div \frac{2}{3}$ c) $\frac{2}{5} + \frac{2}{3}$ d) $\frac{2}{3} - \frac{2}{5}$ e) $\frac{2}{5}$ of 120   f) $\frac{2}{3}$ of 120

2) a) Convert $4\frac{2}{5}$ into an improper fraction.   b) Convert $\frac{22}{3}$ into a mixed number.

3) a) What percentage is the same as $\frac{2}{5}$?   b) What percentage is the same as $\frac{2}{3}$?

4) a) What fraction is the same as 0.4?
   b) What fraction is the same as 0.444444...?
   c) What fraction is the same as 0.45454545...?

5) a) What decimal is the same as $\frac{7}{10}$?   b) What decimal is the same as $\frac{7}{9}$?

Worked Exam Questions

Make sure you understand what's going on in these questions before trying the next page for yourself.

1   Francis owns all the shares of his company.

He sells $\frac{2}{15}$ of the shares to Spencer and $\frac{5}{12}$ of the shares to Jamie.

What fraction of the shares does Francis still own?
Give your answer in its simplest form.

$$1 - \frac{2}{15} - \frac{5}{12} = 1 - \frac{8}{60} - \frac{25}{60}$$

— Write over a common denominator

$$= \frac{27}{60}$$

$$= \frac{9}{20}$$

Remember to give your answer in its simplest form.

$$\frac{9}{20}$$
....
[3 marks]

2   Write $0.2\dot{6}$ in the form $\frac{a}{b}$. Simplify your answer as far as possible, and show your working.

Let r = $0.2\dot{6}$, so 100r = $26.\dot{2}\dot{6}$

Multiply by a power of ten to get one full repeated chunk on the left hand side of the decimal point.

$$100r - r = 26.\dot{2}\dot{6} - 0.\dot{2}\dot{6}$$

$$99r = 26$$

$$r = \frac{26}{99}$$

$$\frac{26}{99}$$
....
[2 marks]

Exam Questions

3 Dean has baked 550 muffins. $\frac{2}{5}$ of the muffins are chocolate, $\frac{3}{11}$ are lemon
and the rest are beetroot. How many beetroot muffins has Dean baked?

....
[4 marks]

4 If $a = \frac{3}{4}$ and $b = 2\frac{1}{2}$, find the value of $\frac{1}{a} + \frac{1}{b}$.

....
[3 marks]

5 Write $\frac{7}{33}$ as a recurring decimal.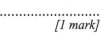

....
[1 mark]

6 Show that $0.5\dot{9}\dot{0} = \frac{13}{22}$. (**7**)

Hint: start by trying to get
only the non-repeating part
before the decimal point.

[2 marks]

Percentages

You shouldn't have any trouble with the <u>simple types</u> of percentage question.
Watch out for the <u>trickier types</u> and make sure you know the <u>proper method</u> for each of them.

Three **Simple** Question Types

Type 1 — "Find x% of y"

Turn the percentage into a <u>decimal</u>, then <u>multiply</u>.

EXAMPLE: **Find 15% of £46.**

1) Write 15% as a <u>decimal</u>: 15% = 15 ÷ 100 = 0.15
2) <u>Multiply</u> £46 by 0.15: 0.15 × £46 = £6.90

Type 2 — "Find the new amount after a % increase/decrease"

Turn the percentage into a <u>decimal</u>, then <u>multiply</u>. Add this on (or subtract from) the original value.

EXAMPLE: **A toaster is reduced in price by 40% in the sales. It originally cost £68. What is the new price of the toaster?**

1) Write 40% as a <u>decimal</u>: 40% = 40 ÷ 100 = 0.4
2) <u>Multiply</u> to find 40% <u>of</u> £68: 0.4 × £68 = £27.20
3) It's a decrease, so subtract from the original: £68 – £27.20 = £40.80

> If you prefer, you can use the <u>multiplier</u> method:
> multiplier = 1 – 0.4
> = 0.6
> 68 × 0.6 = <u>£40.80</u>

Type 3 — "Express x as a percentage of y"

<u>Divide</u> *x* by *y*, then multiply by <u>100</u>.

EXAMPLE: **Give 40p as a percentage of £3.34.**

1) Make sure both amounts are in the <u>same units</u>: £3.34 = 334p
2) <u>Divide</u> 40p by 334p, <u>then multiply</u> by 100: (40 ÷ 334) × 100 = 12.0% (1 d.p.)

Three **Trickier** Question Types

Type 1 — Finding the percentage change

1) This is the formula for giving a <u>change in value</u> as a <u>percentage</u> — <u>LEARN IT, AND USE IT</u>:

2) This is similar to Type 3 above, because you end up with a <u>percentage</u> rather than an amount.

$$\text{Percentage 'Change'} = \frac{\text{Change}}{\text{Original}} \times 100$$

3) Typical questions will ask 'Find the percentage <u>increase</u>/<u>profit</u>/<u>error</u>' or 'Calculate the percentage <u>decrease</u>/<u>loss</u>/<u>discount</u>', etc.

EXAMPLE: **A trader buys watches for £5 and sells them for £7. Find his profit as a percentage.**

1) Here the 'change' is <u>profit</u>, so the formula looks like this: $\text{percentage profit} = \frac{\text{profit}}{\text{original}} \times 100$
2) Work out the <u>actual value</u> of the profit: profit = £7 – £5 = £2
3) Calculate the <u>percentage</u> profit: $\text{percentage profit} = \frac{2}{5} \times 100 = 40\%$

Percentages

Type 2 — Finding the original value

This is the type that <u>most people get wrong</u> — but only because they <u>don't recognise</u> it as this type and don't apply this simple method:

> 1) Write the amount in the question as a <u>percentage of the original value</u>.
>
> 2) <u>Divide</u> to find <u>1%</u> of the original value.
>
> 3) <u>Multiply by 100</u> to give the original value (= 100%).

EXAMPLE: **A house increases in value by 20% to £72 000.** Note: The <u>new</u> value is given,
Find what it was worth before the rise. not the original value.

1) An <u>increase</u> of 20% means £72 000
   represents <u>120% of the original</u> value.

2) Divide by 120 to find <u>1%</u>
   of the original value.

3) Then multiply by 100.

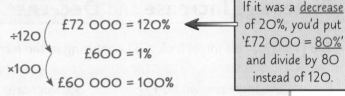

$\div 120$ (£72 000 = 120%
£600 = 1%
$\times 100$ (£60 000 = 100%

So the original value was **£60 000**

> If it was a <u>decrease</u>
> of 20%, you'd put
> '£72 000 = <u>80%</u>'
> and divide by 80
> instead of 120.

Always set them out <u>exactly like this example</u>. The trickiest bit is deciding the top % figure
on the right-hand side — the 2nd and 3rd rows are <u>always</u> 1% and 100%.

Type 3 — Simple Interest vs Compound Interest

1) There are two types of <u>interest</u> you could get asked about — <u>simple interest</u>
   and <u>compound interest</u>. Compound interest is covered on the next page.

2) Simple interest means a certain percentage of the <u>original</u>
   <u>amount only</u> is paid at regular intervals (usually once a year).
   So the amount of interest is <u>the same every time</u> it's paid.

EXAMPLE: **Regina invests £380 in an account which pays 3% simple** 'Per annum' just
interest per annum. How much interest will she earn in 4 years? means 'each year'.

1) Work out the amount of interest earned <u>in one year</u>:   3% = 3 ÷ 100 = 0.03
                                                            3% of £380 = 0.03 × £380 = £11.40

2) Multiply by 4 to get the <u>total interest</u> for <u>4 years</u>:   4 × £11.40 = £45.60

Percentages are one of the most useful things you'll ever learn

Percentages are everywhere — whenever you open a newspaper, see an advert, watch TV
or do a maths exam paper, you will see them all over the place. It's really important you're
confident with using them, so make sure to get lots of practice in now.

Compound Interest and Depreciation

Unlike <u>simple interest</u>, in <u>compound growth and decay</u> the amount added on (or taken away) <u>changes</u> each time — it's a percentage of the <u>new amount</u>, rather than the <u>original amount</u>.

The **Formula**

This topic is simple if you <u>LEARN THIS FORMULA</u>.

N_0 = Initial amount r = Percentage change per day/hour/year

N = Amount after n days/hours/years

$$N = N_0\left(1 + \frac{r}{100}\right)^n$$

n = Number of days/hours/years

Percentage **Increase** and **Decrease**

The $\left(1 + \frac{r}{100}\right)$ bit might look a bit confusing in the formula, but in practice it's really easy:

E.g.   5% increase will be <u>1.05</u>   5% decrease will be <u>0.95</u>   (= 1 – 0.05)
        26% increase will be <u>1.26</u>   26% decrease will be <u>0.74</u>   (= 1 – 0.26)

Two Examples to show you how **EASY** it is:

<u>Compound interest</u> is a popular context for these questions — it means the interest is <u>added on each time</u>, and the next lot of interest is calculated using the <u>new total</u> rather than the original amount.

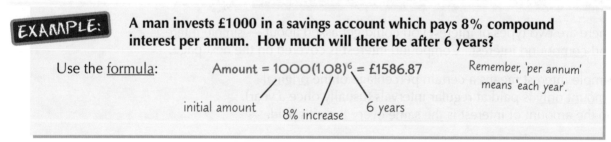

EXAMPLE: A man invests £1000 in a savings account which pays 8% compound interest per annum. How much will there be after 6 years?

Use the <u>formula</u>:   Amount = $1000(1.08)^6$ = £1586.87   Remember, 'per annum' means 'each year'.

initial amount   8% increase   6 years

<u>Depreciation</u> questions are about things (e.g. cars) which <u>decrease in value</u> over time.

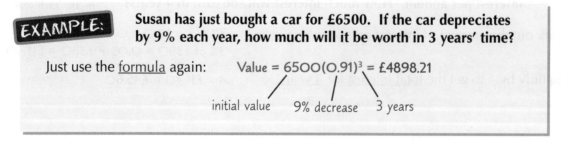

EXAMPLE: Susan has just bought a car for £6500. If the car depreciates by 9% each year, how much will it be worth in 3 years' time?

Just use the <u>formula</u> again: Value = $6500(0.91)^3$ = £4898.21

initial value   9% decrease   3 years

Compound growth and decay — percentages applied again and again

What this method does is to get the original value, increase it by the percentage, then increase that amount by the percentage, then take that amount and increase it by the percentage, then... get it?

Warm-Up and Worked Exam Questions

Have a go at these warm-up questions and see how you get on — the exam questions will be a bit more tricky, so it's important that you can do these first.

Warm-Up Questions

1) Find 15% of £90.
2) A watch is bought for £96 and sold at 135% of its original price. How much did it sell for?
3) Write 36 out of 80 as a percentage.
4) £200 is put in a bank account paying 2% simple interest (per year).
   Find the total amount in the account after 2 years if no money has been withdrawn.
5) £3000 is invested at 3% compound interest (per year).
   Work out how much money is in the account at the end of 4 years, to the nearest penny.

Worked Exam Questions

Another couple of worked exam questions for you. Study them well — they might just help.

1   Ben wants to buy a new laptop. His local shop sells two different laptops.
     VAT is added at a cost of 20% of the laptop's original price.

   a) Laptop A costs £395 before VAT is added. What is the total price including VAT?

       20% = 20 ÷ 100 = 0.2
       so VAT = 0.2 × £395 = £79

       Total price = £395 + £79 = £474

       You could also just do
       £395 × 1.2 = £474

       £ ......474......
       [3 marks]

   b) The VAT on laptop B is £99. What is the total price of the laptop including VAT?

       ÷ 20 ⎰ £99 = 20% of original price
            ⎱ £4.95 = 1% of original price
       × 100 ⎰ £495 = 100% of original price

       Total price = £495 + £99 = £594

       £ ......594......
       [3 marks]

2   A new house cost £120 000, but increased in value by 15% each year.
     Work out its value after 5 years, to the nearest £1000.

     $$N = N_0\left(1 + \frac{r}{100}\right)^n$$

     $$= £120\,000 \times \left(1 + \frac{15}{100}\right)^5$$

     $$= £120\,000 \times 1.15^5 = £241\,362.86\ldots$$

     £ ...241 000 (nearest £1000)...
     [3 marks]

Exam Questions

3   A farmer has 40 pigs. 24 of them are female. **(3)**
    What percentage of the farmer's pigs are male?

.... %

[3 marks]

4   Bill is looking at caravans. **(4)**

    a)   He sees one that cost £18 500 when it was new. It is now worth £12 600.
         Calculate the percentage decrease in value to 1 d.p.

.... %

[3 marks]

    b)   Another caravan has dropped 30% in value. It is now worth £11 549.
         What was its original value to the nearest pound?

£ ....

[3 marks]

5   A barrel has a small leak in it. Each week for the last six weeks, the volume of water
    in the barrel has decreased by 11%. Given that it now contains 3995 ml of water, **(5)**
    work out the volume of water in the barrel six weeks ago, to the nearest 100 ml.

.... ml

[3 marks]

6   Mrs Khan puts £2500 into a high interest savings account.   Compound interest is added to
    the account at the end of each year. After 2 years Mrs Khan's account contains £2704. **(6)**
    What is the interest rate on Mrs Khan's account?

.... %

[3 marks]

Ratios

Ratios are a pretty important topic — the next couple of pages should make the whole thing crystal clear.

Reducing **Ratios** to Their **Simplest Form**

To reduce a ratio to a <u>simpler form</u>, divide <u>all the numbers</u> in the ratio by the <u>same thing</u> (a bit like simplifying a fraction). It's in its <u>simplest form</u> when there's nothing left you can divide by.

> **EXAMPLE:** **Write the ratio 15:18 in its simplest form.**
>
> For the ratio 15:18, both numbers have a <u>factor</u> of 3, so <u>divide them by 3</u>. $\div 3 \diagdown {}^{15:18}_{= \ 5:6} \diagup \div 3$
>
> We can't reduce this any further, so: The simplest form of 15:18 is **5:6**.

> ### A handy trick — use the fraction button
> If you enter a fraction with the ▢ or ▢ button, the calculator automatically cancels it down when you press ▢ . So for the ratio 8:12, just enter $\frac{8}{12}$ as a fraction, and it'll simplify to $\frac{2}{3}$. Now you just change it back to ratio form, i.e. <u>2:3</u>.

The More **Awkward Cases:**

1) If the ratio contains **decimals** or **fractions** — **multiply**

> **EXAMPLES:** **1. Simplify the ratio 2.4:3.6 as far as possible.**
>
> 1) <u>Multiply both sides by 10</u> to get rid of the decimal parts. $= {}^{\times 10} \diagdown {}^{2.4:3.6}_{24:36} \diagup {}^{\times 10}$
> 2) Now <u>divide</u> to reduce the ratio to its simplest form. $= {}^{\div 12} \diagdown {}_{2:3} \diagup {}^{\div 12}$

> **2. Give the ratio $\frac{5}{4}:\frac{7}{2}$ in its simplest form.**
>
> 1) Put the fractions over a <u>common denominator</u> (see p.13). $\frac{5}{4}:\frac{7}{2}$
> 2) Multiply <u>both sides</u> by 4 to get rid of the fractions. $= {}^{\times 4} \left({}^{\frac{5}{4}:\frac{14}{4}} \right) {}^{\times 4}$
> 3) This ratio won't cancel further, so we're done. $5:14$

2) If the ratio has **mixed units** — convert to the **smaller unit**

> **EXAMPLE:** **Reduce the ratio 24 mm:7.2 cm to its simplest form.**
>
> 1) <u>Convert</u> 7.2 cm to millimetres. $24 \text{ mm}:7.2 \text{ cm}$
> 2) <u>Simplify</u> the resulting ratio. Once the units on both sides are the same, <u>get rid of them</u> for the final answer. $= 24 \text{ mm}:72 \text{ mm}$ $= {}^{\div 24} \diagdown {}_{1:3} \diagup {}^{\div 24}$

3) To get the form **1 : n** or **n : 1** — just **divide**

> **EXAMPLE:** **Reduce 3:56 to the form 1:n.** ◄——— This form is often the <u>most useful</u>, since it shows the ratio very clearly.
>
> Divide both sides by 3: $\div 3 \diagdown {}^{3:56}_{1:\frac{56}{3}} \diagup \div 3$
> $= 1:18\frac{2}{3}$ (or 1:18.6̇)

Ratios

Scaling Up **Ratios**

If you know the <u>ratio between parts</u> and the actual size of <u>one part</u>,
you can <u>scale the ratio up</u> to find the other parts.

> **EXAMPLE:**  Mrs Miggins owns tabby cats and ginger cats in the ratio 3:5.
> All her cats are either tabby or ginger, and she has 12 tabby cats.
> How many cats does Mrs Miggins have in total?
>
> Multiply <u>both sides</u> by 4 to go from 3 to 12 on the LHS:
>
> Mrs Miggins has 12 tabby cats and 20 ginger cats.
> So, in total, she has 12 + 20 = 32 cats.
>
> tabby:ginger
> = ×4(3:5)×4
> = 12:20

Proportional **Division**

In a <u>proportional division</u> question, a <u>TOTAL AMOUNT</u> is split into parts <u>in a certain ratio</u>.
The key word here is <u>PARTS</u> — concentrate on 'parts' and it all becomes quite painless:

> **EXAMPLE:** Jess, Mo and Greg share £9100 in the ratio 2:4:7. How much does Mo get?
>
> 1) <u>ADD UP THE PARTS</u>:
>   The ratio 2:4:7 means there will be a total of 13 <u>parts</u>:   2 + 4 + 7 = 13 parts
>
> 2) <u>DIVIDE TO FIND ONE "PART"</u>:
>   Just divide the <u>total amount</u> by the number of <u>parts</u>:   £9100 ÷ 13 = £700 (= 1 part)
>
> 3) <u>MULTIPLY TO FIND THE AMOUNTS</u>:
>   We want to know <u>Mo's share</u>, which is <u>4 parts</u>:   4 parts = 4 × £700 = £2800

Using the **Difference Between Two Parts**

Sometimes questions give you the <u>difference between two parts</u> instead of the <u>total amount</u>.

> **EXAMPLE:** A baguette is cut into 3 pieces in the ratio 1:2:5. The first piece is
> 28 cm smaller than the third piece. How long is the second piece?
>
> 1) Work out <u>how many parts</u> 28 cm makes up.   28 cm = 3rd piece − 1st piece
>   = 5 parts − 1 part = 4 parts
>
> 2) <u>Divide</u> to find <u>one part</u>.   28 cm ÷ 4 = 7 cm
>
> 3) <u>Multiply</u> to find the length of the <u>2nd piece</u>.   2nd piece = 2 parts = 2 × 7 cm = 14 cm

---

You need to know how to simplify all kinds of ratios

You should also understand how to scale up ratios and the three steps for proportional division.
If you're stuck, it's often really helpful to think about what one 'part' is and take it from there...

Proportion

Proportion problems all involve amounts that increase or decrease together.

Learn the **Golden Rule** for **Proportion** Questions

There are lots of exam questions which, at first sight, seem completely different — but in fact they can all be done using the <u>GOLDEN RULE</u>...

> ### DIVIDE FOR ONE, THEN TIMES FOR ALL

EXAMPLE: **5 pints of milk cost £1.30. How much will 3 pints cost?**

The <u>GOLDEN RULE</u> says: | **DIVIDE FOR ONE, THEN TIMES FOR ALL**

which means: <u>Divide the price by 5</u> to find how much <u>FOR ONE PINT</u>, then <u>multiply by 3</u> to find how much <u>FOR 3 PINTS</u>.

So for 1 pint: £1.30 ÷ 5 = 0.26 = 26p
For 3 pints: 26p × 3 = 78p

Use the **Golden Rule** to Scale **Recipes** Up or Down

EXAMPLE: **A fruit punch uses the recipe shown on the right.**

Judy wants to make enough fruit punch to serve 20 people. How much grape juice will she need?

Use the <u>GOLDEN RULE</u> again:

> **Fruit Punch (serves 8)**
> 800 ml orange juice
> 600 ml grape juice
> 200 ml cherry juice
> 140 g fresh pineapple

> ### DIVIDE FOR ONE, THEN TIMES FOR ALL

which means: <u>Divide the amount of grape juice by 8</u> to find how much <u>FOR ONE PERSON</u>, then <u>multiply by 20</u> to find how much <u>FOR 20 PEOPLE</u>.

So for 1 person you need: And for 20 people you need:
600 ml ÷ 8 = 75 ml grape juice   ⇒   20 × 75 ml = 1500 ml grape juice

You'll need to do something a bit different for some proportion questions.

EXAMPLE: **Using the recipe above, Arthur makes enough fruit punch for all the guests at a party. He uses 4 litres of orange juice. How many guests were at the party?**

1) First, convert <u>litres</u> into <u>millilitres</u>.

     4 litres = (4 × 1000) ml = 4000 ml

2) <u>Divide the amount of orange juice</u> in the recipe <u>by 8</u> to find how much <u>FOR ONE PERSON</u>.

     For 1 person: 800 ml ÷ 8 = 100 ml orange juice

3) To find the <u>number of guests</u>, just <u>divide</u> the amount of orange juice Arthur uses by the amount needed <u>for one person</u>.

     4000 ml ÷ 100 ml = 40 people

> Divide for one, but <u>don't</u> multiply for all — you already know the 'all' (4 litres of juice). Instead, <u>divide</u> to find the missing number of people.

Remember the golden rule and these questions will be much easier

Proportion questions are often hidden in wordy contexts, so you need to learn to recognise when to use this method. Luckily, the method itself is pretty easy once you know it well — it's mostly common sense.

Warm-Up and Worked Exam Questions

Make the most of the help on this page by working through everything carefully.

Warm-Up Questions

1) Write these ratios in their simplest forms:
   a) $4:8$ b) $12:27$ c) $1.2:5.4$ d) $\frac{8}{3}:\frac{7}{6}$ e) 0.5 litres : 400 ml

2) Reduce $5:22$ to the form $1:n$.

3) A recipe uses flour and sugar in the ratio $3:2$.
   How much flour do you need if you're using 300 g of sugar?

4) Divide 180 in the ratio $3:4:5$.

5) The ages of Ben, Graham and Pam are in the ratio $3:7:8$.
   Pam is 25 years older than Ben. How old is Graham?

6) It costs £43.20 for 8 people to go on a rollercoaster 6 times.
   How much will it cost for 15 people to go on a rollercoaster 5 times?

Worked Exam Questions

I've gone through these questions and filled in the answers like you'll do in the exam, so take a look.

1   Laura and Ashim are building scale models of a bridge.
    Laura uses a scale of $1:38$ and her model is 133 cm long.
    Ashim's model is 53.2 cm long.

    What scale is Ashim using? Give your answer in the form $1:n$.

    Find the length of the bridge: **model : actual**

    = × 133 (**1 : 38**) × 133
    =   **133 : 5054**

    So the bridge is 5054 cm long.   Make sure the units match
                                                         — both are in cm here.
    Use this to find Ashim's scale: **model : actual**

    = ÷ 53.2 (**53.2 : 5054**) ÷ 53.2
    =   **1 : 95**

                                                    1 : 95
                                                   ....
                                                   [2 marks]

2   Ishmael has bought 23 identical glass slippers for £86.25. (3)
    Work out the total cost of 11 of these slippers.

    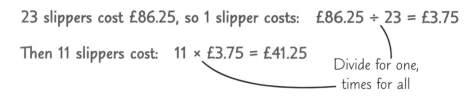

    23 slippers cost £86.25, so 1 slipper costs: £86.25 ÷ 23 = £3.75

    Then 11 slippers cost: 11 × £3.75 = £41.25

                                        Divide for one,
                                        times for all

                                        £ .....**41.25**.....
                                              [2 marks]

Exam Questions

3   The vehicles at a motorshow are cars, motorbikes and hovercrafts in the ratio $13:5:1$. **(3)**
     If there are 286 cars at the show, what is the total number of motorbikes and hovercrafts?

....

[3 marks]

4   Here is a list of ingredients for making flapjacks. **(3)**

> Simple Flapjack Recipe
> (Makes 12)
>
> 250 g oats   150 g butter
> 75 g sugar   75 g syrup

a)   Elenni is making 18 flapjacks. How much butter does she need?

.... g

[2 marks]

b)   Jo has 300 g of syrup. What is the maximum number of flapjacks she can make?

....

[2 marks]

5   Eve is making a bird house. To make the walls, she takes a piece of wood and cuts it into **(4)**
     four pieces in the ratio $5:6:6:7$. The longest wall is 9 cm longer than the shortest wall.
     How long was the original piece of wood?

.... cm

[3 marks]

Rounding Numbers

There are <u>two different ways</u> of specifying <u>where</u> a number should be <u>rounded</u>. The first one is '<u>Decimal Places</u>'.

Decimal Places (d.p.)

To round to a given number of <u>decimal places</u>:

1) <u>Identify</u> the position of the '<u>last digit</u>' from the number of decimal places.

> 'Last digit' = last one in the <u>rounded version</u>, not the original number.

2) Then look at the next digit to the <u>right</u> — called <u>the decider</u>.

3) If the <u>decider</u> is <u>5 or more</u>, then <u>round up</u> the <u>last digit</u>.
   If the <u>decider</u> is <u>4 or less</u>, then leave the <u>last digit</u> as it is.

4) There must be <u>no more digits</u> after the last digit (not even zeros).

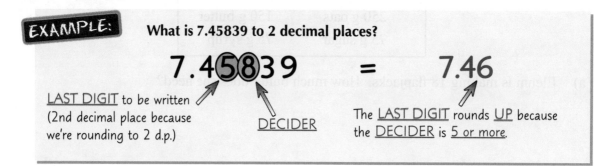

EXAMPLE: **What is 7.45839 to 2 decimal places?**

$$7.45839 \quad = \quad 7.46$$

<u>LAST DIGIT</u> to be written (2nd decimal place because we're rounding to 2 d.p.)

<u>DECIDER</u>

The <u>LAST DIGIT</u> rounds <u>UP</u> because the <u>DECIDER</u> is <u>5 or more</u>.

Trickier Cases with **Nines**

1) If you have to <u>round up</u> a <u>9</u> (to 10), replace the 9 with 0, and <u>carry 1</u> to the left.
2) Remember to keep enough <u>zeros</u> to fill the right number of decimal places.

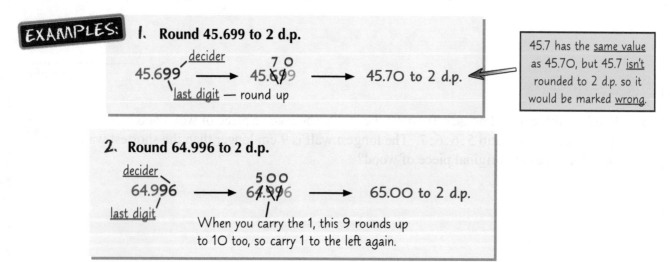

EXAMPLES: **1. Round 45.699 to 2 d.p.**

decider
45.699 ⟶ 45.699 ⟶ 45.70 to 2 d.p.
last digit — round up

> 45.7 has the <u>same value</u> as 45.70, but 45.7 <u>isn't</u> rounded to 2 d.p. so it would be marked <u>wrong</u>.

2. Round 64.996 to 2 d.p.

decider
64.996 ⟶ 64.996 ⟶ 65.00 to 2 d.p.
last digit

When you carry the 1, this 9 rounds up to 10 too, so carry 1 to the left again.

Your answer should have the right number of decimal places

If the question asks for 3 d.p., there should always be 3 digits after the decimal point — even if they're all zeros. If you can remember that, then rounding questions should be nice and easy.

Rounding Numbers

The other method of rounding is 'Significant Figures'. It's a bit tricker than decimal places, but not much.

Significant Figures (s.f.)

The method for significant figures is <u>identical</u> to that for decimal places, except that locating the <u>last digit</u> is more difficult — it wouldn't be so bad, but for the <u>zeros</u>.

> 1) The <u>1st significant figure</u> of any number is simply the <u>first digit which isn't a zero.</u>

> 2) The <u>2nd, 3rd, 4th, etc. significant figures</u> follow on immediately after the 1st, <u>regardless of being zeros or not zeros.</u>

$$0.002309 \qquad\qquad 2.03070$$

SIG. FIGS: 1st 2nd   3rd 4th   1st 2nd   3rd   4th

(If we're rounding to say, 3 s.f., then the LAST DIGIT is simply the 3rd sig. fig.)

> 3) After <u>rounding</u> the <u>last digit</u>, <u>end zeros</u> must be filled in up to, <u>but not beyond</u>, the decimal point.

No <u>extra zeros</u> must ever be put in <u>after</u> the decimal point.

EXAMPLES:

	to 3 s.f.	to 2 s.f.	to 1 s.f.
1) **54.7651**	54.8	55	50
2) **17.0067**	17.0	17	20
3) **0.0045902**	0.00459	0.0046	0.005
4) **30895.4**	30900	31000	30000

Estimating

This is <u>very easy</u>, so long as you don't <u>over-complicate it</u>.

> 1) <u>Round everything off</u> to nice, easy, <u>convenient numbers</u>.
> 2) Then <u>work out the answer</u> using these nice easy numbers.

EXAMPLE: Estimate the value of $\dfrac{127.8 + 41.9}{56.5 \times 3.2}$, showing all your working.

1) Round all the numbers to <u>easier ones</u> — <u>1 or 2 s.f.</u> usually does the trick.

$$\frac{127.8 + 41.9}{56.5 \times 3.2} \approx \frac{130 + 40}{60 \times 3}$$

2) You can <u>round again</u> to make later steps easier if you need to.

$$= \frac{170}{180} \approx 1$$

Remember — the first significant figure is the first non-zero digit

If you're asked to estimate something in the exam, make sure you show all your steps (including what each number is rounded to) to prove that you didn't just use a calculator. Hassle, but it'll pay off.

Bounds

Finding <u>upper and lower bounds</u> is pretty easy, but using them in <u>calculations</u> is a bit trickier.

Upper and Lower Bounds

> **Whenever a measurement is <u>rounded</u> to a <u>given UNIT</u>, the <u>actual measurement</u> can be anything up to <u>HALF A UNIT</u> bigger or smaller.**

EXAMPLE: **A room is 9 m long to the nearest metre. Find upper and lower bounds for its length.**

The actual length could be <u>half a metre</u> either side of 9 m.　　lower bound = 8.5 m
　　　　　　　　　　　　　　　　　　　　　　　　　　　　　　 upper bound = 9.5 m

Note that the actual value is <u>greater than or equal to</u> the <u>lower bound</u> but <u>less than</u> the <u>upper bound</u>. In the example above, the actual length could be <u>exactly</u> 8.5 m, but if it was exactly 9.5 m it would <u>round up</u> to 10 m instead. Or, written as an inequality (see p.69), 8.5 m ≤ actual length < 9.5 m.

EXAMPLE: **The mass of a cake is given as 2.4 kg to the nearest 0.1 kg. What are the upper and lower bounds for the actual mass of the cake?**

The <u>rounding unit</u> here is 0.1 kg, so the actual value 　　lower bound = 2.4 − 0.05 = 2.35 kg
could be anything in the range <u>2.4 kg ± 0.05 kg</u>.　　　　　 upper bound = 2.4 + 0.05 = 2.45 kg

Maximum and Minimum Values for Calculations

When a calculation is done using rounded values there will be a <u>DISCREPANCY</u> between the <u>CALCULATED VALUE</u> and the <u>ACTUAL VALUE</u>:

EXAMPLES: **1. A floor is measured as being 5.3 m by 4.2 m, to the nearest 10 cm. Calculate minimum and maximum possible values for the area of the floor.**

1) The actual dimensions of the floor could be anything 　　minimum possible floor area = 5.25 × 4.15
from <u>5.25 m to 5.35 m</u> and <u>4.15 m to 4.25 m</u>.　　　　　　　　　　　　　　 = 21.7875 m^2

2) Find the <u>minimum</u> area by multiplying the <u>lower bounds</u>, 　maximum possible floor area = 5.35 × 4.25
and the <u>maximum</u> by multiplying the <u>upper bounds</u>.　　　　　　　　　　　　　 = 22.7375 m^2

2. To 1 d.p., a = 5.3 and b = 4.2. What are the maximum and minimum possible values of $a \div b$?

1) First find the <u>bounds</u> for a and b. ———→ 5.25 ≤ a < 5.35,　4.15 ≤ b < 4.25

2) Now the tricky bit... The <u>bigger</u> the number
you <u>divide by</u>, the <u>smaller</u> the answer, so:　　 max. value of $a \div b$ = 5.35 ÷ 4.15
　　　　　　　　　　　　　　　　　　　　　　　　　　　　 = 1.289 (to 3 d.p.)

max($a \div b$) = max(a) ÷ min(b)
min($a \div b$) = min(a) ÷ max(b)　　　　　　 min. value of $a \div b$ = 5.25 ÷ 4.25
　　　　　　　　　　　　　　　　　　　　　　　　　　　　 = 1.235 (to 3 d.p.)

Bounds tell you the possible values of something that's been rounded

When you want to find the maximum or minimum value of a calculation, working out which bound to use for each bit can be pretty confusing — so make sure you always think about it very carefully.

Standard Form

Standard form (or 'standard index form') is useful for writing <u>VERY BIG</u> or <u>VERY SMALL</u> numbers in a more convenient way, e.g. $56\,000\,000\,000$ would be 5.6×10^{10} in standard form.

$0.000\,000\,003\,45$ would be 3.45×10^{-9} in standard form.

But <u>ANY NUMBER</u> can be written in standard form and you need to know how to do it:

What it Actually is:

A number written in standard form must <u>always</u> be in <u>exactly</u> this form:

This <u>number</u> must <u>always</u> be <u>between 1 and 10</u>.

$$A \times 10^n$$

This number is just the <u>number of places</u> the <u>decimal point</u> moves.

(The fancy way of saying this is $1 \leq A < 10$)

Learn the Three Rules:

1) The <u>front number</u> must always be <u>between 1 and 10</u>.
2) The power of 10, n, is <u>how far the decimal point moves</u>.
3) n is <u>positive for BIG numbers</u>, n is <u>negative for SMALL numbers</u>.
   (This is much better than rules based on which way the decimal point moves.)

Four Important Examples:

1 **Express 35 600 in standard form.**

1) <u>Move the decimal point</u> until 35 600 becomes 3.56 ($1 \leq A < 10$).
2) The decimal point has moved <u>4 places</u> so n = 4, giving: 10^4
3) 35 600 is a <u>big number</u> so n is +4, not −4.

35600.0
$= 3.56 \times 10^4$

2 **Express 0.0000623 in standard form.**

1) The decimal point must move <u>5 places</u> to give 6.23 ($1 \leq A < 10$). So the power of 10 is 5.
2) Since 0.0000623 is a <u>small number</u> it must be 10^{-5} not 10^{+5}

0.0000623
$= 6.23 \times 10^{-5}$

3 **Express 4.95×10^{-3} as an ordinary number.**

1) The power of 10 is <u>negative</u>, so it's a <u>small number</u> — the answer will be less than 1.
2) The power is −3, so the decimal point moves <u>3 places</u>.

0004.95×10^{-3}
$= 0.00495$

4 **What is 146.3 million in standard form?**

Too many people get this type of question <u>wrong</u>. Just take your time and do it in <u>two stages</u>:

146.3 million
$= 146300000$
$= 1.463 \times 10^8$

The two favourite <u>wrong answers</u> for this are:

146.3×10^6 — which is kind of right, but it's <u>not in standard form</u> because 146.3 is not between 1 and 10
1.463×10^6 — this one <u>is</u> in standard form, but it's <u>not big enough</u>

Standard Form

Calculations with Standard Form

These are really popular <u>exam questions</u> — you might be asked to add, subtract, multiply or divide using numbers written in <u>standard form</u>.

Multiplying and Dividing — not too bad

1) Rearrange to put the <u>front numbers</u> and the <u>powers of 10 together</u>.
2) Multiply or divide the front numbers, and use the <u>power rules</u> (see p.45) to multiply or divide the powers of 10.
3) Make sure your answer is still in <u>standard form</u>.

EXAMPLES:

1. Find $(2.24 \times 10^3) \times (6.75 \times 10^5)$.
Give your answer in standard form.

Multiply front numbers and powers separately

$(2.24 \times 10^3) \times (6.75 \times 10^5)$
$= (2.24 \times 6.75) \times (10^3 \times 10^5)$
$= 15.12 \times 10^{3+5}$ ——— Add the powers (see p.45)
$= 15.12 \times 10^8$

Not in standard form — convert it
$= 1.512 \times 10 \times 10^8$
$= 1.512 \times 10^9$

2. Calculate $189\,000 \div (5.4 \times 10^{10})$.
Give your answer in standard form.

Convert 189 000 to standard form
$189\,000 \div (5.4 \times 10^{10})$
$= \dfrac{1.89 \times 10^5}{5.4 \times 10^{10}} = \dfrac{1.89}{5.4} \times \dfrac{10^5}{10^{10}}$

Divide front numbers and powers separately
$= 0.35 \times 10^{5-10}$ ——— Subtract the powers (see p.45)
$= 0.35 \times 10^{-5}$

Not in standard form — convert it
$= 3.5 \times 10^{-1} \times 10^{-5}$
$= 3.5 \times 10^{-6}$

Adding and Subtracting — a bit trickier

1) Make sure the <u>powers of 10</u> are <u>the same</u> — you'll probably need to rewrite one of them.
2) Add or subtract the <u>front numbers</u>.
3) Convert the answer to <u>standard form</u> if necessary.

EXAMPLE: Calculate $(9.8 \times 10^4) + (6.6 \times 10^3)$. Give your answer in standard form.

$(9.8 \times 10^4) + (6.6 \times 10^3)$

1) <u>Rewrite one number</u> so both powers of 10 are equal:
$= (9.8 \times 10^4) + (0.66 \times 10^4)$

2) Now add the <u>front numbers</u>:
$= (9.8 + 0.66) \times 10^4$

3) 10.46×10^4 isn't in standard form, so <u>convert it</u>:
$= 10.46 \times 10^4 = 1.046 \times 10^5$

To put standard form numbers into your <u>calculator</u>, use the **EXP** or the **×10ˣ** button.
E.g. enter 2.67×10^{15} by pressing **2.67** **EXP** **15** **=** or **2.67** **×10ˣ** **15** **=** .

Your calculator might <u>display</u> an answer such as 7.986×10^{15} as [7.986 ¹⁵].
If so, <u>don't forget</u> to add in the "×10" bit when you write it down.
Some calculators do display a little "×10" or "E", so check what yours does.

Remember, n tells you how far the decimal point moves

If you aren't a fan of the method above, you can add and subtract numbers in standard form by writing them as ordinary numbers, adding or subtracting as usual, then converting the answer back to standard form.

Warm-Up and Worked Exam Questions

Without a good warm-up you're likely to strain a brain cell or two. So take the time to run through these simple questions and get the basic facts straight before plunging into the exam questions.

Warm-Up Questions

1) Round these numbers to the level of accuracy indicated:
   a) 40.218 to 2 d.p.
   b) 39.888 to 3 s.f.
   c) 27.91 to 2 s.f.

2) By rounding to 1 significant figure, estimate the answer to $\dfrac{94 \times 1.9}{0.328 + 0.201}$.

3) A distance is given as 14 km, to the nearest km.
   Find the upper and lower bounds for the distance.

4) $r = 6.3$ and $s = 2.9$, both to 1 d.p. Find the maximum and minimum possible values for:
   a) $r + s$
   b) $r - s$
   c) $r \times s$
   d) $r \div s$

5) The half-life of a chemical isotope is 0.0000027 seconds. Write this number in standard form.

6) Find each of the following. Give your answers in standard form.
   a) $(3 \times 10^6) \times (8 \times 10^4)$
   b) $(8.4 \times 10^8) \div (4.2 \times 10^4)$
   c) $(7.65 \times 10^6) + (1.47 \times 10^5)$

Worked Exam Questions

With the answers written in, it's very easy to skim these worked examples and think you've understood. But that's not going to help you, so take the time to make sure you've really understood them.

1 The width of a rectangular piece of paper is 23.6 centimetres, correct to 1 decimal place.
  The length of the paper is 54.1 centimetres, correct to 1 decimal place.

   a) Write down the lower bound for the length of the paper.

   Lower bound for length = 54.1 cm − 0.05 cm
                          = 54.05 cm

   .... 54.05 cm
   [1 mark]

   b) Calculate the lower bound for the perimeter of the piece of paper.

   Lower bound for width = 23.6 cm − 0.05 cm
                         = 23.55 cm

   Lower bound for perimeter = (2 × 54.05 cm) + (2 × 23.55 cm)
                             = 108.1 cm + 47.1 cm = 155.2 cm

   .... 155.2 cm
   [2 marks]

2 $A = 2.7 \times 10^5$ and $B = 5.81 \times 10^3$. Work out $A \times B$. Give your answer in standard form.

   Multiply the front numbers together and use the power rules on the powers of 10:

   A × B = (2.7 × 10⁵) × (5.81 × 10³)

   = (2.7 × 5.81) × (10⁵ × 10³)

   = 15.687 × 10⁸

   = 1.5687 × 10⁹ ⟵ *Make sure the final answer is in standard form.*

   .... 1.5687 × 10⁹
   [2 marks]

Exam Questions

3   Look at the following calculation: $\frac{215.7 \times 44.8}{460}$ (4)

    a)   By rounding each of the numbers to 1 significant figure, give an estimate for $\frac{215.7 \times 44.8}{460}$.

....

[3 marks]

    b)   Without using your calculator, will your answer to part a)
    be larger or smaller than the exact answer? Explain why.

....

....

[2 marks]

4   A cruise ship weighs approximately 7.59×10^7 kg.   (5)
Its passengers weigh a total of 2.1×10^5 kg.

> You need matching powers to
> be able to add together two
> numbers in standard form.

    a)   Find the total weight of the ship and passengers,
    giving your answer in standard form. Show all your working.

.... kg

[2 marks]

    b)   Express the weight of the passengers as a percentage of the total combined
    weight of the ship and passengers. Give your answer to 2 decimal places.

.... %

[2 marks]

5   Here is a rectangle.   (7)
$x = 55$ mm to the nearest 5 mm.
$y = 30$ mm to the nearest 5 mm.

Calculate the upper bound for the area of this rectangle.
Give your answer to 3 significant figures.

y

x

Not to scale

.... mm²

[3 marks]

Sets

Sets come with some pretty weird notation, but a <u>set</u> is just a maths word for a <u>collection of things</u>.

Learn How to Use **Set Notation**

1) You can describe a set by listing everything in it, e.g. {2, 4, 6}, or by giving a rule, e.g. {things that are red} or {odd numbers}. ← The <u>curly brackets</u> tell you that this is a set.

2) Each object in a set is called a <u>member</u> or <u>element</u>. There's some special notation for this:

| ∈ | ...IS A MEMBER OF... | | ∉ | ...IS NOT A MEMBER OF... |

E.g. strawberry ∈ {things that are red}, 2 ∉ {odd numbers}

3) You can use a <u>capital letter</u> to stand for <u>a set</u>, e.g. A = {numbers that are multiples of four}, and a <u>lower case letter</u> to stand for <u>a member</u> of a set, e.g. $x \notin$ A.

Two important sets have their own symbols:

| {} or ∅ | THE EMPTY SET | If a set has <u>no members</u> at all, it's called <u>the empty set</u>. E.g. if set B = {negative numbers between 1 and 10} then set B = ∅.

| ξ | THE UNIVERSAL SET | The <u>universal set</u> is the group of things that the members of a set are selected from.

EXAMPLES:

1. ξ = {5, 6, 7, 8, 9, 10, 11, 12, 13, 14, 15, 16, 17}
A = {Even numbers}
Write down all the members of set A.

The members of A are the even numbers within the universal set.

Members of set A:
6, 8, 10, 12, 14, 16

2. ξ = {Positive whole numbers}
B = {Prime numbers}
Is it true that 6 ∈ B?

6 is not a prime number, so 6 is <u>not</u> a member of B.
So 6 ∈ B is **not** true.

You Can Describe Sets Using **Numbers** and **Symbols**

If a set is described using numbers and symbols, work out what the description <u>means in words</u> before you start working with the set.

The <u>colon</u> means 'such that'.

$\{x : x < 0\}$ —— This is <u>the set of numbers, x, such that x is less than 0</u>, i.e. the set of negative numbers.

$\{(x, y) : y = 2x + 2\}$ —— This is <u>the set of all the points (x, y) such that $y = 2x + 2$</u>, i.e. the set of coordinates that lie on the line $y = 2x + 2$.

See p.69 for more on the inequality symbols > and <.

EXAMPLE:

ξ = {Negative integers}, P = {$x : x > -6$}. **List all the members of set P.**

1) Check what the <u>universal set</u> is.   The universal set is the negative whole numbers.

2) Combine this with the <u>definition</u> of set P to find the <u>members</u> of P.

So, P is the set of whole numbers that are bigger than −6 but less than 0.

The members of P are −5, −4, −3, −2 and −1.

Sets can contain more than just numbers

For example, you are a member of the set {People who have read this tip}. Sets can contain anything, including coordinates, shapes or colours — and in probability, you have sets of outcomes (see p.190).

Sets

When there's more than one set, things get more interesting — we're talking <u>UNIONS</u> and <u>INTERSECTIONS</u>.

The **Union** of Two Sets

The <u>UNION</u> of two sets is a <u>set</u> containing <u>all the members</u> that are in <u>either set</u>.
You write "<u>the union of set A and set B</u>" as $A \cup B$.

1. **F = {2, 5, 6} and G = {1, 5, 7}. List all the members of F ∪ G.**

List everything that appears in <u>either</u> F or G.

The members of F ∪ G are 1, 2, 5, 6 and 7.

5 appears in <u>both sets</u> but you <u>must only list it once</u>.

2. **P = {4, 7, 8} and P ∪ Q = {4, 5, 7, 8, 9}. Set Q has 2 members. Find set Q.**

Anything that's a member of P ∪ Q but not a member of P must be a member of Q.

5 and 9 are members of P ∪ Q but not members of P.
So 5 and 9 must be members of Q.
Q has 2 members, so 5 and 9 must be its only members.
So Q = {5, 9}

The **Intersection** of Two Sets

The <u>INTERSECTION</u> of two sets is a <u>set</u> that <u>only</u> contains objects that are <u>members of both sets</u>.
You write "<u>the intersection of set A and set B</u>" like this: $A \cap B$

EXAMPLE:

ξ = {9, 10, 11, 12, 13, 14, 15, 16, 17, 18}, J = {Odd numbers}, K = {Multiples of 3}
List all the members of J ∩ K.

1) Find the members of J and K:

2) Members of J ∩ K are members of <u>both J and K</u>.

Members of J: 9, 11, 13, 15, 17
Members of K: 9, 12, 15, 18

Members of J ∩ K: 9, 15

n(A) — the **Number of Members**

<u>n(A)</u> is shorthand for the <u>number of members</u> of set A. n(A) = 12 means "<u>Set A has 12 members</u>".

ξ = {Positive integers}, L = {x : 3 < x < 8}. What is n(L)?

1) Find the <u>members of L</u>:

2) <u>Count</u> the number of members:

Members of L: 4, 5, 6, 7

n(L) = 4

Make sure you know what all these symbols mean

It's important that you don't get ∪ and ∩ mixed up. If in doubt, say them out loud — the one that looks like a 'u' is the <u>u</u>nion symbol, and the one that looks like an 'n' is the i<u>n</u>tersection symbol.

Sets

Don't worry, there are only a few more sets definitions and symbols left to learn now.

The **Complement** of a Set

The <u>COMPLEMENT</u> of a set is all the members of the <u>universal set</u> that <u>aren't</u> in the set. "The <u>complement of set A</u>" is written as <u>A'</u>.

1. ξ = {1, 2, 3, 4, 5, 6, 7, 8, 9, 10}, F = {Multiples of 3}
List the members of F'.

1) First find the members of F.	The members of F are 3, 6 and 9.
2) The members of F' are the <u>members of</u> <u>the universal set</u> that <u>aren't members of F</u>:	So the members of F' are 1, 2, 4, 5, 7, 8 and 10.

2. ξ = {1, 2, 3, 4, 5, 6, 7, 8}, G = {$x : 2 \le x \le 7$}, H = {Factors of 12}
a) Find G ∩ H'.

1) Write G and H in terms of their <u>members</u>. G = {2, 3, 4, 5, 6, 7}

2) Find H'. H = {1, 2, 3, 4, 6} so H' = {5, 7, 8}

3) Find G ∩ H' — 5 and 7 are the only members of both G and H'. G ∩ H' = {5, 7}

b) Find (G ∩ H)'.

First find G ∩ H, then find its complement. G ∩ H = {2, 3, 4 6}
(G ∩ H)' = {1, 5, 7, 8}

> Watch out for brackets — G ∩ H' means the intersection of G and H', but (G ∩ H)' means the complement of G ∩ H.

Subsets are **Sets Within Sets**

1) A <u>SUBSET</u> is a set that is entirely contained <u>within</u> another set. This means that <u>all</u> the members of the <u>first set</u> are <u>also in the second set</u>.

2) There's another handy symbol for this: ⊂ ...IS A SUBSET OF...
E.g. if A = {5, 7, 11} and B = {prime numbers}, you can write "A ⊂ B".

3) And, of course, there's a symbol meaning the opposite too: ⊄ ...IS NOT A SUBSET OF...
E.g. if set A = {4, 8, 12} and set B = {prime numbers}, you can write "A ⊄ B".

ξ = {Positive integers less than 10},
S = {$x : 5 \le x \le 9$}, T = {Odd numbers}, U = {Prime numbers}
Is (S ∩ T) ⊂ U a true statement?

1) Write S, T and U in terms of their <u>members</u>. S = {5, 6, 7, 8, 9}, T = {1, 3, 5, 7, 9}, U = {2, 3, 5, 7}

2) Find S ∩ T. S ∩ T = {5, 7, 9}

3) If S ∩ T is a <u>subset</u> of U, every member of S ∩ T must also be a member of U. Decide whether this is true. 9 is a member of S ∩ T but not a member of U. So, (S ∩ T) ⊄ U and the statement is false.

There are a lot of words and notation to learn on these pages

This might be one of the toughest bits of this book to get your head around, but don't worry — once you know what all the words and symbols mean, the questions aren't really too bad.

Venn Diagrams

Venn diagrams look a bit odd, but they're actually pretty handy for showing the <u>relationships between sets</u>.

Venn Diagrams Use Circles to Represent Sets

1) Each set is represented by a <u>circle</u> — the space inside the circle represents everything in the set.
2) Each circle is labelled with a <u>letter</u> — this tells you which set each circle represents.
3) There might be a <u>number</u> inside the circle — this tells you the <u>number of members</u> of the set.

E.g. T = {People called Tammy in my class}

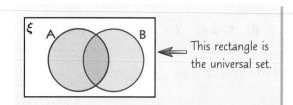

This tells you there are 3 people called Tammy in my class — so n(T) = 3.

4) The universal set is shown as a <u>rectangle</u> that goes <u>around all of the circles</u>, like this:

This rectangle is the universal set.

Venn diagrams can also show the <u>actual</u> <u>elements</u> of the sets, not just the numbers of elements.

Venn Diagrams Show Intersections and Unions

The <u>intersection</u> of sets is where the circles <u>overlap</u>. If two sets have no shared members then their circles won't overlap at all.

There are <u>12</u> objects that are <u>only members of A</u>.

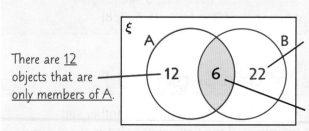

There are <u>22</u> objects that are <u>only</u> <u>members of B</u>.

The shaded area is A ∩ B. <u>6</u> objects are members of <u>both A and B</u>, so n(A ∩ B) = 6

The <u>union</u> of sets is all the space covered by the circles representing those sets.

You can find n(A ∪ B) by <u>adding</u> the number of members in each part of A ∪ B. So here: n(A ∪ B) = 12 + 6 + 22 = 40

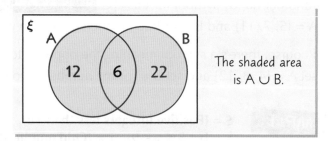

The shaded area is A ∪ B.

They Can Also Show Subsets and Complements

On a Venn diagram, the <u>complement</u> of a set is everything outside the circle representing that set.

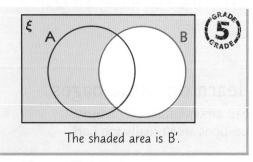

The shaded area is B'.

If set A is a <u>subset</u> of set B then on a Venn diagram the circle representing set A lies <u>completely inside</u> the circle representing set B.

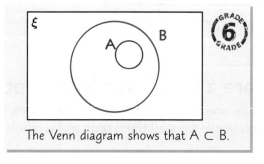

The Venn diagram shows that A ⊂ B.

Venn Diagrams

Using the **Numbers**

EXAMPLE: **P and Q are sets. $n(\xi) = 40$ and $n(P \cup Q) = 32$.**
Some other numbers of members have been filled in on the Venn diagram below.

a) **Find x.** $n(P \cup Q) = 15 + 7 + x$

So, $32 = 15 + 7 + x$

$x = 32 - 15 - 7 = 10$

b) **Find $n(P' \cap Q')$.**

$P' \cap Q'$ is the set of objects that are members of <u>neither P nor Q</u>.
This is represented by the <u>region outside both circles</u>:

$n(P' \cap Q') = n(\xi) - n(P \cup Q) = 40 - 32 = 8$

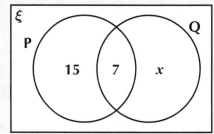

Drawing a Venn Diagram

To draw a Venn diagram you need to work out whether the <u>intersections</u> of each pair of sets have any members — this will tell you if the circles should overlap. Look out for any <u>subsets</u> too.

EXAMPLE: $\xi = $ {Positive integers less than 20},
A = {Odd numbers}, B = {Multiples of 3}, C = {Multiples of 6}
Draw a Venn Diagram representing the relationships between A, B and C.

A = {1, 3, 5, 7, 9, 11, 13, 15, 17, 19},
B = {3, 6, 9, 12, 15, 18}, C = {6, 12, 18}

$A \cap B = $ {3, 9, 15}, so circles A and B overlap.

C is a subset of B, so circle C is completely inside circle B.

$A \cap C = \emptyset$, so circles A and C do not overlap.

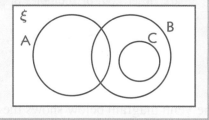

Venn Diagrams with **Three Intersecting Sets**

Venn diagrams can show <u>three intersecting sets</u>.
For sets A, B and C, the area where <u>all three circles overlap</u> represents $A \cap B \cap C$.
This is the set containing the objects that are <u>members of all three sets</u>.

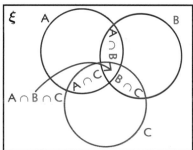

EXAMPLE: **Using set notation, describe the shaded area of the Venn diagram below.**

Everything in the shaded area is a member of Z, but not a member of X and not a member of Y.

So, they're members of Z <u>and</u> X' <u>and</u> Y'.

So the set is $X' \cap Y' \cap Z$. —— $(X \cup Y)' \cap Z$ would also be correct here.

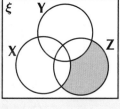

Make sure you know what unions and intersections look like

Getting $A \cup B$ mixed up with $A \cap B$ is a sorry way to lose marks. Fortunately, you'll have a bit more practice at this later on — set notation and Venn diagrams are also used to talk about probability.

Warm-Up and Worked Exam Questions

Hopefully, you now know everything you need from Section One. Just to make sure, have a go at these warm-ups. Once you're happy with those, move on to the exam questions.

Warm-Up Questions

1) ξ = {Members of a sports club}, K = {People who play badminton}.
   Peter is a member of the sports club and Peter $\notin$ K. What does this tell you about Peter?

2) C = {Trees}, D = {Things over 3 m tall}. Describe the members of C $\cap$ D'.

3) ξ = {2, 3, 4, 5, 6, 7, 8, 9, 10, 11, 12}
   J = {Odd numbers}, K = {Factors of 24}, L = {Prime numbers}
   a) Find K $\cap$ L.   b) What is n(K $\cap$ L)?   c) Is L $\subset$ (J $\cup$ K) a true statement?
   d) Draw a Venn diagram showing all the elements in these sets.

Worked Exam Questions

Have a read through these worked exam questions before having a go at some yourself.

1 ξ = {3, 5, 6, 8, 9, 11, 12, 14, 15}, A = {Even numbers}, B = {Multiples of 3}
   Write down the members of the following sets:

a) $A \cup B$

    A $\cup$ B is all the numbers that
    are either even <u>or</u> multiples of 3:

                3, 6, 8, 9, 12, 14, 15
                          [1 mark]

b) $A \cap B$

    A $\cap$ B is all the numbers that
    are both even <u>and</u> multiples of 3:

                  6, 12
                     [1 mark]

2 The Venn diagram below shows the sets A, B, C and the universal set ξ.
   Each number on the diagram represents the **number** of elements. Find:

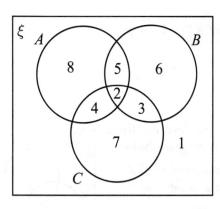

a) n($A \cup C$)

    A $\cup$ C is everything that is in A or C:
    8 + 5 + 4 + 2 + 7 + 3 = 29

                        29
                       [1 mark]

b) n($B \cap C'$)

    B $\cap$ C' is everything that is in B but not in C:
             5 + 6 = 11

                        11
                       [1 mark]

c) n($A' \cup B \cup C$)

    A' $\cup$ B $\cup$ C is anything that is either outside of A, inside B or inside C
    — this will be everything except those that are only in A.
         5 + 6 + 4 + 2 + 3 + 7 + 1 = 28

                        28
                       [1 mark]

Exam Questions

3   ξ = {Students at Hilltop College}

    B = {Students in basketball club}

    C = {Students in cycling club}

    F = {Students in football club}

Write a statement to interpret each of the following pieces of information.

a) $B \cap F = \varnothing$ 

....

[1 mark]

b) $n(C \cap F) = 5$

....

[1 mark]

4   L, M and N are three sets. L and M are shown on the diagram below.

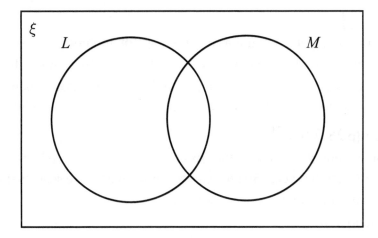

a) Shade the region represented by $L \cap M'$.

[1 mark]

b) Given that $L \cap N = \varnothing$ and $N \subset M$, draw the set N on the diagram.

[1 mark]

5   ξ = {Odd numbers}, R = {3, 5, 7, 9, 11, 13, 15}

    Set S is a subset of R such that $R \cap S' = \{5, 7, 11, 13\}$ and $n(S) = 3$.

    Write down the members of set S.

....

[2 marks]

Revision Questions for Section One

Well, that wraps up <u>Section One</u> — time to put yourself to the test and find out <u>how much you really know</u>.
- Try these questions and <u>tick off each one</u> when you <u>get it right</u>.
- When you've done <u>all the questions</u> for a topic and are <u>completely happy</u> with it, tick off the topic.

Types of Number, Roots, Factors and Multiples (p.1-9) ☑

1) What are: a) integers?   b) rational numbers?   c) prime numbers?

2) Complete the following: a) $13^2 = $ __   b) $\sqrt{49} = $ __   c) $\sqrt[3]{27} = $ __   d) $5^3 = $ __

3) Express each of these as a product of powers of prime factors: a) 1050   b) 360

4) a) Write 320 and 880 as products of their prime factors.
   b) Use the prime factorisations to find the LCM and HCF of 320 and 880.

Fractions, Decimals and Percentages (p.12-17) ☑

5) a) Write $\frac{74}{9}$ as a mixed number   b) Write $4\frac{5}{7}$ as an improper fraction

6) What are the rules for multiplying, dividing and adding/subtracting fractions?

7) Calculate: a) $\frac{2}{11} \times \frac{7}{9}$ b) $5\frac{1}{2} \div 1\frac{3}{4}$ c) $\frac{5}{8} - \frac{1}{6}$ d) $3\frac{3}{10} + 4\frac{1}{4}$

8) How do you convert: a) a fraction to a decimal?   b) a terminating decimal to a fraction?

9) Write: a) 0.04 as: (i) a fraction (ii) a percentage   b) 65% as: (i) a fraction (ii) a decimal

10) Show that $0.5\dot{1} = \frac{17}{33}$.

Percentages (p.20-22) ☑

11) What's the method for finding one amount as a percentage of another?

12) A tree's height has increased by 15% in the last year to 20.24 m. What was its height a year ago?

13) I have £850 to invest for 4 years. Which will pay more interest, and how much more:
    an account paying 6% simple interest, or an account paying 4% compound interest?

Ratios and Proportion (p.25-27) ☑

14) Sarah is in charge of ordering stock for a clothes shop. The shop usually sells red scarves and blue
    scarves in the ratio 5:8. Sarah orders 150 red scarves. How many blue scarves should she order?

15) What are the three steps of the method of proportional division?

16) Divide 3000 in the ratio 5:8:12.

17) Rick bought 5 pints of milk for £2.35. How much would 3 pints cost?

Rounding and Bounds (p.30-32) ☑

18) Round 427.963 to: a) 2 d.p.   b) 1 d.p.   c) 2 s.f.   d) 4 s.f.

19) Estimate the value of $(124.6 + 87.1) \div 9.4$

20) A rectangle measures 15.6 m by 8.4 m, to the nearest 0.1 m. Find its maximum possible area.

Standard Form (p.33-34) ☑

21) What are the three rules for writing numbers in standard form?

22) Write these numbers in standard form: a) 970 000   b) 3 560 000 000   c) 0.00000275

23) Calculate: a) $(2.54 \times 10^6) \div (1.6 \times 10^3)$ b) $(1.75 \times 10^{12}) + (9.89 \times 10^{11})$
    Give your answers in standard form.

Sets and Venn Diagrams (p.37-41) ☑

24) $\xi = $ {Positive integers less than 16}, A = {Multiples of 5}, B = $\{x : x \le 10\}$
    a) List the members of A ∩ B.
    b) Fill in the boxes in the Venn diagram on the right to show
       the number of members in each part of the diagram.
    c) Find n(A ∪ B).

Powers and Roots

> **Powers** are a very useful <u>shorthand</u>:
> $2 \times 2 \times 2 \times 2 \times 2 \times 2 \times 2 = 2^7$ ('two to the power 7')

That bit is easy to remember. Unfortunately, there are also <u>ten special rules</u> for powers that you need to learn — eight on this page and two trickier ones on the next page.

Learn these **Eight** Rules

1) When <u>MULTIPLYING</u>, you <u>ADD THE POWERS</u>.

e.g. $3^4 \times 3^6 = 3^{4+6} = 3^{10}$, $a^2 \times a^7 = a^{2+7} = a^9$

Warning: Rules 1 & 2 don't work for things like $2^3 \times 3^7$, only for powers of the same number.

2) When <u>DIVIDING</u>, you <u>SUBTRACT THE POWERS</u>.

e.g. $5^4 \div 5^2 = 5^{4-2} = 5^2$, $b^8 \div b^5 = b^{8-5} = b^3$

3) When <u>RAISING</u> one power to another, you <u>MULTIPLY THEM</u>.

e.g. $(3^2)^4 = 3^{2 \times 4} = 3^8$, $(c^3)^6 = c^{3 \times 6} = c^{18}$

4) $x^1 = x$, <u>ANYTHING</u> to the <u>POWER 1</u> is just <u>ITSELF</u>.

e.g. $3^1 = 3$, $d \times d^3 = d^1 \times d^3 = d^{1+3} = d^4$

5) $x^0 = 1$, <u>ANYTHING</u> to the <u>POWER 0</u> is just <u>1</u>.

e.g. $5^0 = 1$, $67^0 = 1$, $e^0 = 1$

6) $1^x = 1$, <u>1 TO ANY POWER</u> is <u>STILL JUST 1</u>.

e.g. $1^{23} = 1$, $1^{89} = 1$, $1^2 = 1$

7) <u>FRACTIONS</u> — Apply the power to <u>both TOP and BOTTOM</u>.

e.g. $\left(1\frac{3}{5}\right)^3 = \left(\frac{8}{5}\right)^3 = \frac{8^3}{5^3} = \frac{512}{125}$, $\left(\frac{u}{v}\right)^5 = \frac{u^5}{v^5}$

8) <u>NEGATIVE Powers</u> — Turn it Upside Down.

People have real difficulty remembering this — whenever you see a negative power you need to immediately think: "Aha, that means turn it the other way up and make the power positive".

e.g. $7^{-2} = \frac{1}{7^2} = \frac{1}{49}$, $a^{-4} = \frac{1}{a^4}$, $\left(\frac{3}{5}\right)^{-2} = \left(\frac{5}{3}\right)^{+2} = \frac{5^2}{3^2} = \frac{25}{9}$

Remember that rules 1 & 2 only work for powers of the same number

If you can add, subtract and multiply, there's nothing on this page you can't do — as long as you learn the rules. Try copying them over and over until you can do it with your eyes closed.

Powers and Roots

These **Two** Rules are a bit more **Tricky**

9) FRACTIONAL POWERS

The power $\frac{1}{2}$ means <u>Square Root</u>.

The power $\frac{1}{3}$ means <u>Cube Root</u>.

The power $\frac{1}{4}$ means <u>Fourth Root</u> etc.

e.g. $25^{\frac{1}{2}} = \sqrt{25} = 5$

$64^{\frac{1}{3}} = \sqrt[3]{64} = 4$

$81^{\frac{1}{4}} = \sqrt[4]{81} = 3$

$z^{\frac{1}{5}} = \sqrt[5]{z}$

See page 4 for more on roots.

You'll be able to use your calculator in the exam if you get a root that's really hard to evaluate.

The one to really watch is when you get a <u>negative fraction</u> like $49^{-\frac{1}{2}}$ — people get mixed up and think that the minus is the square root, and forget to turn it upside down as well.

e.g. $49^{-\frac{1}{2}} = \frac{1}{\sqrt{49}} = \frac{1}{7}$

10) TWO-STAGE FRACTIONAL POWERS

With fractional powers like $64^{\frac{5}{6}}$, always <u>split the fraction</u> into a <u>root</u> and a <u>power</u>, and do them in that order: <u>root</u> first, then <u>power</u>: $(64)^{\frac{1}{6} \times 5} = (64^{\frac{1}{6}})^5 = (2)^5 = 32$.

EXAMPLES:

1. Simplify $28p^5q^3 \div 14p^3q^3$ **(5)**

Just deal with each bit separately:

$= (28 \div 14)(p^5 \div p^3)(q^3 \div q^3)$

$= (28 \div 14)p^{5-3}q^{3-3}$

$= 2p^2$

$q^{3-3} = q^0 = 1$

You simplify algebraic fractions using the <u>power rules</u> (though you might not realise it).

So if you had to simplify e.g. $\frac{p^3q^6}{p^2q^3}$, you'd just <u>cancel</u> using the power rules to get $p^{3-2}q^{6-3} = pq^3$.

2. Evaluate $\left(\frac{216}{27}\right)^{\frac{2}{3}}$ **(7)**

1) Break down the <u>two-stage fractional power</u> into a <u>root</u> and a <u>power</u>. Remember to do everything to both the <u>top and the bottom</u>.

$$\left(\frac{216}{27}\right)^{\frac{2}{3}} = \left(\left(\frac{216}{27}\right)^{\frac{1}{3}}\right)^2 = \left(\frac{216^{\frac{1}{3}}}{27^{\frac{1}{3}}}\right)^2 = \left(\frac{\sqrt[3]{216}}{\sqrt[3]{27}}\right)^2$$

2) Work out the <u>roots</u> and deal with the <u>power</u> that's left.

$$= \left(\frac{6}{3}\right)^2 = 2^2 = 4$$

These two rules might be a bit trickier — but they are essential

Because these are things which people often get muddled, examiners love to sneak them into the exam — so scribble down these rules and learn them. Then in the exam you'll have the last laugh.

Algebra Basics

Before you can really get your teeth into <u>algebra</u>, there are some basics you need to get your head around.

Negative Numbers

Negative numbers crop up everywhere so you need to learn these rules for dealing with them:

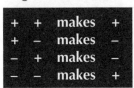

+	+	makes	+
+	−	makes	−
−	+	makes	−
−	−	makes	+

Use these rules when:

1) <u>Multiplying or dividing</u>.
   e.g. $-2 \times 3 = -6$, $-8 \div -2 = +4$, $-4p \times -2 = +8p$

2) <u>Two signs are together</u>.
   e.g. $5 - -4 = 5 + 4 = 9$, $x + -y - -z = x - y + z$

Be careful when squaring or cubing. <u>Squaring</u> a negative number gives a <u>positive</u> number, e.g. $(-2)^2 = 4$ but <u>cubing</u> a negative number gives a <u>negative</u> number, e.g. $(-3)^2 = -27$.

Letters Multiplied Together

Watch out for these combinations of letters in algebra that regularly catch people out:

1) abc means $a \times b \times c$. The ×'s are often left out to make it clearer.

2) gn^2 means $g \times n \times n$. Note that only the n is squared, not the g as well — e.g. πr^2 means $\pi \times r \times r$.

3) $(gn)^2$ means $g \times g \times n \times n$. The brackets mean that <u>BOTH</u> letters are squared.

4) $p(q - r)^3$ means $p \times (q - r) \times (q - r) \times (q - r)$. Only the brackets get cubed.

5) -3^2 is a bit ambiguous. It should either be written $(-3)^2 = 9$, or $-(3^2) = -9$ (you'd usually take -3^2 to be -9).

Terms

Before you can do anything else with algebra, you must understand what a term is:

> **A <u>TERM</u> is a collection of numbers, letters and brackets, all multiplied/divided together**

Terms are separated by <u>+ and − signs</u>. Every term has a + or − attached to the <u>front of it</u>.

If there's no sign in front of the first term, it means there's an invisible + sign.

$4xy$ + $5x^2$ − $2y$ + $6y^2$ + 4

'xy' term   'x^2' term   'y' term   'y^2' term   'number' term

Simplifying or 'Collecting Like Terms'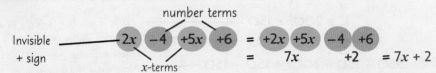

To <u>simplify</u> an algebraic expression, you combine '<u>like terms</u>' — terms that have the <u>same combination of letters</u> (e.g. all the x terms, all the y terms, all the number terms etc.).

EXAMPLE: Simplify $2x - 4 + 5x + 6$

number terms

Invisible + sign → $2x$ -4 $+5x$ $+6$ = $+2x$ $+5x$ -4 $+6$

x-terms

= $7x$ $+2$ = $7x + 2$

1) Put <u>bubbles</u> round each term — be sure you capture the <u>+/− sign</u> in front of each.

2) Then you can move the bubbles into the <u>best order</u> so that <u>like terms</u> are together.

3) <u>Combine like terms</u>.

These simple bits and bobs are the key to all algebra

Algebra gets people fazed at first. If you don't get these basics in your head you will be really baffled in a few pages' time. Always remember — every term has a + or − stuck to the front (even if it's invisible).

Making Formulas from Words

Before we get started, there are a few <u>definitions</u> you need to know:

> 1) EXPRESSION — a <u>collection</u> of <u>terms</u> (see p.47). Expressions <u>DON'T</u> have an = sign in them.
> 2) EQUATION — an expression with an = sign in it (so you can solve it).
> 3) FORMULA — a <u>rule</u> that helps you work something out (it will also have an = sign in it).

Making a **Formula** from **Given Information**

Making <u>formulas</u> from <u>words</u> can be a bit confusing as you're given a lot of <u>information</u> in one go. You just have to go through it slowly and carefully and <u>extract the maths</u> from it.

EXAMPLES:

1. **Tiana is x years old. Leah is 5 years younger than Tiana. Martin is 4 times as old as Tiana.**

a) **Write an expression for Leah's age in terms of x.**

Tiana's age is x
So Leah's age is $x - 5$
Leah is 5 years younger, so subtract 5

b) **Write an expression for Martin's age in terms of x.**

Tiana's age is x
So Martin's age is $4 \times x = 4x$
4 times older

2. **Windsurfing lessons cost £15 per hour, plus a fixed fee of £20 for equipment hire. h hours of lessons cost £W. Write a formula for W in terms of h.**

One hour costs 15, so h hours will cost $15 \times h$

$W = 15h + 20$

Don't forget to add on the fixed fee (20)

Because you're asked for a formula, you must include the 'W =' bit to get full marks (i.e. don't just put 15h + 20).

3. **In rugby union, tries score 5 points and conversions score 2 points. In a game, Morgan scores a total of M points, made up of t tries and c conversions. Write a formula for M in terms of t and c.**

Tries score 5 points ——— t tries will score $5 \times t = 5t$ points
Conversions score 2 points ——— c conversions will score $2 \times c = 2c$ points
So total points scored are $M = 5t + 2c$

Using Your **Formula** to **Solve Equations**

Sometimes, you might be asked to <u>use</u> a formula to <u>solve an equation</u>.

EXAMPLE: **A decorator uses the formula $C = 200r + 150$, where C is the cost in £ and r is the number of rooms. Gabrielle spends £950. How many rooms does she have decorated?**

$$C = 200r + 150$$
$$950 = 200r + 150$$
(-150) $\quad 950 - 150 = 200r + 150 - 150$
$$800 = 200r$$
$(\div 200)$ $\quad 800 \div 200 = 200r \div 200$
$$4 = r \qquad \text{So Gabrielle has 4 rooms decorated}$$

Write down the formula first.
Replace C with the value given in the question (£950).
Now solve the equation.

Check out p.54-55 for how to solve equations.

All the information you need will be somewhere in the question

Don't be overwhelmed by wordy questions — read each sentence slowly and then write down the maths that you can extract from it. Then, if you're asked to, solve it just like any other equation.

Multiplying Out Brackets

You often find <u>brackets</u> in <u>algebraic expressions</u>. The first thing you need to be able to do is to <u>expand them</u> (multiply them out).

Single Brackets

The main thing to remember when multiplying out brackets is that the thing <u>outside</u> the bracket multiplies <u>each separate term</u> inside the bracket.

EXAMPLE: Expand the following:

a) $4a(3b - 2c)$

$= (4a \times 3b) + (4a \times -2c)$
$= 12ab - 8ac$

b) $-4(3p^2 - 7q^3)$

$= (-4 \times 3p^2) + (-4 \times -7q^3)$
$= -12p^2 + 28q^3$

<u>Note</u>: both signs have been reversed.

Double Brackets

<u>Double</u> brackets are trickier than single brackets — this time, you have to multiply <u>everything</u> in the <u>first bracket</u> by <u>everything</u> in the <u>second bracket</u>. You'll get <u>4 terms</u>, and usually 2 of them will combine to leave <u>3 terms</u>. There's a handy way to multiply out double brackets — it's called the <u>FOIL method</u>:

<u>F</u>irst — multiply the first term in each bracket together

<u>O</u>utside — multiply the outside terms (i.e. the first term in the first bracket by the second term in the second bracket)

<u>I</u>nside — multiply the inside terms (i.e. the second term in the first bracket by the first term in the second bracket)

<u>L</u>ast — multiply the second term in each bracket together

EXAMPLE: Expand and simplify $(2p - 4)(3p + 1)$.

$(2p - 4)(3p + 1) = (2p \times 3p) + (2p \times 1) + (-4 \times 3p) + (-4 \times 1)$
$= 6p^2 + 2p - 12p - 4$
$= 6p^2 - 10p - 4$

The two p terms <u>combine together</u>.

Always write out <u>SQUARED BRACKETS</u> as <u>TWO BRACKETS</u> (to avoid mistakes), then multiply out as above.
So $(3x + 5)^2 = (3x + 5)(3x + 5) = 9x^2 + 15x + 15x + 25 = 9x^2 + 30x + 25$.
(DON'T make the mistake of thinking that $(3x + 5)^2 = 9x^2 + 25$ — this is <u>wrong</u>.)

Triple Brackets

1) For <u>three</u> brackets, just multiply <u>two</u> together as above, then multiply the result by the remaining bracket.

It doesn't matter which pair of brackets you multiply together first.

2) If you end up with <u>three terms</u> in one bracket, you <u>won't</u> be able to use FOIL. Instead, you can reduce it to a <u>series</u> of <u>single bracket multiplications</u> — like in the example below.

EXAMPLE: Expand and simplify $(x + 2)(x + 3)(2x - 1)$.

$(x + 2)(x + 3)(2x - 1) = (x + 2)(2x^2 + 5x - 3) = x(2x^2 + 5x - 3) + 2(2x^2 + 5x - 3)$
$= (2x^3 + 5x^2 - 3x) + (4x^2 + 10x - 6)$
$= 2x^3 + 9x^2 + 7x - 6$

Use the FOIL method to make sure you don't miss out any terms

When multiplying squared brackets, write them as two brackets and remember that you should get four terms (two of which will combine). If you're given cubed brackets, write them as three brackets like above.

Factorising

Right, now you know how to expand brackets, it's time to put them back in. This is known as <u>factorising</u>.

Factorising — Putting Brackets In

This is the <u>exact reverse</u> of multiplying out brackets. Here's the method to follow:

1) Take out the <u>biggest number</u> that goes into all the terms.
2) <u>For each letter in turn</u>, take out the <u>highest power</u> (e.g. x, x^2 etc.) that will go into EVERY term.
3) Open the brackets and fill in all the bits needed to <u>reproduce each term</u>.
4) <u>Check</u> your answer by <u>multiplying out</u> the brackets and making sure it matches the original expression.

1. **Factorise $3x^2 + 6x$**

Biggest number that'll divide into 3 and 6

Highest power of x that will go into both terms

$$3x(x + 2)$$

Check: $3x(x + 2) = 3x^2 + 6x$ ✓

2. **Factorise $8x^2y + 2xy^2$**

Biggest number that'll divide into 8 and 2

Highest powers of x and y that will go into both terms

$$2xy(4x + y)$$

Check: $2xy(4x + y) = 8x^2y + 2xy^2$ ✓

<u>REMEMBER</u>: The bits <u>taken out</u> and put at the front are the <u>common factors</u>. The bits <u>inside the brackets</u> are what's needed to get back to the <u>original terms</u> if you multiply the brackets out again.

D.O.T.S. — The Difference Of Two Squares

The 'difference of two squares' (D.O.T.S. for short) is where you have 'one thing squared' <u>take away</u> 'another thing squared'. There's a quick and easy way to factorise it — just use the rule below:

$$a^2 - b^2 = (a + b)(a - b)$$

EXAMPLE: **Factorise:** a) $x^2 - 1$ **Answer:** $x^2 - 1 = (x + 1)(x - 1)$
Don't forget that 1 is a square number (it's 1^2).

b) $9p^2 - 16q^2$ **Answer:** $9p^2 - 16q^2 = (3p + 4q)(3p - 4q)$
Here you had to spot that 9 and 16 are square numbers.

c) $3x^2 - 75y^2$ **Answer:** $3x^2 - 75y^2 = 3(x^2 - 25y^2) = 3(x + 5y)(x - 5y)$
This time, you had to take out a factor of 3 first.

Watch out — the difference of two squares can creep into other algebra questions. A popular <u>exam question</u> is to put a difference of two squares on the top or bottom of a <u>fraction</u> and ask you to simplify it. There's more on algebraic fractions on p.68.

EXAMPLE: **Simplify** $\dfrac{x^2 - 36}{5x + 30}$

The numerator is a difference of two squares.

$$\frac{x^2 - 36}{5x + 30} = \frac{(x + 6)(x - 6)}{5(x + 6)} = \frac{x - 6}{5}$$

Factorise the denominator.

D.O.T.S. is straightforward as long as you recognise the pattern

Once you've seen one D.O.T.S. question, you've seen them all — they all follow the same basic pattern. If it doesn't look like a D.O.T.S. because there's a factor in it, taking out the factor might make things clearer.

Manipulating Surds

Surds are expressions with <u>irrational square roots</u> in them (remember from p.3 that irrational numbers are ones which <u>can't</u> be written as <u>fractions</u>, such as most square roots, cube roots and π).

Manipulating Surds — **6 Rules** to Learn

There are 6 rules you need to learn for dealing with surds...

1 $\boxed{\sqrt{a} \times \sqrt{b} = \sqrt{a \times b}}$ e.g. $\sqrt{2} \times \sqrt{3} = \sqrt{2 \times 3} = \sqrt{6}$ — also $(\sqrt{b})^2 = \sqrt{b} \times \sqrt{b} = b$

2 $\boxed{\dfrac{\sqrt{a}}{\sqrt{b}} = \sqrt{\dfrac{a}{b}}}$ e.g. $\dfrac{\sqrt{8}}{\sqrt{2}} = \sqrt{\dfrac{8}{2}} = \sqrt{4} = 2$

3 $\boxed{\sqrt{a} + \sqrt{b} - \underline{\text{DO NOTHING}}}$ — in other words it is definitely <u>NOT</u> $\sqrt{a+b}$

4 $\boxed{(a + \sqrt{b})^2 = (a + \sqrt{b})(a + \sqrt{b}) = a^2 + 2a\sqrt{b} + b}$ — <u>NOT</u> just $a^2 + (\sqrt{b})^2$ (see p.49)

5 $\boxed{(a + \sqrt{b})(a - \sqrt{b}) = a^2 + a\sqrt{b} - a\sqrt{b} - (\sqrt{b})^2 = a^2 - b}$ (see p.50)

6 $\boxed{\dfrac{a}{\sqrt{b}} = \dfrac{a}{\sqrt{b}} \times \dfrac{\sqrt{b}}{\sqrt{b}} = \dfrac{a\sqrt{b}}{b}}$ ← This is known as 'RATIONALISING the denominator' — it's where you get rid of the $\sqrt{}$ on the bottom of the fraction. For denominators of the form $a \pm \sqrt{b}$, multiply by the denominator but <u>change the sign</u> in front of the root (see example 2 below).

EXAMPLE: **1.** Write $\dfrac{3}{\sqrt{5}}$ in the form $\dfrac{a\sqrt{5}}{b}$, where a and b are whole numbers.

You have to rationalise the denominator — so multiply top and bottom by $\sqrt{5}$:

$$\frac{3\sqrt{5}}{\sqrt{5}\sqrt{5}} = \frac{3\sqrt{5}}{5} \text{ — so } a = 3 \text{ and } b = 5$$

---

2. Write $\dfrac{3}{2 + \sqrt{5}}$ in the form $a + b\sqrt{5}$, where a and b are integers.

To rationalise the denominator, multiply top and bottom by $2 - \sqrt{5}$:

$$\frac{3}{2+\sqrt{5}} = \frac{3(2-\sqrt{5})}{(2+\sqrt{5})(2-\sqrt{5})}$$

$$= \frac{6 - 3\sqrt{5}}{2^2 - 2\sqrt{5} + 2\sqrt{5} - (\sqrt{5})^2}$$

$$= \frac{6 - 3\sqrt{5}}{4 - 5} = \frac{6 - 3\sqrt{5}}{-1} = -6 + 3\sqrt{5}$$

Leave **Surds** in **Exact Answers**

If a question asks for an <u>exact answer</u>, just <u>leave</u> the surds in your answer. The same goes for calculations involving π — if you're asked for an <u>exact</u> answer, leave π in instead of using your π calculator button.

EXAMPLES: **1.** A rectangle has area 32 cm². It has length x cm and width $4x$ cm. Find the exact value of x, giving your answer in its simplest form.

Area of rectangle = length × width = $x \times 4x = 4x^2$

So $4x^2 = 32$. This means $x^2 = 8$, so $x = \pm\sqrt{8}$

Now get $\sqrt{8}$ into its simplest form:

$\sqrt{8} = \sqrt{4 \times 2} = \sqrt{4}\sqrt{2} = 2\sqrt{2}$ So $x = 2\sqrt{2}$

You can ignore the negative square root (see p.55) as length must be positive.

2. Find the exact area of a circle with radius 4 cm.

Area = $\pi r^2 = \pi \times 4^2$
= 16π cm²

Once you get used to them, surds are quite easy

They do seem a bit fiddly but all you have to do is learn these six rules, then practise, practise, practise.

Warm-Up and Worked Exam Questions

Take a deep breath and go through these warm-up questions one by one. Then you'll be ready for the really exciting bit (well, slightly more exciting anyway) — the exam questions.

Warm-Up Questions

1) Evaluate: a) $4^5 \times 4^{-2}$ b) $\left(1\frac{2}{7}\right)^2$ c) $27^{\frac{2}{3}}$ d) $\left(\frac{2}{3}\right)^{-2}$

2) Simplify: a) $4a + c - 2a - 6c$ b) $3r^2 - 2r + 4r^2 - 1 - 3r$

3) The cost of hiring a wallpaper-stripper is £12 per day, plus a deposit of £18. If the cost for hiring it for d days is $£C$, find a formula for C in terms of d.

4) Multiply out: a) $4(2p + 7)$ b) $(4x - 2)(2x + 1)$ c) $a(5a - 3)$.

5) Factorise: a) $6p - 12q + 4$ b) $4cd^2 - 2cd + 10c^2d^3$.

6) Factorise $x^2 - 4y^2$.

7) Work out $\sqrt{5} \times \sqrt{6}$, leaving your answer as a surd.

Worked Exam Questions

Don't skip over these worked exam questions just because they already have the answers written in. Work through them yourself so you know what's going on, then have a go at the next page.

1 Factorise the following expressions fully.

a) $x^2 - 16$

This is a difference of two squares:
$$x^2 - 16 = x^2 - 4^2$$
$$= (x + 4)(x - 4)$$

$(x + 4)(x - 4)$
....
[1 mark]

b) $9n^2 - 4m^2$

Here you have to spot that
9 and 4 are square numbers.

$$9n^2 - 4m^2 = (3n)^2 - (2m)^2$$
$$= (3n + 2m)(3n - 2m)$$

$(3n + 2m)(3n - 2m)$
....
[2 marks]

2 Write $2\sqrt{50} - \left(\sqrt{2}\right)^3$ in the form $a\sqrt{b}$, where a and b are integers.

$$2\sqrt{50} = 2\sqrt{25 \times 2} = 2 \times 5\sqrt{2}$$
$$= 10\sqrt{2}$$

$$\left(\sqrt{2}\right)^3 = \sqrt{2} \times \sqrt{2} \times \sqrt{2} = \left(\sqrt{2}\right)^2 \times \sqrt{2}$$
$$= 2\sqrt{2}$$

So $2\sqrt{50} - \left(\sqrt{2}\right)^3 = 10\sqrt{2} - 2\sqrt{2}$
$$= 8\sqrt{2}$$

$8\sqrt{2}$
....
[2 marks]

Exam Questions

3   The cost per person of a flight from Manchester to Aberdeen is £73 plus £27 tax and an extra £15 for each piece of luggage. Write down a formula to calculate the total cost (T) of a flight for p people with a total of l pieces of luggage.

....

[2 marks]

4   Fully factorise $2v^3w + 8v^2w^2$

....

[2 marks]

5   Write an expression for the area of the triangle below. Simplify your expression as much as possible.

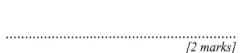

The formula for the area of a triangle is:
Area = ½ × base × height

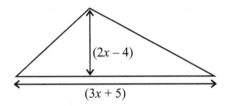

Diagram not accurately drawn

....

[3 marks]

6   Completely simplify the expression $(9a^4)^{\frac{1}{2}} \times \dfrac{2ab^2}{6a^3b}$

....

[3 marks]

7   Express $\dfrac{1+\sqrt{7}}{3-\sqrt{7}}$ in the form $a + b\sqrt{7}$, where a and b are integers.

....

[4 marks]

Section Two — Algebra

Solving Equations

The basic idea of <u>solving equations</u> is very simple — keep <u>rearranging</u> until you end up with x = number. The two most common methods for <u>rearranging</u> equations are: 1) '<u>same to both sides</u>' and 2) do the <u>opposite</u> when you cross the '='. I'll use the 'same to both sides' method on these pages.

Rearrange Until You Have x = Number

The easiest ones to solve are where you just have a <u>mixture</u> of x's and numbers.

1) First, <u>rearrange</u> the equation so that all the <u>x's</u> are on one side and the <u>numbers</u> are on the other. <u>Combine</u> terms where you can.

2) Then <u>divide</u> both sides by the <u>number multiplying x</u> to find the value of x.

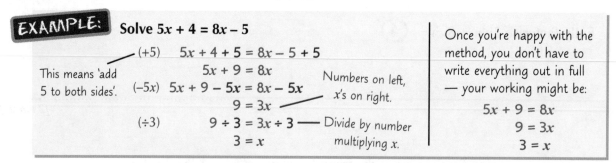

EXAMPLE: Solve $5x + 4 = 8x - 5$

This means 'add 5 to both sides'.
$(+5) \quad 5x + 4 + 5 = 8x - 5 + 5$
$5x + 9 = 8x$
$(-5x) \quad 5x + 9 - 5x = 8x - 5x$ — Numbers on left, x's on right.
$9 = 3x$
$(\div 3) \quad 9 \div 3 = 3x \div 3$ — Divide by number multiplying x.
$3 = x$

Once you're happy with the method, you don't have to write everything out in full — your working might be:
$5x + 9 = 8x$
$9 = 3x$
$3 = x$

Multiply Out Brackets First

If your equation has <u>brackets</u> in it...
1) <u>Multiply</u> them out <u>before rearranging</u>.
2) <u>Solve it</u> in the same way as above.

EXAMPLE: Solve $3(3x - 2) = 5x + 10$

$9x - 6 = 5x + 10$
$(-5x) \quad 9x - 6 - 5x = 5x + 10 - 5x$
$4x - 6 = 10$
$(+6) \quad 4x - 6 + 6 = 10 + 6$
$4x = 16$
$(\div 4) \quad 4x \div 4 = 16 \div 4$
$x = 4$

Get Rid of Fractions

1) <u>Fractions</u> make everything more complicated — so you need to get rid of them <u>before doing anything else</u> (yep, even before multiplying out brackets).

2) To get rid of fractions, multiply <u>every term</u> of the equation by whatever's on the <u>bottom</u> of the fraction. If there are <u>two</u> fractions, multiply by <u>both</u> denominators (or by a <u>common multiple</u> of them).

EXAMPLES:

1. Solve $\frac{x+2}{4} = 4x - 7$

Multiply <u>every</u> term by 4 to get rid of the fraction.
$(\times 4) \quad \frac{4(x+2)}{4} = 4(4x) - 4(7)$
$x + 2 = 16x - 28$
$30 = 15x$ — And solve.
$2 = x$

2. Solve $\frac{3x+5}{2} = \frac{4x+10}{3}$

Multiply <u>everything</u> by 2 then by 3.
$(\times 2), (\times 3) \quad \frac{2 \times 3 \times (3x+5)}{2} = \frac{2 \times 3 \times (4x+10)}{3}$
$3(3x+5) = 2(4x+10)$
And solve. $9x + 15 = 8x + 20$
$x = 5$

Remember that you're trying to get x on its own

You can always check your answer by putting your value of x back into both sides of the original equation — you should get the same number on each side. If you don't, you've made a mistake somewhere.

Solving Equations

Now you know the basics of solving equations, it's time to put it all together into a handy step-by-step method.

Solving Equations Using the **6-Step Method**

Here's the method to follow (just ignore any steps that don't apply to your equation):

1) Get rid of any <u>fractions</u>.
2) <u>Multiply out</u> any brackets.
3) Collect all the <u>x-terms</u> on one side and all <u>number terms</u> on the other.
4) Reduce it to the form '<u>Ax = B</u>' (by <u>combining like terms</u>).
5) Finally <u>divide both sides by A</u> to give '$x =$ ', and that's your answer.
6) If you had '$x^2 =$ ' instead, <u>square root</u> both sides to end up with '$x = \pm$ '.

EXAMPLE: Solve $\dfrac{3x+4}{5} + \dfrac{4x-1}{3} = 14$

Multiply everything by 5 then by 3.

1) Get rid of any <u>fractions</u>.   (×5), (×3) $\dfrac{5 \times 3 \times (3x+4)}{5} + \dfrac{5 \times 3 \times (4x-1)}{3} = 5 \times 3 \times 14$

$$3(3x + 4) + 5(4x - 1) = 210$$

2) <u>Multiply out</u> any brackets. $9x + 12 + 20x - 5 = 210$

3) Collect all the <u>x-terms</u> on one side and all <u>number terms</u> on the other.

(−12), (+5) $9x + 20x = 210 - 12 + 5$

4) Reduce it to the form '<u>Ax = B</u>' (by <u>combining like terms</u>).

$$29x = 203$$

5) Finally <u>divide both sides by A</u> to give '$x =$ ', and that's your answer.

(÷29) $x = 7$ (You're left with '$x =$ ' so you can ignore step 6.)

Dealing with **Squares**

If you're unlucky, you might get an x^2 in an equation. If this happens, you'll end up with '$x^2 = ...$' at step 5, and then step 6 is to take <u>square roots</u>. There's one very important thing to remember: whenever you take the square root of a number, the answer can be <u>positive</u> or <u>negative</u>.

EXAMPLE: Solve $3x^2 = 75$.

(÷3) $x^2 = 25$

($\sqrt{\ }$) $x = \pm 5$

You always get a +ve and −ve version of the <u>same number</u> (your calculator only gives the +ve answer). This shows why:
$5^2 = 5 \times 5 = 25$ but also
$(-5)^2 = (-5) \times (-5) = 25$.

Learn the 6-step method for solving equations

You might not need to use all 6 steps to solve your equation — ignore any that you don't need and move onto the next step. Make sure you do them in the right order though — otherwise you'll get it wrong.

Rearranging Formulas

Rearranging formulas means making one letter the subject, e.g. getting '$y =$ ' from '$2x + z = 3(y + 2p)$' — you have to get the subject on its own.

Use the Solving Equations Method to Rearrange Formulas

Rearranging formulas is remarkably similar to solving equations. The method below is identical to the method for solving equations, except that I've added an extra step at the start.

1) Get rid of any square root signs by squaring both sides.
2) Get rid of any fractions.
3) Multiply out any brackets.
4) Collect all the subject terms on one side and all non-subject terms on the other.
5) Reduce it to the form '$Ax = B$' (by combining like terms). You might have to do some factorising here too.
6) Divide both sides by A to give '$x =$ '.
7) If you're left with '$x^2 =$ ', square root both sides to get '$x = \pm$ ' (don't forget the ±).

> x is the subject term here. A and B could be numbers or letters (or a mix of both).

> Don't panic if you have some other root/power, e.g. cubes (see p.4). Steps 1) and 7) still work in the same sort of way.

What to Do If...

...the Subject Appears in a Fraction

You won't always need to use all 7 steps in the method above — just ignore the ones that don't apply.

EXAMPLE: Make b the subject of the formula $a = \dfrac{5b + 3}{4}$.

There aren't any square roots, so ignore step 1.

2) Get rid of any fractions.	(by multiplying every term by 4, the denominator)	(×4) $4a = \dfrac{4(5b + 3)}{4}$

$$4a = 5b + 3$$

There aren't any brackets, so ignore step 3.

4) Collect all the subject terms on one side and all non-subject terms on the other.

(remember that you're trying to make b the subject)   (−3) $5b = 4a - 3$

5) It's now in the form $Ax = B$.	(where A = 5 and B = 4a − 3)

6) Divide both sides by 5 to give '$b =$ '.	(÷5) $b = \dfrac{4a - 3}{5}$

b isn't squared, so you don't need step 7.

The subject is the letter on its own

Remember that rearranging formulas is exactly the same as solving equations, except that instead of ending up with '$x =$ number' (e.g. $x = 3$), you'll end up with '$x =$ expression' (e.g. $x = 2y + 4$).

Rearranging Formulas

Carrying straight on from the previous page, now it's time for what to do if...

...there's a **Square** or **Square Root** Involved

If the subject appears as a <u>square</u> or in a <u>square root</u>, you'll have to use steps 1 and 7 (not necessarily both).

EXAMPLE: Make v the subject of the formula $u = 4v^2 + 5w$.

There aren't any square roots, fractions or brackets so ignore steps 1-3 (this is pretty easy so far).

4) Collect all the <u>subject terms</u> on one side and all <u>non-subject terms</u> on the other.

$$(-5w) \quad 4v^2 = u - 5w$$

5) It's now in the form $\underline{Ax^2 = B}$ (where A = 4 and B = $u - 5w$)

6) <u>Divide both sides by 4</u> to give '$v^2 =$ '. $\quad (\div 4) \quad v^2 = \dfrac{u - 5w}{4}$

7) <u>Square root</u> both sides to get '$v = \pm$ '. $\quad (\sqrt{\ }) \quad v = \pm\sqrt{\dfrac{u - 5w}{4}} \quad$ <u>Don't forget</u> the $\pm$

EXAMPLE: Make n the subject of the formula $m = \dfrac{\sqrt{n + 5}}{k}$.

1) Get rid of any <u>square roots</u> by <u>squaring</u> both sides. $\quad m^2 = \dfrac{n + 5}{k^2} \quad$ $\sqrt{a}$ means the <u>positive</u> square root, so you <u>don't</u> need a $\pm$.

2) Get rid of any <u>fractions</u>. $\quad k^2 m^2 = n + 5$

There aren't any brackets, so ignore step 3.

4) Collect all the <u>subject terms</u> on one side and all <u>non-subject terms</u> on the other.

$(-5) \quad n = k^2 m^2 - 5 \qquad$ This is in the form '$n =$ ' so you don't need to do steps 5-7.

...the Subject Appears **Twice**

You'll just have to do some <u>factorising</u>, usually in step 5.

EXAMPLE: Make p the subject of the formula $p = \dfrac{p + 1}{q - 1}$.

There aren't any square roots, so ignore step 1.

2) Get rid of any <u>fractions</u>. $\quad p(q - 1) = p + 1 \qquad$ 3) <u>Multiply out</u> any brackets. $\quad pq - p = p + 1$

4) Collect all the <u>subject terms</u> on one side and all <u>non-subject terms</u> on the other.

$pq - 2p = 1$

5) <u>Combine like terms</u> on each side of the equation. $\quad p(q - 2) = 1 \qquad$ This is where you factorise — p was in both terms on the LHS, so it comes out as a common factor.

6) <u>Divide both sides by $(q - 2)$</u> to give '$p =$ '. $\quad p = \dfrac{1}{q - 2} \quad$ (p isn't squared, so you don't need step 7.)

Remember — you square first and square root last

Rearranging formulas is a bit harder if the subject appears twice. But if this happens, don't panic — just follow the 7-step method and be prepared to do some factorising (see page 50 if you need a reminder).

Warm-Up and Worked Exam Questions

It's easy to think you've learnt everything in the section until you try the warm-up questions. Don't panic if there are bits you've forgotten. Just go back over them until they're firmly fixed in your brain.

Warm-Up Questions

1) Solve these equations to find the value of x:
   a) $8x - 5 = 19$ b) $3(2x + 7) = 3$ c) $4x - 9 = x + 6$

2) What is the subject of these formulas?
   a) $p = \sqrt{\dfrac{ml^2}{h}}$ b) $t = px - y^3$

3) Make q the subject of the formula $p = \dfrac{q}{7} + 2r$

4) Make z the subject of the formula $x = \dfrac{y + 2z}{3}$

Worked Exam Questions

Here are a couple of exam questions that I've done for you. You won't get any help for the questions on the next page though — so make the most of it whilst you can.

1 Solve the equation $\dfrac{5}{4}(2c - 1) = 3c - 2$ **(5)**

$$\frac{5}{4}(2c - 1) = 3c - 2$$

Get rid of the fraction... $(\times 4)$ $5(2c - 1) = 4(3c - 2)$

...multiply out the brackets... $10c - 5 = 12c - 8$

...and solve. $(-10c)$ $-5 = 2c - 8$

$(+8)$ $3 = 2c$

$(\div 2)$ $1.5 = c$ $c = \underline{\quad 1.5 \quad}$

[3 marks]

2 The formula $s = \dfrac{1}{2}gt^2$ is often used in physics. **(5)**

a) Work out the value of s when $g = -9.8$ and $t = 8$.

Just substitute into the equation: $s = \dfrac{1}{2} \times -9.8 \times 8^2 = -313.6$ $s = \underline{\quad -313.6 \quad}$

[2 marks]

b) Rearrange the equation to make t the subject, where t is positive.

Follow the 7-step method $s = \dfrac{1}{2}gt^2$
to get t on its own:

$(\times 2)$ $2s = gt^2$

$(\div g)$ $\dfrac{2s}{g} = t^2$

Don't forget the ± when
you take the square root... $(\sqrt{\ })$ $\pm\sqrt{\dfrac{2s}{g}} = t$ ...but you're told you only
need to give the +ve root $t = \sqrt{\dfrac{2s}{g}}$
in your final answer.

[3 marks]

Exam Questions

3   The diagram on the right shows two rectangles.

Rectangle A has sides of length $5x - 8$ cm and $2x + 3$ cm.
Rectangle B has sides of length $3x + 6$ cm and y cm.

$5x - 8$ cm

$2x + 3$ cm   Rectangle A

a)   Rectangle B has the same perimeter as rectangle A.
Write an equation for y in terms of x. Give your equation
in the form $y = ux + v$, where u and v are integers to be found.

$3x + 6$ cm

y cm   Rectangle B

Diagrams not
drawn to scale

....
[3 marks]

b)   The perimeter of each rectangle is 32 cm. Find the value of y.

$y =$ ....
[3 marks]

4   The relationship between a, b and y is given by the formula $a + y = \dfrac{b - y}{a}$

a)   Rearrange this formula to make y the subject.

....
[4 marks]

b)   Find the value of y when $a = 3$ and $b = 6$.

$y =$ ....
[2 marks]

5   Rearrange this formula to make n the subject: $x = \sqrt{\dfrac{(1 + n)}{(1 - n)}}$

....
[5 marks]

Factorising Quadratics

There are several ways of <u>solving</u> a <u>quadratic equation</u>, as detailed on the following pages.
You need to know <u>all the methods</u> as they sometimes ask for specific ones in the exam.

Factorising a Quadratic

1) 'Factorising a quadratic' means '<u>putting it into 2 brackets</u>'.

2) The standard format for quadratic equations is: $\underline{ax^2 + bx + c = 0}$.

3) Most exam questions have $\underline{a = 1}$, making them <u>much easier</u>. E.g. $x^2 + 3x + 2 = 0$ *See the next page for when 'a' is not 1.*

4) As well as factorising a quadratic, you might be asked to <u>solve</u> it.
This just means finding the values of x that make each bracket $\underline{0}$ (see example below).

Factorising Method when a = 1

1) <u>ALWAYS</u> rearrange into the <u>STANDARD FORMAT</u>: $x^2 + bx + c = 0$.

2) Write down the <u>TWO BRACKETS</u> with the x's in: $(x\quad)(x\quad) = 0$.

3) Then <u>find 2 numbers</u> that <u>MULTIPLY to give c</u> (the end number)
but also <u>ADD/SUBTRACT to give b</u> (the coefficient of x).   *Ignore any minus signs at this stage.*

4) Fill in the +/– signs and make sure they work out properly.

5) As an <u>ESSENTIAL CHECK</u>, <u>expand</u> the brackets to make sure
they give the original equation.

6) Finally, <u>SOLVE THE EQUATION</u> by <u>setting each bracket equal to 0</u>.

You <u>only</u> need to do step 6) if the question asks you to <u>solve</u> the quadratic
— if it just tells you to <u>factorise</u>, you can <u>stop</u> at step 5).

EXAMPLE: **Solve $x^2 - x = 12$.**

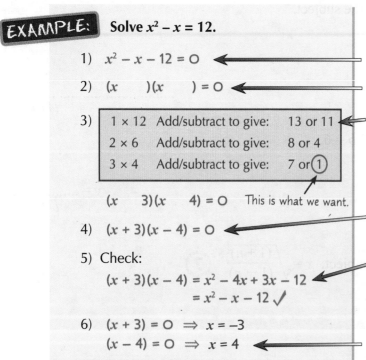

1) $x^2 - x - 12 = 0$ 1) <u>Rearrange</u> into the standard format.

2) $(x\quad)(x\quad) = 0$ 2) Write down the <u>initial brackets</u>.

3)
1×12	Add/subtract to give:	13 or 11
2×6	Add/subtract to give:	8 or 4
3×4	Add/subtract to give:	7 or ①

3) Find the right <u>pairs of numbers</u> that <u>multiply to give c</u> (= 12), and <u>add or subtract to give b</u> (= 1) (remember, we're ignoring the +/– signs for now).

$(x\quad 3)(x\quad 4) = 0$ This is what we want.

4) $(x + 3)(x - 4) = 0$ 4) <u>Now fill in the +/– signs</u> so that 3 and 4 add/subtract to give –1 (= b).

5) Check:
$(x + 3)(x - 4) = x^2 - 4x + 3x - 12$
$= x^2 - x - 12$ ✓

5) <u>ESSENTIAL check</u> — <u>EXPAND the brackets</u> to make sure they give the original equation.

But we're not finished yet — we've only factorised it, we still need to...

6) $(x + 3) = 0 \Rightarrow x = -3$
$(x - 4) = 0 \Rightarrow x = 4$

6) <u>SOLVE THE EQUATION</u> by setting each bracket <u>equal to 0</u>.

Factorising quadratics is not easy — but it is important

To help you work out which signs you need, look at c. If c is positive, the signs will be the same (both positive or both negative), but if c is negative the signs will be different (one positive and one negative).

Factorising Quadratics

It gets a bit more complicated when a isn't 1, but don't panic — just follow the method on this page.

When 'a' is Not 1

The basic method is still the same but it's a bit messier — the initial brackets are different as the first terms in each bracket have to multiply to give a. This means finding the other numbers to go in the brackets is harder as there are more combinations to try. The best way to get to grips with it is to have a look at an example.

EXAMPLE: Solve $3x^2 + 7x - 6 = 0$.

1) $3x^2 + 7x - 6 = 0$

2) $(3x\quad)(x\quad) = 0$

3) Number pairs: 1×6 and 2×3

$(3x\quad 1)(x\quad 6)$ multiplies to give $18x$ and $1x$ which add/subtract to give $17x$ or $19x$

$(3x\quad 6)(x\quad 1)$ multiplies to give $3x$ and $6x$ which add/subtract to give $9x$ or $3x$

$(3x\quad 3)(x\quad 2)$ multiplies to give $6x$ and $3x$ which add/subtract to give $9x$ or $3x$

$(3x\quad 2)(x\quad 3)$ multiplies to give $9x$ and $2x$ which add/subtract to give $11x$ or $7x$ ✓

$(3x\quad 2)(x\quad 3)$

4) $(3x - 2)(x + 3)$

5) $(3x - 2)(x + 3) = 3x^2 + 9x - 2x - 6$
$= 3x^2 + 7x - 6$ ✓

6) $(3x - 2) = 0 \Rightarrow x = \dfrac{2}{3}$
$(x + 3) = 0 \Rightarrow x = -3$

1) Rearrange into the standard format.

2) Write down the initial brackets — this time, one of the brackets will have a $3x$ in it.

3) The tricky part: first, find pairs of numbers that multiply to give c (= 6), ignoring the minus sign for now.

Then, try out the number pairs you just found in the brackets until you find one that gives $7x$. But remember, each pair of numbers has to be tried in 2 positions (as the brackets are different — one has $3x$ in it).

4) Now fill in the +/– signs so that 9 and 2 add/subtract to give +7 (= b).

5) ESSENTIAL check — EXPAND the brackets.

6) SOLVE THE EQUATION by setting each bracket equal to 0 (if a isn't 1, one of your answers will be a fraction).

EXAMPLE: Solve $2x^2 - 9x = 5$.

1) Put in the standard format: $2x^2 - 9x - 5 = 0$

2) Initial brackets: $(2x\quad)(x\quad) = 0$

3) Number pairs: 1×5

$(2x\quad 5)(x\quad 1)$ multiplies to give $2x$ and $5x$ which add/subtract to give $3x$ or $7x$

$(2x\quad 1)(x\quad 5)$ multiplies to give $1x$ and $10x$ which add/subtract to give $9x$ or $11x$ ✓

$(2x\quad 1)(x\quad 5)$

4) Put in the signs: $(2x + 1)(x - 5)$

5) Check:
$(2x + 1)(x - 5) = 2x^2 - 10x + x - 5$
$= 2x^2 - 9x - 5$ ✓

6) Solve:
$(2x + 1) = 0 \Rightarrow x = -\dfrac{1}{2}$
$(x - 5) = 0 \Rightarrow x = 5$

Factorising quadratics when 'a' is not 1 is quite a bit harder

The problem is that it's a lot harder to work out the right combination of numbers to go in the brackets. Don't get stressed out, just take your time and work through the possibilities one at a time.

The Quadratic Formula

The solutions to ANY quadratic equation $ax^2 + bx + c = 0$ are given by this formula:

$$x = \frac{-b \pm \sqrt{b^2 - 4ac}}{2a}$$

<u>LEARN THIS FORMULA</u> — and <u>how to use it</u>. It's usually given in the exam, but if you don't learn it, you won't know how to use it. Using it isn't that hard, but there are a few pitfalls — so <u>TAKE HEED of these crucial details</u>:

Quadratic Formula — Five **Crucial Details**

1) Take it nice and slowly — always write it down in stages as you go.

2) **WHENEVER YOU GET A MINUS SIGN, <u>THE ALARM BELLS SHOULD ALWAYS RING</u>!**

3) Remember it's <u>2a</u> on the bottom line, not just a — and you <u>divide ALL of the top line by 2a</u>.

4) The ± sign means you end up with <u>two solutions</u> (by replacing it in the final step with '+' and '−').

5) If you get a <u>negative</u> number inside your square root, go back and <u>check your working</u>. Some quadratics do have a negative value in the square root, but they won't come up in the exam.

If either 'a' or 'c' is negative, the −4ac effectively becomes +4ac, so watch out. Also, be careful if b is negative, as −b will be positive.

EXAMPLE: Solve $3x^2 + 7x = 1$, giving your answers to 2 decimal places.

$3x^2 + 7x - 1 = 0$

$a = 3, \quad b = 7, \quad c = -1$

$x = \dfrac{-b \pm \sqrt{b^2 - 4ac}}{2a}$

$= \dfrac{-7 \pm \sqrt{7^2 - 4 \times 3 \times -1}}{2 \times 3}$

$= \dfrac{-7 \pm \sqrt{49 + 12}}{6}$

$= \dfrac{-7 \pm \sqrt{61}}{6}$

$= \dfrac{-7 + 7.81...}{6}$ or $\dfrac{-7 - 7.81...}{6}$

$= 0.1350...$ or $-2.468...$

So to 2 d.p. the solutions are:
$x = 0.14$ or -2.47

1) First get it into the form <u>$ax^2 + bx + c = 0$</u>.

2) Then carefully identify a, b and c.

3) Put these values into the quadratic formula and <u>write down each stage</u>.

4) Finally, <u>as a check</u> put these values back into the <u>original equation</u>:
E.g. for $x = 0.1350...$:
$3 \times 0.1350...^2 + 7 \times 0.1350... = 1$

Notice that you do two calculations at the final stage — one + and one −.

When to use the quadratic formula:
- If you have a quadratic that <u>won't</u> easily <u>factorise</u>.
- If the question mentions <u>decimal places</u> or <u>significant figures</u>.
- If the question asks for <u>surds</u>.

Looks nightmarish — but you'll soon be chanting it in your sleep

This formula looks difficult to use and learn, but after you've said "minus b plus or minus the square root of b squared minus four a c all over 2 a" a few times, you'll wonder what all the fuss was about.

Completing the Square

There's just <u>one more method</u> to learn for solving quadratics — and it's a bit of a nasty one. It's called '<u>completing the square</u>', and takes a bit to get your head round it.

Solving Quadratics by 'Completing the Square'

To 'complete the square' you have to:

1) Write down a <u>SQUARED</u> bracket, and then   2) Stick a number on the end to '<u>COMPLETE</u>' it.

$$x^2 + 12x - 5 = (x + 6)^2 - 41$$

The SQUARE...   ...COMPLETED

It's not that bad if you learn all the steps — some of them aren't all that obvious.

1) As always, <u>REARRANGE THE QUADRATIC INTO THE STANDARD FORMAT</u>: $ax^2 + bx + c$ (the rest of this method is for $a = 1$).

2) <u>WRITE OUT THE INITIAL BRACKET</u>: $\left(x + \frac{b}{2}\right)^2$ — just divide the value of b by 2.

3) <u>MULTIPLY OUT THE BRACKETS</u> and <u>COMPARE TO THE ORIGINAL</u> to find what you need to add or subtract to complete the square.

4) Add or subtract the <u>ADJUSTING NUMBER</u> to make it <u>MATCH THE ORIGINAL</u>.

If a isn't 1, you have to divide through by a or take out a factor of a at the start — see the next page.

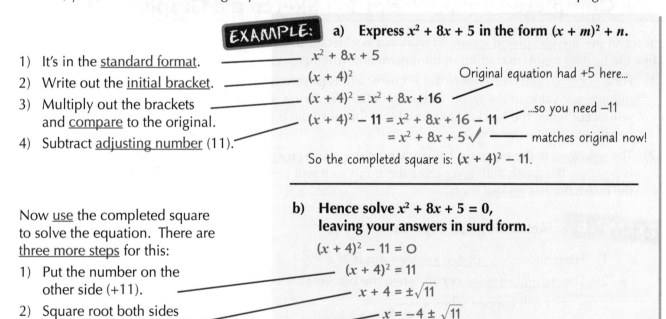

EXAMPLE: a) Express $x^2 + 8x + 5$ in the form $(x + m)^2 + n$.

1) It's in the <u>standard format</u>. $x^2 + 8x + 5$

2) Write out the <u>initial bracket</u>. $(x + 4)^2$ Original equation had +5 here...

3) Multiply out the brackets and <u>compare</u> to the original. $(x + 4)^2 = x^2 + 8x + 16$
   $(x + 4)^2 - 11 = x^2 + 8x + 16 - 11$ ...so you need −11

4) Subtract <u>adjusting number</u> (11). $= x^2 + 8x + 5$ ✓ — matches original now!

So the completed square is: $(x + 4)^2 - 11$.

Now <u>use</u> the completed square to solve the equation. There are <u>three more steps</u> for this:

b) **Hence solve $x^2 + 8x + 5 = 0$, leaving your answers in surd form.**

$(x + 4)^2 - 11 = 0$

1) Put the number on the other side (+11). $(x + 4)^2 = 11$

2) Square root both sides (don't forget the ±!) ($\sqrt{\ }$). $x + 4 = \pm\sqrt{11}$

3) Get x on its own (−4). $x = -4 \pm \sqrt{11}$

So the two solutions (in surd form) are:
$x = -4 + \sqrt{11}$ and $x = -4 - \sqrt{11}$

If you really don't like steps 3-4, just remember that the value you need to add or subtract is <u>always</u> $c - \left(\frac{b}{2}\right)^2$.

Make a SQUARE (bracket) and COMPLETE it (add or take away)

Completing the square basically means working out a squared bracket which is almost the same as your quadratic and then working out what has to be added or subtracted to make it the same as the original.

Completing the Square

Completing the square can still be done when <u>a isn't 1</u>, it just takes an extra step.

Completing the Square When 'a' Isn't 1

If a isn't 1, completing the square is a bit trickier. You follow the <u>same method</u> as on the previous page, but you have to take out a <u>factor of a</u> from the x^2 and x-terms before you start (which often means you end up with awkward <u>fractions</u>). This time, the number in the brackets is $\frac{b}{2a}$.

EXAMPLE: Write $2x^2 + 5x + 9$ in the form $a(x + m)^2 + n$.

1) It's in the <u>standard format</u>. —— $2x^2 + 5x + 9$
2) Take out a <u>factor</u> of 2. —— $2\left(x^2 + \frac{5}{2}x\right) + 9$
3) Write out the <u>initial bracket</u>. —— $2\left(x + \frac{5}{4}\right)^2$
4) Multiply out the bracket and <u>compare</u> to the original.—— $2\left(x + \frac{5}{4}\right)^2 = 2x^2 + 5x + \frac{25}{8}$
5) Add on <u>adjusting number</u> $\left(\frac{47}{8}\right)$. —— $2\left(x + \frac{5}{4}\right)^2 + \frac{47}{8} = 2x^2 + 5x + \frac{25}{8} + \frac{47}{8}$
$$= 2x^2 + 5x + 9 \checkmark$$

Original equation had +9 here...

...so you need $9 - \frac{25}{8} = \frac{47}{8}$

matches original now!

So the completed square is: $2\left(x + \frac{5}{4}\right)^2 + \frac{47}{8}$

The **Completed Square** Helps You **Sketch** the **Graph**

You can use the <u>completed square</u> to work out key details about the graph —
like the <u>turning point</u> (maximum or minimum) and whether it <u>crosses</u> the x-axis.

1) For a <u>positive</u> quadratic (where the x^2 coefficient is positive), the <u>adjusting number</u> tells you the <u>minimum</u> y-value of the graph. If the completed square is $a(x + m)^2 + n$, this minimum y-value will occur when the brackets are equal to 0 (because the bit in brackets is squared, so is never negative) — i.e. when $x = -m$.

2) The <u>solutions</u> to the equation tell you where the graph <u>crosses</u> the <u>x-axis</u>. If the adjusting number is <u>positive</u>, the graph will <u>never</u> cross the x-axis as it will always be greater than 0 (this means that the quadratic has <u>no real roots</u>).

EXAMPLE: Sketch the graph of $y = 2x^2 + 5x + 9$.

1) From above, <u>completed square form</u> is $2\left(x + \frac{5}{4}\right)^2 + \frac{47}{8}$.

2) The <u>minimum point</u> occurs when the brackets are equal to <u>0</u>
   — this will happen when $x = -\frac{5}{4}$.

3) At this point, the graph takes its minimum value,
   which is the <u>adjusting number</u> $\left(\frac{47}{8}\right)$.

4) The <u>adjusting number</u> is <u>positive</u>, so the graph will
   <u>never</u> cross the x-axis.

5) Find where the curve crosses the y-axis by substituting $x = 0$
   into the equation and mark this on your graph. $y = 0 + 0 + 9$
   $= 9$

This is only a sketch, so label the points you know.

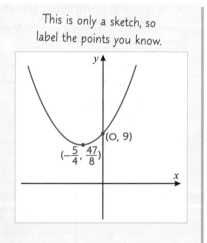

Take out a factor of 'a' from the x^2 and x-terms

After you've done that, you can complete the square like usual, just don't forget to multiply out the brackets properly — you need to multiply by the number in front of them. It's tricky, but practice helps.

Quadratic Equations — Tricky Ones

Now it's time to have a go at some tricky 'hidden quadratic' questions that sometimes pop up in the exam.

Shape Questions Involving Quadratics

Sometimes examiners like to <u>disguise</u> quadratic equations by pretending the question is about a <u>shape</u> — it might look like an <u>area</u> or <u>volume</u> question where you have to find the <u>length</u> of a side. Don't be fooled though.

EXAMPLE: **The rectangle on the right has sides of length x cm and $(2x + 1)$ cm. The area of the rectangle is 15 cm². Find the value of x.**

x cm

$(2x + 1)$ cm

1) You're told the <u>side lengths</u> and the <u>area</u>, and you know the <u>formula</u> for the area of a rectangle ($A = l \times w$), so this gives you:

$$x \times (2x + 1) = 15$$
$$2x^2 + x = 15$$

2) This is a <u>quadratic</u>, so just <u>rearrange</u> into the <u>standard format</u> and solve:

See p.60-61 if you need some help factorising.

$$2x^2 + x - 15 = 0$$
$$(2x - 5)(x + 3) = 0 \qquad \text{so } x = \tfrac{5}{2} \text{ or } x = -3$$

You couldn't have a shape with sides of length −3 cm and −5 cm.

3) However, you're looking for a <u>length</u>, which means x <u>can't be negative</u> — so $x = \tfrac{5}{2}$

Quadratics Hidden as Fractions

This is a nasty exam question — you're given an <u>equation</u> to solve that looks like it's an <u>algebraic fractions</u> question (more about these on p.68), but after some <u>rearranging</u>, it turns out you've got a <u>quadratic</u>.

EXAMPLE: **Solve $x - \dfrac{5}{x-1} = 2$, giving your answers to 3 significant figures.**

At first glance, this doesn't look like a quadratic, but wait and see...

1) The first thing to do is to get <u>rid of the fraction</u> (by multiplying every term by $(x - 1)$):

$$x(x - 1) - \frac{5(x - 1)}{x - 1} = 2(x - 1)$$
$$\Rightarrow x(x - 1) - 5 = 2(x - 1)$$

This is using the method for solving equations from p.55.

2) Next, <u>multiply out the brackets</u>: $x^2 - x - 5 = 2x - 2$

3) It's starting to look like a <u>quadratic</u> now, so write it out in the <u>standard format</u>:

$$x^2 - 3x - 3 = 0$$

4) <u>Solve it</u> — you're going to need the <u>quadratic formula</u> (see p.62):

$$a = 1, b = -3, c = -3$$

The mention of significant figures in the question is a hint that you're going to need to use the quadratic formula.

$$x = \frac{-b \pm \sqrt{b^2 - 4ac}}{2a} = \frac{-(-3) \pm \sqrt{(-3)^2 - (4 \times 1 \times -3)}}{2 \times 1}$$
$$= \frac{3 \pm \sqrt{9 - (-12)}}{2} = \frac{3 \pm \sqrt{21}}{2}$$
$$x = \frac{3 + \sqrt{21}}{2} = 3.7912... = 3.79 \text{ (3 s.f.)} \quad \text{or} \quad x = \frac{3 - \sqrt{21}}{2} = -0.7912... = -0.791 \text{ (3 s.f.)}$$

Always rearrange into the form ax² + bx + c

You can't solve a quadratic until it's in the form $ax^2 + bx + c = 0$, so always get hidden quadratics into this form before doing anything else. Only then can you use the methods on the last few pages to solve it.

Warm-Up and Worked Exam Questions

This quadratic stuff isn't everyone's cup of tea. But once you get the knack of it, through lots of practice, you'll find a lot of the questions are really similar. Which is nice.

Warm-Up Questions

1) Factorise: a) $x^2 + 11x + 28$ b) $x^2 + 16x + 28$ c) $x^2 + 12x - 28$
2) Solve by factorisation: a) $x^2 + 8x + 15 = 0$ b) $x^2 + 5x - 14 = 0$ c) $x^2 - 7x + 7 = -5$
3) Factorise $3x^2 + 32x + 20$.
4) Solve $5x^2 - 13x = 6$.
5) Solve $3x^2 - 3x = 2$, giving your answers to 2 decimal places.
6) Express $x^2 - 10x + 9$ as a completed square, and hence solve $x^2 - 10x + 9 = 0$.
7) Complete the square for the expression $2x^2 + 16x + 39$.

Worked Exam Questions

Now, the exam questions — the good news is, if you've got the hang of the warm-up questions, you'll find that the exam questions are pretty much the same.

1   The expression $5x^2 - 19x + 18$ is an example of a quadratic expression.

   a)   Fully factorise the expression $5x^2 - 19x + 18$.

     Number pairs are 1×18, 2×9, 3×6.
     $(5x \quad 9)(x \quad 2)$ multiplies to give $9x$ and $10x$ which add to give $19x$.

     $5x^2 - 19x + 18 = (5x - 9)(x - 2)$

     Be careful, you want $-19x$, so the signs are both $-$.

        $(5x - 9)(x - 2)$
        [2 marks]

   b)   Use your answer to part a) to solve the equation $5x^2 - 19x + 18 = (x - 2)^2$.

   Replace the left-hand side with the ——— $(5x - 9)(x - 2) = (x - 2)^2$
     factorisation from part a). $(5x - 9)(x - 2) - (x - 2)^2 = 0$ —— Get one side equal to 0.

   Factorise — you can take $(x - 2)((5x - 9) - (x - 2)) = 0$ —— Tidy up what's
   out a factor of $(x - 2)$ here. $(x - 2)(4x - 7) = 0$ inside the brackets.

     Set each bracket ——— $x - 2 = 0$ or $4x - 7 = 0$
     equal to 0 and solve.

        $x = 2$ or $x = \dfrac{7}{4}$ $x = \underline{\ 2\ }$ or $x = \underline{\ \frac{7}{4}\ }$
        [4 marks]

2   Solve the quadratic equation $x^2 + 5x + 3 = 0$, giving your answers to 2 decimal places.

   2 d.p. suggests you should use the quadratic formula:

   $a = 1$, $b = 5$ and $c = 3$

$$x = \frac{-b \pm \sqrt{b^2 - 4ac}}{2a} = \frac{-5 \pm \sqrt{5^2 - 4 \times 1 \times 3}}{2 \times 1} = \frac{-5 \pm \sqrt{13}}{2} = -0.697... \text{ or } -4.302...$$

   The answers are to 2 d.p. so you ——— $x = \underline{\ -0.70\ }$ or $x = \underline{\ -4.30\ }$
   need to include the 0s on the end.
        [3 marks]

Exam Questions

3   Solve the equation $3x^2 + 18x + 24 = 0$. **(5)**

Start by dividing everything by 3.

$x =$ .... or $x =$ ....

[3 marks]

4   The shape on the right is made from a square and a triangle. **(7)**

The sides of the square are $(x + 3)$ cm long and the height of the triangle is $(2x + 2)$ cm. The area of the whole shape is 60 cm². Find the value of x.

Don't forget, a length can't have a negative value.

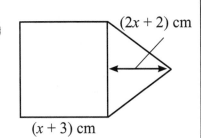

(2x + 2) cm

(x + 3) cm

Diagram NOT drawn to scale

$x =$ ....

[7 marks]

5   A curve has equation $y = 2x^2 - 8x + 19$. **(9)**

a)   Write the expression $2x^2 - 8x + 19$ in the form $a(x + b)^2 + c$.

....

[3 marks]

b)   Find the coordinates of the minimum point of the graph of $y = 2x^2 - 8x + 19$.

....

[1 mark]

c)   State if and where the graph of the equation crosses the x-axis.

Think about the minimum value of the graph.

....

[1 mark]

Algebraic Fractions

Unfortunately, fractions aren't limited to numbers — you can get <u>algebraic fractions</u> too.
Fortunately, everything you learnt about fractions on p.12-14 can be applied to algebraic fractions as well.

Simplifying Algebraic Fractions

You can <u>simplify</u> algebraic fractions by <u>cancelling</u> terms on the top and bottom — just deal with each <u>letter</u> individually and cancel as much as you can. You might have to <u>factorise</u> first (see pages 50 and 60-61).

1. Simplify $\dfrac{21x^3y^2}{14xy^3}$

÷7 on the top and bottom

÷x on the top and bottom
to leave x^2 on the top

÷y^2 on the top and bottom
to leave y on the bottom

$$\dfrac{\overset{3}{\cancel{21}}\,\overset{x^2}{\cancel{x^3}}\,y^2}{\underset{2}{\cancel{14}}\,x\,\underset{y}{\cancel{y^3}}} = \dfrac{3x^2}{2y}$$

2. Simplify $\dfrac{x^2-16}{x^2+2x-8}$

Factorise the top
using D.O.T.S.

$$\dfrac{(x+4)(x-4)}{(x-2)(x+4)} = \dfrac{x-4}{x-2}$$

Factorise the quadratic
on the bottom

Then cancel the common
factor of $(x+4)$

Multiplying/Dividing Algebraic Fractions

1) To <u>multiply</u> two fractions, just multiply tops and bottoms <u>separately</u>.

2) To <u>divide</u>, turn the second fraction <u>upside down</u> then <u>multiply</u>.

EXAMPLE: Simplify $\dfrac{x^2}{4} \times \dfrac{2}{x+1}$

Cancel the number
terms first...

$$\dfrac{x^2}{\underset{2}{\cancel{4}}} \times \dfrac{\cancel{2}}{x+1} = \dfrac{x^2}{2(x+1)}$$

EXAMPLE: Simplify $\dfrac{2}{x} \div \dfrac{x^3}{5}$

$$\dfrac{2}{x} \div \dfrac{x^3}{5} = \dfrac{2}{x} \times \dfrac{5}{x^3} = \dfrac{10}{x^4}$$

Adding/Subtracting Algebraic Fractions

For the common denominator, find
something both denominators divide into.

Adding or <u>subtracting</u> is a bit more difficult:

1) Work out the <u>common denominator</u> (see p.13).

2) Multiply <u>top and bottom</u> of each fraction by whatever gives you the common denominator.

3) Add or subtract the <u>numerators</u> only.

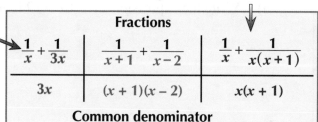

Fractions		
$\dfrac{1}{x} + \dfrac{1}{3x}$	$\dfrac{1}{x+1} + \dfrac{1}{x-2}$	$\dfrac{1}{x} + \dfrac{1}{x(x+1)}$
$3x$	$(x+1)(x-2)$	$x(x+1)$
Common denominator		

EXAMPLE: Write $\dfrac{3x}{(x+3)} + \dfrac{x-3}{(x-2)}$ as a single fraction.

1st fraction: × top & bottom by $(x-2)$

2nd fraction: × top & bottom by $(x+3)$

$$\dfrac{3x}{(x+3)} + \dfrac{x-3}{(x-2)} = \dfrac{3x(x-2)}{(x+3)(x-2)} + \dfrac{(x+3)(x-3)}{(x+3)(x-2)}$$

Common denominator
will be $(x+3)(x-2)$

Add the numerators

$$= \dfrac{3x^2-6x}{(x+3)(x-2)} + \dfrac{x^2-9}{(x+3)(x-2)} = \dfrac{4x^2-6x-9}{(x+3)(x-2)}$$

Put fractions over a common denominator

One more thing — never do this: $\dfrac{x}{x+y} = \dfrac{1}{y}$ ✗. It's WRONG and will lose you marks.

Inequalities

Inequalities aren't <u>half as difficult as they look</u>. Once you've learned the tricks involved, most of the algebra for them is <u>identical to ordinary equations</u> (have a look back at p.54-55 if you need a reminder).

The **Inequality Symbols**

> > means 'Greater than'   ≥ means 'Greater than or equal to'
> < means 'Less than'   ≤ means 'Less than or equal to'

<u>REMEMBER</u> — the one at the <u>big</u> end is <u>biggest</u> so '$x > 4$' and '$4 < x$' both mean: '<u>x is greater than 4</u>'.

Algebra with **Inequalities**

The key thing about inequalities is to solve them <u>just like regular equations</u> but <u>WITH ONE BIG EXCEPTION</u>:

> Whenever you <u>MULTIPLY</u> OR <u>DIVIDE</u> by a <u>NEGATIVE NUMBER</u>, you must <u>FLIP THE INEQUALITY SIGN</u>.

EXAMPLES:

1. x is an integer such that $-4 < x \le 3$. Write down all the possible values of x.

1) Work out what <u>each bit</u> of the inequality is telling you:

   $-4 < x$ means 'x is greater than -4', $x \le 3$ means 'x is less than or equal to 3'.

2) Now just write down <u>all the values</u> that x can take. (Remember, integers are just +ve or –ve <u>whole numbers</u>.)

   $-3, -2, -1, 0, 1, 2, 3$

> -4 <u>isn't</u> included because of the $<$, but 3 <u>is</u> included because of the $\le$.

2. Solve $2x + 7 > x + 11$.

Just solve it like an <u>equation</u>:

(-7) $2x + 7 - 7 > x + 11 - 7$
$\qquad 2x > x + 4$
$(-x)$ $2x - x > x + 4 - x$
$\qquad x > 4$

3. Solve $9 - 2x > 15$.

Again, solve it like an <u>equation</u>:

(-9) $9 - 2x - 9 > 15 - 9$
$\qquad -2x > 6$
$(\div -2)$ $-2x \div (-2) < 6 \div (-2)$
$\qquad x < -3$

> The $>$ has turned into a $<$, because we divided by a <u>negative number</u>.

4. Solve $-2 \le \dfrac{x+4}{4} \le 5$.

Don't be put off because there are two inequality signs — just do the same thing to each bit of the inequality.

1) First <u>multiply</u> everything by 4:

$4 \times -2 \le \dfrac{4 \times (x+4)}{4} \le 4 \times 5$
$-8 \le x + 4 \le 20$

2) Then <u>subtract</u> 4 to finish it off:

$-8 - 4 \le x + 4 - 4 \le 20 - 4$
$-12 \le x \le 16$

You Can Show Inequalities on **Number Lines**

Drawing inequalities on a <u>number line</u> is dead easy — all you have to remember is that you use an <u>open circle</u> (O) for $>$ or $<$ and a <u>coloured-in circle</u> (●) for $\ge$ or $\le$.

EXAMPLE: Show the inequality $-4 < x \le 3$ on a number line.

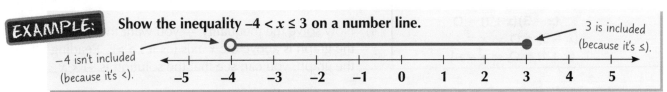

-4 isn't included (because it's $<$).

3 is included (because it's $\le$).

$-5 \quad -4 \quad -3 \quad -2 \quad -1 \quad 0 \quad 1 \quad 2 \quad 3 \quad 4 \quad 5$

Treat inequalities like equations — but remember the exception

The good news is, if you know how to solve equations, you also know how to solve inequalities. The bad news is, if you forget to flip the inequality sign when dividing by a negative number, you'll lose marks.

Inequalities

Quadratic inequalities can get pretty tough. Because they involve an x^2 term, they'll have <u>two</u> bounds for x.

Take Care with **Quadratic Inequalities**

If $x^2 = 4$, then $x = \underline{+2 \text{ or } -2}$. Remember this when solving quadratic inequalities.

EXAMPLES:

1. Solve the inequality $x^2 \leq 25$.

If $x^2 = 25$, then $x = \pm 5$.
As $x^2 \leq 25$, then $-5 \leq x \leq 5$

This means x is between -5 and 5, possibly equal to either. It looks like this on a number line:

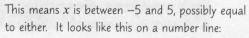

2. Solve the inequality $x^2 > 9$.

If $x^2 = 9$, then $x = \pm 3$.
As $x^2 > 9$, then $x < -3$ or $x > 3$

This means x is less than -3 or greater than 3. It looks like this on a number line:

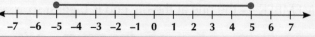

Harder **Quadratic Inequalities**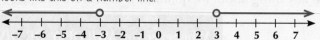

If the examiners are feeling particularly mean, you might get a harder quadratic inequality that <u>takes more steps</u> to solve. Worst case scenario, you might even need to sketch a graph...

EXAMPLES:

1. Solve the inequality $3x^2 \geq 48$.

Just solve it like an equation:

$(\div 3) \quad \dfrac{3x^2}{3} \geq \dfrac{48}{3}$

$x^2 \geq 16$

$x \leq -4$ or $x \geq 4$

2. Solve the inequality $-2x^2 + 8 > 0$.

$(-8) \quad -2x^2 + 8 - 8 > 0 - 8$

$-2x^2 > -8$

$(\div -2) \quad -2x^2 \div -2 < -8 \div -2$

$x^2 < 4$

$-2 < x < 2$

You're dividing by a <u>negative number</u>, so flip the sign.

3. Solve the inequality $-x^2 + 2x + 3 > 0$.

1) Start off by setting the quadratic <u>equal to 0</u>:

$-x^2 + 2x + 3 = 0$

2) Now <u>solve</u> the equation to find where the graph of $y = -x^2 + 2x + 3$ equals zero — i.e. where it crosses the x-axis.

Multiply everything by -1 and factorise:

$x^2 - 2x - 3 = 0$
$(x - 3)(x + 1) = 0$
$(x - 3) = 0$, so $x = 3$
$(x + 1) = 0$, so $x = -1$

3) Then sketch the graph of $y = -x^2 + 2x + 3$ — it'll cross the x-axis at -1 and 3. As the x^2 term is <u>negative</u>, it'll be an n-shaped curve (see p.95).

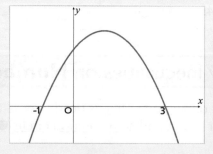

This is all the information you need to make a quick sketch to help you answer the question.

4) Now <u>solve</u> the inequality — you want the bit where the graph is <u>above</u> the x-axis (as it's a $>$). Reading off the graph, you can see that the solution is $-1 < x < 3$.

You can sketch graphs to help you solve quadratic inequalities

When you're sketching a quadratic graph, remember that if it has a positive x^2 term it will be a u-shaped graph, and if it has a negative x^2 term it will be an n-shaped graph. There's more on this on p.95.

Graphical Inequalities

These questions always involve <u>shading a region on a graph</u>. The method sounds very complicated, but once you've seen it in action with an example, you'll see that it's O...

Showing **Inequalities** on a **Graph**

Here's the method to follow:

1) <u>CONVERT each INEQUALITY to an EQUATION</u>
   by simply putting an '=' in place of the inequality sign.
2) <u>DRAW THE GRAPH FOR EACH EQUATION</u> — if the inequality sign
   is < or > draw a <u>dotted line</u>, but if it's ≥ or ≤ draw a <u>solid line</u>.
3) <u>Work out WHICH SIDE of each line you want</u> — put a point (usually the
   origin, (0, 0)) into the inequality to see if it's on the correct side of the line.
4) <u>SHADE THE REGION this gives you.</u>

If using the origin doesn't work (e.g. if the origin lies on a line), just pick another point with easy coordinates and use that instead.

EXAMPLE: **Shade the region that satisfies all three of the following inequalities:**
$x + y < 5$ $\qquad y \le x + 2$ $\qquad y > 1$

1) CONVERT EACH INEQUALITY TO AN EQUATION:
   $x + y = 5$, $y = x + 2$ and $y = 1$

2) DRAW THE GRAPH FOR EACH EQUATION (see p.89)
   You'll need a <u>dotted</u> line for $x + y = 5$ and $y = 1$ and a <u>solid</u> line for $y = x + 2$.

3) WORK OUT WHICH SIDE OF EACH LINE YOU WANT
   This is the fiddly bit. Put $x = 0$ and $y = 0$ (the origin) into
   each inequality and see if this makes the inequality <u>true</u> or <u>false</u>.

   <u>$x + y < 5$:</u>
   $x = 0$, $y = 0$ gives $0 < 5$ which is <u>true</u>.
   This means the <u>origin</u> is on the <u>correct</u> side of the line.

   <u>$y \le x + 2$:</u>
   $x = 0$, $y = 0$ gives $0 \le 2$ which is <u>true</u>.
   So the origin is on the <u>correct</u> side of this line.

   <u>$y > 1$:</u>
   $x = 0$, $y = 0$ gives $0 > 1$ which is <u>false</u>.
   So the origin is on the <u>wrong side</u> of this line.

   Dotted lines mean the region <u>doesn't</u> include the points on the line. *A <u>solid line</u> means the region <u>does</u> include the points on the line.*

4) SHADE THE REGION
   You want the region that satisfies all of these:
   - below $x + y = 5$ (because the origin <u>is</u> on this side)
   - right of $y = x + 2$ (because the origin <u>is</u> on this side)
   - above $y = 1$ (because the origin <u>isn't</u> on this side).

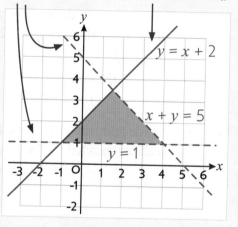

Make sure you read the question <u>carefully</u> — you might be asked to <u>label</u> the region instead of shade it, or just <u>mark on points</u> that satisfy all three inequalities. No point throwing away marks because you didn't read the question properly.

Just draw the graphs and shade the region

Don't panic if you're not quite sure how to sketch the graphs — you'll find out how on p.89.
Then you just have to make sure you shade the right region — pick a point (usually (0, 0)) and try it.

Warm-Up and Worked Exam Questions

OK, the topics in this section look a bit nasty — but for all of them, it's just a case of learning the symbols and methods and practising lots of questions...

Warm-Up Questions

1) Simplify: a) $\dfrac{16ab^2c^2}{4bc^4}$ b) $\dfrac{x^4 - 4y^2}{x^3 - 2xy}$

2) List all integer values of n if: a) $12 < n < 17$ b) $-3 \le n \le 3$ c) $8 < 4n < 20$

3) Solve these inequalities: a) $2q + 2 \le 12$ b) $4p + 12 > 30$

4) a) On the same axis, draw the graphs of $y = 0$, $y = 2x$, $y = 6 - x$.
   b) R is the region defined by the inequalities $y \le 2x$, $y \le 6 - x$, $y \ge 0$. Shade this region and label it R.

Worked Exam Questions

I'll show you how to do three exam questions, then you're on your own for the questions on the next page. Enjoy.

1   Write down the inequality that is shown on the number line below.

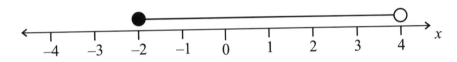

Think about what a coloured-in circle and an open circle mean.

$$-2 \le x < 4$$

[1 mark]

2   Look at the grid on the right.

a) Use the grid to draw the graphs of $2x + y = 10$ and $y = x + 2$.

It can help to rearrange the equations into the form $y = mx + c$ first.
$$y = 10 - 2x \qquad \textit{[2 marks]}$$

b) Shade and label, using the letter S, the area represented by the inequalities:
$$x \ge 1, \ 2x + y \le 10, \ y \ge x + 2.$$
[2 marks]

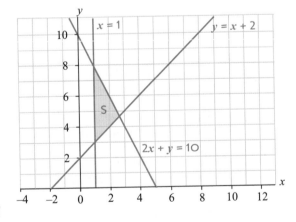

3   Write $\dfrac{2}{3} + \dfrac{m - 2n}{m + 3n}$ as a single fraction.

$$\frac{2}{3} + \frac{m - 2n}{m + 3n} = \frac{2 \times (m + 3n)}{3 \times (m + 3n)} + \frac{3 \times (m - 2n)}{3 \times (m + 3n)} = \frac{2m + 6n + 3m - 6n}{3(m + 3n)} = \frac{5m}{3(m + 3n)}$$

Finding the common denominator is the tricky bit — you often just need to multiply the denominators together.

$$\frac{5m}{3(m + 3n)}$$

[3 marks]

Exam Questions

4   Solve $\frac{2x}{5} \leq 3$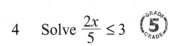

....
[2 marks]

5   Look at the grid on the right.

On the grid, shade the region
that represents these inequalities:

$x < 5$

$y \geq -2$

$y - x \leq 1$

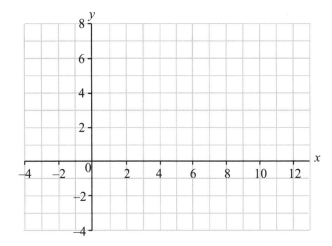

[4 marks]

6   Write $\frac{1}{x-5} + \frac{2}{x-2}$ as a single fraction.

....
[3 marks]

7   Show that $(x + 3) \div \left(\frac{x^2 + 4x + 3}{x + 4} \right) + 2 = \frac{3(x + 2)}{x + 1}$.

[4 marks]

8   Solve the following inequalities:

a) $x^2 + 1 > 37$

Remember — when you
take the square root
you get two answers.

....
[2 marks]

b) $x^2 + 1 < x + 7$

....
[3 marks]

Simultaneous Equations and Graphs

You can use <u>graphs</u> to solve <u>simultaneous equations</u> — just plot the graph of each equation, and the solutions are the points where the graphs <u>cross</u> (you can usually just read off the coordinates from the graph).

Plot **Both Graphs** and See Where They **Cross**

EXAMPLE: Draw the graphs of $y = 2x + 3$ and $y = 6 - 4x$ and use the diagram to solve the equations simultaneously.

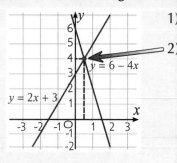

There's more on drawing straight-line graphs on p.89.

1) <u>DRAW BOTH GRAPHS.</u>

2) <u>LOOK FOR WHERE THE GRAPHS CROSS.</u>

The straight lines cross at <u>one point</u>.
Reading the <u>x- and y-values</u> of this point

gives the solution $x = \frac{1}{2}$ and $y = 4$.

If you were asked for the <u>point</u> where the graphs cross, give your answer in <u>coordinate form</u> — i.e. (x, y).

The point at which the two graphs cross is actually the <u>solution</u> you'd find if you set the two equations <u>equal to each other</u> (so in the first example, you're actually solving $2x + 3 = 6 - 4x$).
This fact comes in handy for the next (trickier) example.

EXAMPLE: The equation $y = x^2 - 4x + 3$ is shown on the graph below.
By drawing a suitable straight line, solve the equation $x^2 - 5x + 3 = 0$.

1) <u>WORK OUT WHICH STRAIGHT LINE YOU NEED.</u>

This is a bit nasty — the trick is to rearrange the given equation $x^2 - 5x + 3 = 0$ so that you have $x^2 - 4x + 3$ (the graph) on one side.

$x^2 - 5x + 3 = 0$

Adding x to both sides:

$x^2 - 4x + 3 = x$ ←——— The sides of this equation represent the two graphs $y = x^2 - 4x + 3$ and $y = x$.

So the line needed is $y = x$.

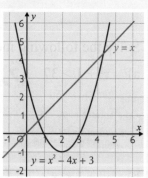

2) <u>DRAW IN THE LINE AND READ OFF THE SOLUTIONS.</u>

Once you have two graphs, read off the x-values where they cross.

You only need the x-values because that's the only variable in your equation.

The graphs cross at <u>two points</u>.
Reading the <u>x-values</u> of these points gives the solutions $x = 0.7$ and $x = 4.3$.

The actual solutions are 0.69722... and 4.30277...
You won't be expected to read the graph to that level of accuracy, so you'll get the marks if you're near enough.

The solutions lie where the graphs intersect

Try and be as accurate as possible with your drawings. If either of your graphs are wrong then the intersections will be in the wrong place and you'll end up with the wrong solutions.

Simultaneous Equations

You've seen one way to solve simultaneous equations using graphs. Now it's time to learn how to solve them using algebra. The rules are quite simple, but you must follow <u>ALL</u> the steps, in the <u>right order</u>, and treat them as a strict method.

There are two types of simultaneous equations you could get:

EASY ONES (where both equations are linear) and TRICKY ONES (where one's quadratic).

1 $2x = 6 - 4y$ and $-3 - 3y = 4x$ **2** $7x + y = 1$ and $2x^2 - y = 3$

1 Six Steps for **Easy Simultaneous Equations**

EXAMPLE: **Solve the simultaneous equations $2x = 6 - 4y$ and $-3 - 3y = 4x$.**

1) <u>Rearrange both equations</u> into the form <u>$ax + by = c$</u>, and label the two equations ① and ②.

> a, b and c are numbers
> (which can be negative)

$2x + 4y = 6$ — ①
$-4x - 3y = 3$ — ②

2) <u>Match up the numbers in front</u> (the 'coefficients') of either the x's or y's in both equations. You may need to multiply one or both equations by a suitable number. Relabel them ③ and ④.

① × 2: $4x + 8y = 12$ — ③
           $-4x - 3y = 3$ — ④

3) <u>Add or subtract the two equations</u> to eliminate the terms with the same coefficient.

③ + ④ $0x + 5y = 15$

> If the coefficients have <u>the same sign</u> (both +ve or both –ve) then <u>subtract</u>. If the coefficients have <u>opposite signs</u> (one +ve and one –ve) then <u>add</u>.

4) <u>Solve</u> the resulting equation.

$5y = 15 \Rightarrow \underline{y = 3}$

5) Substitute the value you've found <u>back</u> into equation ① and solve it.

Sub $y = 3$ into ①: $2x + (4 × 3) = 6 \Rightarrow 2x + 12 = 6 \Rightarrow 2x = -6 \Rightarrow \underline{x = -3}$

6) Substitute both these values into equation ② to make sure it works. If it doesn't then you've done something wrong and you'll have to do it all again.

Sub x and y into ②: $(-4 × -3) - (3 × 3) = 12 - 9 = 3$, which is right, so it's worked.
So the solutions are: $x = -3$, $y = 3$

And these are the easy simultaneous equations

It might just be me, but I think simultaneous equations are quite fun... well, maybe not fun... but quite satisfying. Anyway, it doesn't matter whether you like them or not — you have to learn how to do them.

Simultaneous Equations

EXAMPLE: Solve these two equations simultaneously:

$$7x + y = 1 \quad \text{and} \quad 2x^2 - y = 3$$

1) Rearrange the quadratic equation so that you have the non-quadratic unknown on its own. Label the two equations ① and ②.

$$7x + y = 1 \quad — ①$$
$$y = 2x^2 - 3 \quad — ②$$

2) Substitute the quadratic expression into the other equation. You'll get another equation — label it ③.

$$7x + y = 1 \quad — ①$$
$$y = \boxed{2x^2 - 3} \quad — ②$$

$$\Rightarrow 7x + (2x^2 - 3) = 1 \quad — ③$$

In this example, put the expression for y into equation ① in place of y.

3) Rearrange to get a quadratic equation. And guess what... You've got to solve it.

$$2x^2 + 7x - 4 = 0$$
$$(2x - 1)(x + 4) = 0$$
So $2x - 1 = 0$ OR $x + 4 = 0$
$x = 0.5$ OR $x = -4$

Remember — if it won't factorise, you can use the formula. Have a look at p.62 for more details.

4) Stick the first value back in one of the original equations (pick the easy one).

① $7x + y = 1$

Substitute in $x = 0.5$: $3.5 + y = 1$, so $y = 1 - 3.5 = -2.5$

5) Stick the second value back in the same original equation (the easy one again).

① $7x + y = 1$

Substitute in $x = -4$: $-28 + y = 1$, so $y = 1 + 28 = 29$

6) Substitute both pairs of answers back into the other original equation to check they work.

② $y = 2x^2 - 3$

Substitute in $x = 0.5$: $y = (2 \times 0.25) - 3 = -2.5$
Substitute in $x = -4$: $y = (2 \times 16) - 3 = 29$

7) Write the pairs of answers out again, clearly, at the bottom of your working.

The two pairs of solutions are: $x = 0.5, y = -2.5$ and $x = -4, y = 29$

Remember to write out the two pairs clearly

You're basically combining the two equations to make one quadratic equation.
Solve that equation and stick the solutions back in to get the other two corresponding answers.

Warm-Up and Worked Exam Questions

Have a go at these warm-up questions and check that you're comfortable with them before moving on to the exam questions. If you find anything a bit tricky, go back and read over it until you understand it.

Warm-Up Questions

1) Solve these simultaneous equations:
   a) $y = x$
      $y = 9 - 2x$
   b) $y = 2x$
      $y = x + 1$
   c) $x + y = 5$
      $x - y = 1$

2) By sketching the graphs, find the solutions of the simultaneous equations $y = 4x - 4$ and $y = 6 - x$.

3) Solve the simultaneous equations $2x + 3y = 19$ and $2x + y = 9$.

4) Solve the simultaneous equations $y = 2 - 3x$ and $y + 2 = x^2$.

5) Find x and y given that $2x - 10 = 4y$ and $3y = 5x - 18$.

Worked Exam Questions

To ease you into the exam questions on the next page, I've done two for you (aren't I kind?). Have a look at these worked exam questions, and make sure you understand each step.

1   Clare wants to use the graph of $x^3 + 4x^2 - 3x + 2$ to solve the equation $x^3 + 4x^2 - 3x - 1 = 0$.
    Find the equation of the straight line she should draw on the graph. **(8)**

> Rearrange the equation that
> Clare wants to solve so that it has
> $x^3 + 4x^2 - 3x + 2$ on one side.

$x^3 + 4x^2 - 3x - 1 = 0$
$x^3 + 4x^2 - 3x - 1 (+ 3) = 0 (+ 3)$
$x^3 + 4x^2 - 3x + 2 = 3$

> Whatever is on the other side is
> the line that she needs to draw.

$\underline{\qquad y = 3 \qquad}$

[2 marks]

2   Solve the following pair of simultaneous equations. **(8)**
    $x^2 + y = 4$
    $y = 4x - 1$

$y = 4x - 1$ ① $\qquad y = 4 - x^2$ ②

Substitute ② into ①:

$(4 - x^2) = 4x - 1$

$x^2 + 4x - 5 = 0$

$(x + 5)(x - 1) = 0$

So $x = -5$ or $x = 1$.

When $x = 1$, $y = (4 \times 1) - 1 = 3$

When $x = -5$, $y = (4 \times -5) - 1 = -21$

So the solutions are $x = 1$, $y = 3$ and $x = -5$, $y = -21$

> Rearrange the quadratic equation to get y on
> its own, then sub the expression for y into the
> other equation. Then you just need to solve it.

$x = \underset{1}{\ldots\ldots\ldots} , \quad y = \underset{3}{\ldots\ldots\ldots}$

and $x = \underset{-5}{\ldots\ldots\ldots} , \quad y = \underset{-21}{\ldots\ldots\ldots}$

[5 marks]

Exam Questions

3   Solve this pair of simultaneous equations.

$$2x + 3y = 12$$
$$5x + 4y = 9$$

$x = $ .... , $y = $ ....

[4 marks]

4   By drawing two straight lines on the grid provided, solve these simultaneous equations:

$$y = x + 1$$
$$3y = x + 9$$

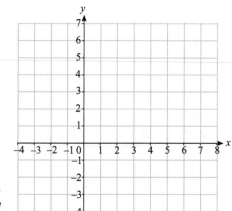

$x = $ .... , $y = $ ....

[3 marks]

5   The diagram below shows part of the graph of $y = 4x - x^2$.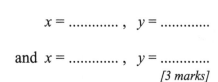
Use the graph to solve these simultaneous equations:

$$y = 5x - 2$$
$$y = 4x - x^2$$

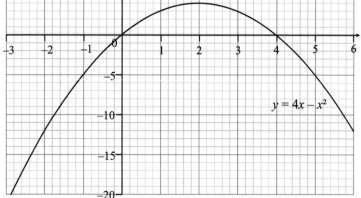

$x = $ .... , $y = $ ....

and $x = $ .... , $y = $ ....

[3 marks]

6   Solve the following pair of simultaneous equations.

$$2x^2 + y^2 = 51$$
$$y = x + 6$$

$x = $ .... , $y = $ ....

and $x = $ .... , $y = $ ....

[6 marks]

Number Patterns and Sequences

Sequences are just <u>patterns</u> of <u>numbers</u> or <u>shapes</u> that follow a <u>rule</u>. You need to be able to spot what the rule is.

Finding **Number Patterns**

The trick to <u>finding the rule</u> for number patterns is to <u>write down</u> what you have to do to get from one number to the next in the <u>gaps</u> between the numbers. There are <u>two main types</u> to look out for:

1) <u>Add</u> or <u>subtract</u> the <u>same number</u>

E.g.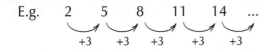

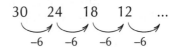

| **The RULE:** | **'Add 3 to the <u>previous term</u>'** | **'Subtract 6 from the <u>previous term</u>'** |

2) <u>Multiply</u> or <u>divide</u> by the <u>same</u> number <u>each time</u>

E.g.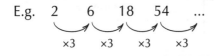

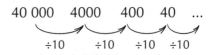

| **The RULE:** | **'Multiply the <u>previous term</u> by 3'** | **'Divide the <u>previous term</u> by 10'** |

You might sometimes get patterns that follow a <u>different</u> rule — for example, you might have to add or subtract a <u>changing number</u> each time, or add together the <u>two previous terms</u>. You probably don't need to worry about this, but if it comes up, just <u>describe</u> the pattern and use your <u>rule</u> to find the next term.

Shape Patterns

If you have a pattern of <u>shapes</u>, you need to be able to <u>continue</u> the pattern. You might also have to find the <u>rule</u> for the pattern to work out <u>how many</u> shapes there'll be in a later pattern.

EXAMPLE: On the right, there are some patterns made of circles.
  a) Draw the next pattern in the sequence.
  b) Work out how many circles there will be in the 10th pattern.

a) Just continue the pattern —
each 'leg' increases by one circle.

In an exam question, you might be given a table and asked to complete it.

b) Set up a table to find the rule:

Pattern number	1	2	3	4	5	6	7	8	9	10
Number of circles	1	3	5	7	9	11	13	15	17	19

The rule is '**add 2 to the previous term**'.

So just keep on <u>adding 2</u> to extend the table until you get to the 10th term — which is **19**.

Look out for patterns to spot sequence rules

When you're given a sequence, start by checking the difference between each term. If that doesn't tell you the rule (i.e. the differences aren't the same), divide each term by the one before it to see if it's a × or ÷ rule.

Number Patterns and Sequences

You'll often be asked to "find an <u>expression</u> for the <u>nth term</u> of a sequence" — this is just a formula with *n* in, like 5*n* – 3. It gives you <u>every term in a sequence</u> when you put in different values for *n*.

Finding the **nth Term** of a **Sequence**

The two methods below work for <u>linear</u> sequences — ones with a <u>common difference</u> (where the sequence <u>increases</u> or <u>decreases</u> by the <u>same number</u> each time).

EXAMPLE:

Find an expression for the *n*th term of the sequence that starts 5, 8, 11, 14, ...

n:	1	2	3	4
term:	5	8	11	14

+3   +3   +3

> The common difference is <u>3</u>, so '<u>3n</u>' is in the formula.

3n:	3	6	9	12

+2   +2   +2   +2

term:	5	8	11	14

> You have to <u>+ 2</u> to get to the term.

So the expression for the nth term is 3n + 2

Method 1 — Work it out

1) <u>Find the common difference</u> — this tells you what to multiply *n* by. So here, 3 gives '3*n*'.

2) <u>Work out what to add or subtract</u>. So for *n* = 1, '3*n*' is 3 so add 2 to get to the term (5).

3) <u>Put both bits together</u>. So you get 3*n* + 2.

Always <u>check</u> your formula by putting the first few values of *n* back in, e.g. putting *n* = 1 into 3*n* + 2 gives 5, *n* = 2 gives 8, etc. which is the <u>original sequence</u> you were given.

Method 2 — Learn the formula

$$n\text{th term} = a + (n - 1)d$$

'*d*' is the common difference and '*a*' is the first term.

The other approach is to simply <u>learn this formula</u> and stick in the values of *a* and *d* (you don't need to replace the *n* though):

So for the example above, *d* = 3 and *a* = 5. Putting these in the formula gives:
*n*th term = 5 + (*n* – 1) × 3 = 5 + 3*n* – 3 = <u>3*n* + 2</u>.
Again, <u>check</u> it by putting in values for *n*.

Deciding if a Term is in a Sequence

You might be given the *n*th term and asked if a <u>certain value</u> is in the sequence. The trick here is to <u>set the expression equal to that value</u> and solve to find *n*. If *n* is a <u>whole number</u>, the value is <u>in</u> the sequence.

EXAMPLE: **The *n*th term of a sequence is given by 3*n* + 8.**

> Have a look at p.54-55 for more on solving equations.

a) Find the 6th term in the sequence.

This is straightforward — just put *n* = 6 into the expression:

3 × 6 + 8 = 18 + 8
= 26

b) Is 45 a term in this sequence?

Set it equal to 45... 3*n* + 8 = 45
3*n* = 37 ...and solve for *n*.
$n = \frac{37}{3} = 12.33333...$

n is not a whole number, so 45 is not in the sequence 3n + 8.

Look for the common difference

Whichever of the methods you use to find the *n*th term, you're going to need to work out the common difference, *d*. Then, if you're sure you've learnt it right you can go ahead and use the formula — but if you're in any doubt then it's better to go the long way around and stick with method 1.

Number Patterns and Sequences

Sometimes you might have to do a bit more <u>working out</u> before you can get an <u>expression</u> for the <u>nth term</u>.

Finding the **nth Term** from any **Two Terms**

Any two terms can be used to find the *n*th term. As long as you know <u>where</u>
they are in the sequence, you can set up <u>simultaneous equations</u> to find *a* and *d*.

EXAMPLE:
In an arithmetic sequence, the 3rd term is 14, and the 7th term is 30.
Find an expression for the *n*th term of this sequence.

> An <u>arithmetic</u> sequence is just a fancier way of saying <u>linear</u> sequence.

1) Use the <u>formula</u> for the *n*th term to form <u>two equations</u> in *a* and *d*:

$$a + (3 - 1)d = 14 \qquad a + (7 - 1)d = 30$$
$$① \; a + 2d = 14 \qquad ② \; a + 6d = 30$$

> From the question, you know that when n = 3 the term is 14, and when n = 7 the term is 30.

2) Doing ② − ① <u>cancels</u> the *a*'s out:

$$a - a + 6d - 2d = 30 - 14 \Rightarrow 4d = 16 \Rightarrow \underline{d = 4}$$

3) Now, <u>substitute</u> *d* = 4 back into ① to find *a*:

> Have a look back at pages 75-76 to brush up on your simultaneous equations skills.

$$a + 2 \times 4 = 14 \Rightarrow \underline{a} = 14 - 8 = \underline{6}$$

4) Now put *d* = 4 and *a* = 6 back into the *n*th term <u>formula</u> to get $6 + (n - 1) \times 4 = 4n + 2$

A **Series** is when you **Add** the Terms to Find the **Total**

You could be asked to find the <u>sum</u> of the first *n* terms of an arithmetic series, written S_n.
There are <u>two different formulas</u>, depending on whether or not you know the <u>last term</u> in the sum.

1) If you know the last term...

...the formula you use is fairly simple: $\boxed{S_n = \dfrac{n}{2}(a + \text{the last term})}$

EXAMPLE: **An arithmetic series has 1st term 3 and 22nd term 87. Find the sum of the first 22 terms.**

$a = 3$, $n = 22$ and the last term is 87.

Put these values into the formula to get:

$$S_{22} = \frac{22}{2}(3 + 87) = 11 \times 90 = 990$$

2) If you don't know the last term...

...the formula is a bit trickier: $\boxed{S_n = \dfrac{n}{2}[2a + (n-1)d]}$ ←

> This version will be given to you on the formula sheet in your exam.

EXAMPLE: **For the arithmetic series starting −5 + −2 + 1 + 4 + 7 + ...**
find the sum of the first 20 terms.

$a = -5$, $d = 3$ and $n = 20$

$$S_{20} = \frac{20}{2}[2 \times -5 + (20 - 1) \times 3] = 10[-10 + 19 \times 3] = 470$$

> You might get a question in the exam where you have to calculate a and d first, before substituting them into the formula.

You need to learn that first formula off by heart

Make sure you know the difference between sequences and series — a sequence is a bunch of numbers
in a pattern (1, 6, 11, 16, ...), while a series is the <u>sum</u> of a sequence (1 + 6 + 11 + 16 + ...).

Proof

I'm not going to lie — <u>proof questions</u> can look a bit terrifying. The trick is to understand which <u>bit of maths</u> the question actually <u>wants</u> you to do. Once you've got that, the rest isn't so bad.

Show Things Are **Odd**, **Even** or **Multiples** by **Rearranging**

Before you get started, there are a few things you need to know —
they'll come in very handy when you're trying to prove things.

> - Any <u>even number</u> can be written as <u>$2n$</u> — i.e. 2 × something.
> - Any <u>odd number</u> can be written as <u>$2n + 1$</u> — i.e. 2 × something + 1.
> - <u>Consecutive numbers</u> can be written as <u>n</u>, <u>$n + 1$</u>, <u>$n + 2$</u> etc. — you can apply this to e.g. consecutive even numbers too (they'd be written as $2n$, $2n + 2$, $2n + 4$). (In all of these statements, n is just any <u>integer</u>.)
> - The <u>sum</u>, <u>difference</u> and <u>product</u> of integers is <u>always</u> an integer.

This can be extended to multiples of other numbers too — e.g. to prove that something is a <u>multiple of 3</u>, show that it can be written as <u>3 × something</u>.

EXAMPLE: **Prove that the sum of any three odd numbers is odd.**

Take three odd numbers:
$2a + 1$, $2b + 1$ and $2c + 1$ (they don't have to be consecutive)   (7ᴳᴿᴬᴰᴱ)

Add them together:

$2a + 1 + 2b + 1 + 2c + 1 = 2a + 2b + 2c + 2 + 1$ — *You'll see why I've written 3 as 2 + 1 in a second.*
$\qquad\qquad\qquad\qquad\qquad = 2(a + b + c + 1) + 1$
$\qquad\qquad\qquad\qquad\qquad = 2n + 1$ where n is an integer $(a + b + c + 1)$

So the sum of any three odd numbers is odd.

So what you're trying to do here is show that the sum of three odd numbers can be written as (2 × integer) + 1.

EXAMPLE: **Prove that for any integer n, $(n + 3)^2 - (n - 2)^2$ is a multiple of 5.**   (6ᴳᴿᴬᴰᴱ)

Play about with the expression until you get it into the form '5 × something':

$(n + 3)^2 - (n - 2)^2 = n^2 + 6n + 9 - (n^2 - 4n + 4)$
$\qquad\qquad\qquad\qquad\quad = n^2 + 6n + 9 - n^2 + 4n - 4$
$\qquad\qquad\qquad\qquad\quad = 10n + 5$
$\qquad\qquad\qquad\qquad\quad = 5(2n + 1)$

Because you can take a 5 outside the brackets, this must be a multiple of 5 for any integer n.

As n is an integer, $2n + 1$ is also an integer, so $5(2n + 1)$ is a multiple of 5 for any integer n.

Disprove Things by Finding a **Counter Example**

If you're asked to prove a statement <u>isn't</u> true, all you have to do is find <u>one example</u> that the statement doesn't work for — this is known as <u>disproof by counter example</u>.

EXAMPLE: **Ellie says, "If $x > y$, then $x^2 > y^2$". Is she correct? Explain your answer.**   (6ᴳᴿᴬᴰᴱ)

Try some different values for x and y:
$\quad x = 2, y = 1$: $x > y$ and $x^2 = 4 > 1 = y^2$
$\quad x = 5, y = 2$: $x > y$ and $x^2 = 25 > 4 = y^2$

Make sure you try positive and negative numbers when you're trying to find a counter example. Sometimes it's worth trying zero too.

At first glance, Ellie seems to be correct. BUT... $x = -1, y = -2$: $x > y$ but $x^2 = 1 < 4 = y^2$, so Ellie is wrong as the statement does not hold for all values of x and y.

Proof questions aren't as bad as they look

If you're asked to prove that two things are equal, a bit of rearranging should do the trick. If you're asked to prove something is wrong, just find a counter example. And <u>always</u> keep in mind what you're aiming for.

Direct and Inverse Proportion

Proportion questions involve two variables (often x and y) which are linked in some way. You'll have to figure out the relationship between them, and use this to find values of x or y, given one value.

Simple Proportions

The easiest types of proportions you might get are direct proportion ($y \propto x$) and inverse proportion ($y \propto \frac{1}{x}$).

$\propto$ means 'is proportional to'.

Direct Proportion	BOTH INCREASE TOGETHER

The graph is a straight line through the origin: $y = kx$

If it doesn't go through the origin, it's not a direct proportion.

Inverse Proportion	One INCREASES, one DECREASES

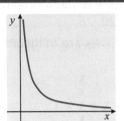

The graph is $y = \frac{k}{x}$.

See p.96 for more on these graphs.

Trickier Proportions

More complex proportions involve y varying proportionally or inversely to some function of x, e.g. x^2, x^3, $\sqrt{x}$. You can always turn a proportion statement into an equation by replacing '$\propto$' with '$= k$' like this:

	Proportionality	Equation
'y is proportional to the square of x'	$y \propto x^2$	$y = kx^2$
't is proportional to the square root of h'	$t \propto \sqrt{h}$	$t = k\sqrt{h}$
'D varies with the cube of t'	$D \propto t^3$	$D = kt^3$
'V is inversely proportional to r cubed'	$V \propto \frac{1}{r^3}$	$V = \frac{k}{r^3}$

k is just some constant (unknown number).

Handling Questions on Proportion

1) Convert the sentence into a proportionality.
2) Replace '$\propto$' with '$= k$' to make an equation (as above).

Once you've got it in the form of an equation with k, the rest is easy.

3) Find a pair of values of x and y somewhere in the question, and substitute them into the equation with the sole purpose of finding k.
4) Put the value of k into the equation and it's now ready to use, e.g. $y = 3x^2$.
5) Inevitably, they'll ask you to find y, having given you a value for x (or vice versa).

EXAMPLE: G is inversely proportional to the square root of H. When $G = 2$, $H = 16$.
Find an equation for G in terms of H, and use it to work out the value of G when $H = 36$.

1) Convert to a proportionality. $G \propto \dfrac{1}{\sqrt{H}}$

2) Replace $\propto$ with '$= k$' to form an equation. $G = \dfrac{k}{\sqrt{H}}$

3) Use the values of G and H (2 and 16) to find k. $2 = \dfrac{k}{\sqrt{16}} = \dfrac{k}{4} \Rightarrow k = 8$

4) Put the value of k back into the equation. $G = \dfrac{8}{\sqrt{H}}$ This is the equation for G in terms of H.

5) Use your equation to find the value of G.

$$G = \frac{8}{\sqrt{H}} = \frac{8}{\sqrt{36}}$$
$$= \frac{8}{6}$$
$$= \frac{4}{3}$$

Direct proportion means 'as one thing increases, so does the other'

With inverse proportion, as one increases, the other decreases. Don't get them muddled up.

Warm-Up and Worked Exam Questions

There was a lot of maths to take in over the last few pages — but you can breathe a sigh of relief as you've made it to the end of the algebra section. Just a few pages of questions to go.

Warm-Up Questions

1) a) Find the first 6 terms of the sequence whose nth term is $5n + 3$.
   b) Find the first 6 terms of the sequence whose nth term is $3n + 5$.

2) Find the nth term of the following sequences:
   a) 5, 10, 15, 20, 25, ...   b) 7, 10, 13, 16, 19, ...

3) How many crosses are in the nth pattern?

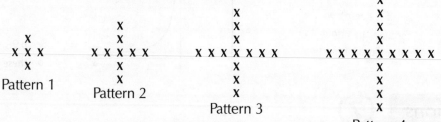

4) Prove that the sum of two consecutive even numbers is even.

5) $4x + 2 = 3(3a + x)$. For odd integer values of a, prove that x is never a multiple of 8.

6) Write each of the following as an equation:
   a) A is proportional to the square of r b) $D \propto \dfrac{1}{R}$
   c) H is inversely proportional to the cube of D d) $V \propto S^3$

Worked Exam Questions

Here are a couple of worked examples for you. Make the most of them, because the next page is full of exam-type questions for you to have a go at on your own.

1   Prove that the difference between the squares of two consecutive even numbers is always a multiple of 4.   (7)

   n is an integer. 2n represents any even number, so the difference between the squares of two consecutive even numbers will be given by:

   $(2n + 2)^2 - (2n)^2 = (4n^2 + 8n + 4) - 4n^2 = 8n + 4 = 4(2n + 1)$
   $= 4x$ (where x is an integer given by x = 2n + 1)

   Any integer multiplied by 4 is a multiple of 4, so 4x must be a multiple of 4 and therefore the difference between the squares of two consecutive even numbers will always be a multiple of 4.

   [3 marks]

2   The gravitational force, f, between two objects is inversely proportional to the square of the distance, d, between them. When $d = 100$, $f = 20$.   (7)
   Write an equation connecting f and d and use it to find the value of f when $d = 800$.

   $f \propto \dfrac{1}{d^2}$, so $f = \dfrac{k}{d^2}$

   When d = 100 and f = 20, $20 = \dfrac{k}{100^2}$, so k = 20 × 100² = 200 000

   So the equation is $f = \dfrac{200\,000}{d^2}$

   When d = 800, $f = \dfrac{200\,000}{800^2} = 0.3125$

   $f =$ ....0.3125.......
   [3 marks]

Exam Questions

3 The first four terms in a sequence are 3, 8, 13, 18, ...

a) Find the nth term of the sequence. **(4)**

....
[2 marks]

b) Is 107 a term in this sequence? Explain your answer. **(5)**

[2 marks]

4 The signal strength, S%, on Habib's mobile phone is inversely proportional to **(7)** the distance, d km, he is from the nearest radio mast.

a) When Habib is 15 km from the nearest radio mast his signal strength is 60%. Express S in terms of d.

....
[3 marks]

b) On the axes to the right, sketch the graph of S against d.

[1 mark]

5 The 3rd term of an arithmetic series is 11. The 8th term of the same series is 31. **(9)** Find the sum of the first 65 terms of the series.

....
[5 marks]

6 Show that the number $2^{64} - 1$ is not prime. **(9)**

Try thinking of this as a difference of two squares.

[3 marks]

Revision Questions for Section Two

There's no denying, Section Two has some really nasty maths — so check now how much you've learned.
- Try these questions and <u>tick off each one</u> when you <u>get it right</u>.
- When you've done <u>all the questions</u> for a topic and are <u>completely happy</u> with it, tick off the topic.

Algebra (p.45-57) ☑

1) Simplify the following: a) $x^3 \times x^6$ b) $y^7 \div y^5$ c) $(z^3)^4$ ☑

2) Simplify by collecting like terms: $3x + 2y - 5 - 6y + 2x$ ☑

3) Imran buys d DVDs and c CDs. DVDs cost £7 each and CDs cost £5 each. He spends £P in total. Write a formula for P in terms of d and c. ☑

4) Multiply out these brackets: a) $3(2x + 1)$ b) $(x + 2)(x - 3)$ c) $(x - 1)(x + 3)(x + 5)$ ☑

5) Factorise: a) $7x^2y + 21xz^2$ b) $49 - 81p^2q^2$ c) $12x^2 - 48y^2$ ☑

6) Simplify the following: a) $\sqrt{27}$ b) $\sqrt{125} \div \sqrt{5}$ ☑

7) Solve these equations: a) $5(x + 2) = 8 + 4(5 - x)$ b) $x^2 - 21 = 3(5 - x^2)$ ☑

8) Make p the subject of these: a) $\frac{1}{p} = \frac{1}{q} + \frac{1}{r}$ b) $\frac{p}{p + y} = 4$ ☑

Quadratics (p.60-65) ☑

9) Solve the following by factorising them first: a) $x^2 + 9x + 18 = 0$ b) $5x^2 - 17x - 12 = 0$ ☑

10) Find the solutions of these equations (to 2 d.p.) using the quadratic formula:
    a) $x^2 + x - 4 = 0$ b) $5x^2 + 6x = 2$ c) $(2x + 3)^2 = 15$ ☑

11) Find the exact solutions of these equations by completing the square:
    a) $x^2 + 12x + 15 = 0$ b) $2x^2 - 5x = 3$ ☑

Algebraic Fractions (p.68) ☑

12) Write $\frac{2}{x + 3} + \frac{1}{x - 1}$ as a single fraction. ☑

Inequalities (p.69-71) ☑

13) Solve these inequalities: a) $4x + 3 \le 6x + 7$ b) $-9 \le 3 - 2x < 5$ ☑

14) Solve $4x^2 > 100$ ☑

15) Show on a graph the region described by these conditions: $x + y \le 6$, $y > 0.5$, $y \le 2x - 2$ ☑

Simultaneous Equations (p.74-76) ☑

16) Solve the following pair of simultaneous equations: $4x + 5y = 23$ and $3y - x = 7$ ☑

17) Solve these simultaneous equations: $y = 3x + 4$ and $x^2 + 2y = 0$ ☑

Number Patterns and Sequences (p.79-81) ☑

18) For each of the following sequences, find the next term and write down the rule you used.
    a) 3, 10, 17, 24, ... b) 1, 4, 16, 64, ... c) 2, 5, 7, 12, ... ☑

19) Find the expression for the nth term in the following sequences: a) 5, 9, 13, 17 b) 11, 8, 5, 2 ☑

20) Find the sum of the first 30 terms of these series:
    a) $7 + 9 + 11 + 13...$ b) $12 + 23 + 34 + 45...$ ☑

Proof (p.82) ☑

21) Prove that the product of an odd number and an even number is even. ☑

Direct and Inverse Proportion (p.83) ☑

22) Write the following statement as an equation: "y is proportional to the square of x". ☑

23) p is proportional to the cube of q. When $p = 9$, $q = 3$. Find the value of p when $q = 6$. ☑

Coordinates

To start off with, here's some basic stuff about <u>coordinates</u>.
Get stuck into it — it'll get you off to a running start.

The Four **Quadrants**

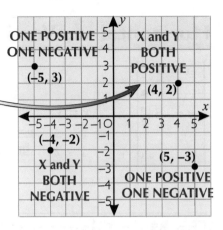

1) A graph has <u>four different quadrants</u> (regions). The top-right region is the easiest because here <u>all the coordinates in it are positive</u>.

2) You have to be careful in the <u>other regions</u> though, because the x- and y- coordinates could be <u>negative</u>, and that makes life much more difficult.

3) Coordinates are always written in brackets like this: (x, y) — remember x is <u>across</u>, and y is <u>up</u>.

Finding the **Midpoint** of a Line Segment

Finding the coordinates of a midpoint is pretty easy...

> A line segment is part of a line. Lines continue forever in both directions, but line segments have two end points. Things that are actually line segments are often referred to as lines though.

> **Find the <u>average</u> of the <u>two x-coordinates</u>, then do the same for the <u>y-coordinates</u>. These will be the coordinates of the <u>midpoint</u>.**

EXAMPLE:

Point P has coordinates (8, 3) and point Q has coordinates (–4, 8). Find the midpoint of the line PQ.

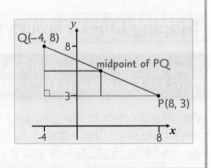

See p.155 for finding the length of a line segment.

1) Average of x-coordinates $= \dfrac{8 + (-4)}{2} = \underline{2}$

2) Average of y-coordinates $= \dfrac{3 + 8}{2} = \underline{5.5}$

So, coordinates of midpoint = (2, 5.5)

Finding Coordinates Using **Geometrical Information**

EXAMPLE:

A parallelogram has vertices (3, 1), (5, 4) and (9, 1). The x and y coordinates of its fourth vertex are both positive. What are their values?

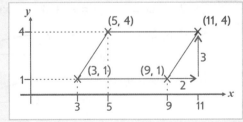

Do a quick <u>sketch</u> and it's dead easy — just mark in the 4th vertex by eye.

<u>Check</u>: to get from (3, 1) to (5, 4) you go <u>along 2 and up 3</u> — the missing point needs to be the same distance from (9, 1).

Midpoints — add the x's together and halve, then do the same for the y's

Don't forget the basics otherwise you'll lose marks needlessly — x comes before y in (x, y), and x goes <u>aCROSS</u> while y goes up and down. Finding a line's midpoint is as simple as finding the average of the x's and y's.

Straight-Line Graphs

There are some <u>straight lines</u> you should be able to immediately recognise from their <u>equation</u>.

Horizontal and Vertical lines: 'x = a' and 'y = a'

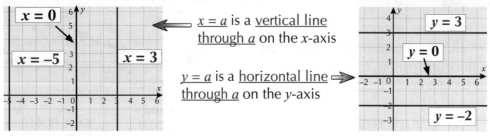

$x = a$ is a <u>vertical line</u> through a on the x-axis

$y = a$ is a <u>horizontal line</u> through a on the y-axis

A common error is to mix up $x = 3$ and $y = 3$, etc. Remember — all the points on $x = 3$ have an x-coordinate of 3, and all the points on $y = 3$ have a y-coordinate of 3.

The Main Diagonals: 'y = x' and 'y = –x'

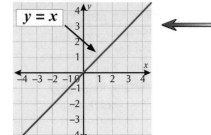

$y = x$ is the <u>main diagonal</u> that goes UPHILL from left to right.
The x- and y-coordinates of each point are <u>the same</u>.

$y = -x$ is the <u>main diagonal</u> that goes DOWNHILL from left to right.
The x- and y-coordinates of each point are <u>negatives of each other</u>, e.g. $(-4, 4)$.

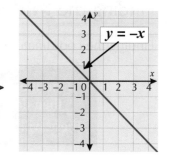

Other Sloping Lines Through the Origin: 'y = ax' and 'y = –ax'

$y = ax$ and $y = -ax$ are the equations for **A SLOPING LINE THROUGH THE ORIGIN**

The value of $\underline{a}$ (known as the <u>gradient</u>) tells you the steepness of the line. The bigger a is, the steeper the slope. A <u>MINUS SIGN</u> tells you it slopes <u>DOWNHILL</u>.

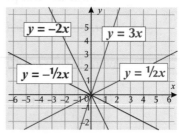

See p.90 for how to find a gradient.

Learn to Spot Straight Lines from Their Equations

All other straight-line equations just contain '<u>something x, something y and a number</u>'.

EXAMPLE: **Decide whether each of the following are equations of straight lines.**

$2y - 4x = 7$ $y = x^2 + 3$ $xy + 3 = 0$ $6y - 8 = x$ $\dfrac{2}{y} - \dfrac{1}{x} = 7$

Straight lines: $2y - 4x = 7$
$6y - 8 = x$

Not straight lines: $y = x^2 + 3$
$xy + 3 = 0$
$\dfrac{2}{y} - \dfrac{1}{x} = 7$

These equations only have <u>something x</u>, <u>something y</u> and <u>a number</u>. These 'terms' can be added or subtracted in any order.

x^2, xy, $\dfrac{2}{y}$ and $\dfrac{1}{x}$ mean that these <u>aren't</u> straight-line equations.

Simple lines you have to learn — it'll only take a second

Vertical line: $x = a$, horizontal line: $y = a$, main diagonals: $y = x$ and $y = -x$. Things get a bit more involved with other types of straight line but drawing a sketch will help if you're stuck — see the next page for more.

Plotting Straight-Line Graphs

You could be asked to <u>draw</u> a <u>straight-line graph</u> in the exam. We'll cover <u>two</u> methods on this page.

The 'Table of 3 Values' Method

You can <u>easily</u> draw the graph of <u>any equation</u> using this <u>easy</u> method:

Don't forget to use a <u>ruler</u> to draw your line — you can lose exam marks if you don't.

1) Choose <u>3 values of x</u> and <u>draw up a table</u>.
2) <u>Work out the corresponding y-values</u>.
3) <u>Plot the coordinates</u> and <u>draw the line</u>.

If it's a <u>straight-line equation</u>, the 3 points will be in a <u>dead straight line</u> with each other.
If they aren't, you need to go back and <u>CHECK YOUR WORKING</u>.

EXAMPLE: **Draw the graph of $y = 2x - 3$ for values of x from –1 to 4.**

1) <u>Draw up a table</u> with some suitable values of x.

x	0	2	4
y			

2) <u>Find the y-values</u> by putting each x-value into the equation:

x	0	2	4
y	–3	1	5

When $x = 4$, $y = 2x - 3$
$= 2 \times 4 - 3 = \underline{5}$

3) <u>Plot the points</u> and <u>draw the line</u>.

The table gives the points (0, –3), (2, 1) and (4, 5)

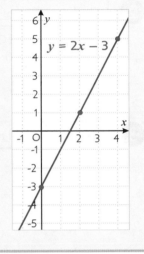

The '$x = 0$, $y = 0$' Method

1) <u>Set $x = 0$</u> in the equation, and <u>find y</u> — this is where it <u>crosses the y-axis</u>.
2) <u>Set $y = 0$</u> in the equation and <u>find x</u> — this is where it <u>crosses the x-axis.</u>
3) <u>Plot these two points</u> and <u>join them up with a straight line</u>.

Make sure it's definitely a straight line before using this method — have a look at the previous page to see how you can check.

EXAMPLE: **Draw the graph of $3x + 5y = 15$ between $x = -1$ and $x = 6$.**

Putting $x = 0$ gives "$5y = 15$" $\Rightarrow$ $y = 3$
Putting $y = 0$ gives "$3x = 15$" $\Rightarrow$ $x = 5$

So plot (0, 3) and (5, 0) on the graph and join them up with a straight line.

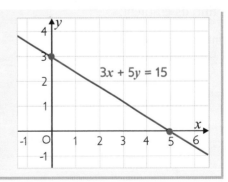

Drawing straight-line graphs isn't as scary with these simple methods

This page gives you two simple methods for drawing straight-line graphs. Usually, you'll be able to use whichever you find easiest — but learn them both, just in case you're told to use a specific one in the exam.

Finding the Gradient

A <u>gradient</u> is just the <u>slope</u> of a line or a curve. This page will show you how to find it.

The **Gradient** is the **Steepness** of the **Line**

The <u>gradient</u> of the line is how <u>steep</u> it is — the <u>larger</u> the gradient, the <u>steeper</u> the slope.
A <u>negative gradient</u> tells you it slopes <u>downhill</u>. You find it by dividing the <u>change in *y*</u> by the <u>change in *x*</u>.

Find the gradient of the straight line on the right.

1 Choose <u>two accurate points</u> on the line.

A: (6, 50)
B: (1, 10)

2 Find the <u>change in *y*</u> and <u>change in *x*</u>.

Change in *y* = 50 − 10 = 40
Change in *x* = 6 − 1 = 5

Make sure you subtract the *y* and *x*-coordinates in the same order.
E.g. $y_A − y_B$ and $x_A − x_B$

3 Use this <u>formula</u>:

$$\text{GRADIENT} = \frac{\text{CHANGE IN Y}}{\text{CHANGE IN X}}$$

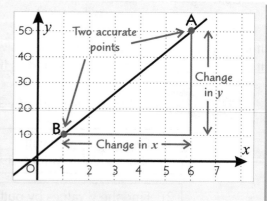

Gradient = $\frac{40}{5}$ = 8

<u>Always</u> check the <u>sign</u> of your gradient.
Remember, uphill = <u>positive</u> and downhill = <u>negative</u>

Draw a **Tangent** to Estimate a **Curve's Gradient**

A tangent is a straight line that just touches the curve.

The gradient of a curve is <u>constantly changing</u>. To <u>estimate</u> the <u>gradient</u> at a particular point, draw in the <u>tangent</u> at that point, and find the gradient of the tangent.

Find an estimate for the gradient of the curve below at the point where *x* = 3.5.

1) Draw in a <u>tangent</u> to the curve at *x* = 3.5.

2) Use two points on the tangent to find its <u>gradient</u>:

Points on the tangent:
(2, −22) and (4, −2)

Gradient = $\dfrac{\text{Change in } y}{\text{Change in } x}$

$= \dfrac{-2 - (-22)}{4 - 2} = \dfrac{20}{2} = 10$

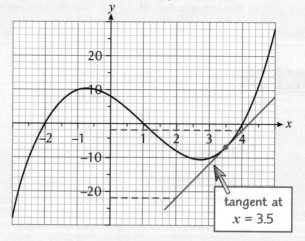

tangent at *x* = 3.5

Uphill = positive gradient, downhill = negative gradient

If the gradient is far away from 0 (e.g. 15, −20, etc.) then the graph will be quite steep. If it's pretty close to 0, (e.g. −0.5, 0.0001, etc.) then the gradient is fairly shallow. A gradient of 0 means the graph is horizontal.

"y = mx + c"

Using '$y = mx + c$' is one of the most common ways of dealing with straight-line equations, and it's useful in exams. The first thing you have to do though is <u>rearrange</u> the equation into the standard format like this:

Straight line:	Rearranged into '$y = mx + c$'	
$y = 2 + 3x$	→	$y = 3x + 2$	($m = 3$, $c = 2$)
$x - y = 0$	→	$y = x + 0$	($m = 1$, $c = 0$)
$4x - 3 = 5y$	→	$y = 0.8x - 0.6$	($m = 0.8$, $c = -0.6$)

REMEMBER:

m = <u>gradient</u> of the line

c = '<u>y-intercept</u>' (where it hits the y-axis)

<u>WATCH OUT</u>: people mix up m and c when they get something like $y = 5 + 2x$.
Remember, m is the number <u>in front of the x</u> and c is the number <u>on its own</u>.

Sketching a **Straight Line** Using y = mx + c

EXAMPLE: **Draw the graph of $y - 2x = 1$.**

1 Get the equation into the form $y = mx + c$.

$y - 2x = 1$
$\rightarrow \ y = 2x + 1$

2 Put a dot on the y-axis at the <u>value of c</u>.

$c = 1$, so put a dot here

3 Go <u>along 1 unit</u> and <u>up or down</u> by m. Make another dot, then repeat this step a few times in both directions.

Go <u>1 along</u> and <u>2 up</u> because $m = +2$.

(If m was -2, you'd go down.)

4 When you have 4 or 5 dots, draw a <u>straight line</u> through them.

5 Finally check that the <u>gradient</u> looks right.

A gradient of <u>+2</u> should be <u>quite steep</u> and <u>uphill</u> left to right — which it is, so it looks OK.

Finding the **Equation** of a Straight-Line **Graph**

When you're given the graph itself, it's quick and easy to find the <u>equation</u> of the straight line.

EXAMPLE: **Find the equation of the line on this graph in the form $y = mx + c$.**

1) Find <u>m</u> (gradient) and <u>c</u> (y-intercept).

$m = \dfrac{\text{change in } y}{\text{change in } x} = \dfrac{15}{30} = \dfrac{1}{2}$

$c = \underline{15}$

2) Use these to write the equation in the form $y = mx + c$.

$y = \dfrac{1}{2}x + 15$

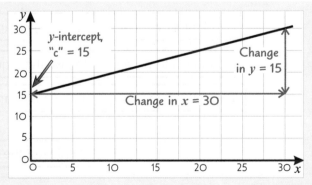

---

m is the gradient and c is the y-intercept

The key thing to remember is that m is the number in front of the x, and c is the number on its own.
If you remember that, then $y = mx + c$ is a very easy way of identifying straight lines.

Parallel and Perpendicular Lines

On the previous page, you saw how to write the <u>equation of a straight line</u>. You also have to be able to write the equation of a line that's <u>parallel</u> or <u>perpendicular</u> to the straight line you're given.

Parallel Lines Have the Same Gradient (6)

Parallel lines all have the <u>same gradient</u>, which means their $y = mx + c$ equations all have the same value of <u>m</u>.
So the lines: $y = 2x + 3$, $y = 2x$ and $y = 2x - 4$ are all parallel.

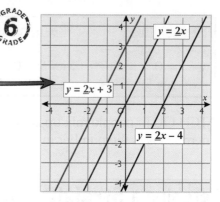

EXAMPLE: Line J has a gradient of –0.25. Find the equation of Line K, which is parallel to Line J and passes through point (2, 3).

Lines J and K are <u>parallel</u> so their <u>gradients</u> are the same $\Rightarrow$ m = –0.25 ◀

$y = -0.25x + c$ ◀

When $x = 2$, $y = 3$: ◀
$3 = (-0.25 \times 2) + c \Rightarrow 3 = -0.5 + c$
$c = 3.5$

$y = -0.25x + 3.5$ ◀

1) First find the <u>m value</u> for Line K.
2) Substitute the value for m into $\underline{y = mx + c}$ to give you the 'equation so far'.
3) Substitute the <u>x and y values</u> for the given point on Line K and solve for <u>c</u>.
4) Write out the <u>full equation</u>.

Perpendicular Line Gradients (7)

Perpendicular lines cross at a <u>right angle</u>, and if you <u>multiply</u> their <u>gradients</u> together you'll get <u>–1</u>.

> If the gradient of the first line is m, the gradient of the other line will be $-\frac{1}{m}$, because $m \times -\frac{1}{m} = -1$.

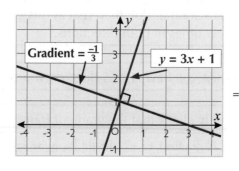

Product of gradients $= -\frac{1}{3} \times 3 = -1$

EXAMPLE: Lines A and B are perpendicular and intersect at (3, 3). If Line A has the equation $3y - x = 6$, what is the equation of Line B?

Find <u>m</u> (the gradient) for Line A.	$3y - x = 6 \Rightarrow 3y = x + 6$ $\Rightarrow y = \frac{1}{3}x + 2$, so $m_A = \frac{1}{3}$
Find the m value for the <u>perpendicular</u> line (Line B).	$m_B = -\frac{1}{m_A} = -1 \div \frac{1}{3} = -3$
Put this into $y = mx + c$ to give the 'equation so far'.	$y = -3x + c$
Put in the <u>x and y values</u> of the point and solve for <u>c</u>.	$x = 3$, $y = 3$ gives: $3 = (-3 \times 3) + c$ $\Rightarrow 3 = -9 + c \Rightarrow c = 12$
Write out the full equation.	$y = -3x + 12$

Parallel lines have the same gradient

Perpendicular lines can be a little more tricky, so it's important that you remember that their gradients multiply together to give –1. Make sure the equation of your first line is in the form $y = mx + c$ before you try to find $-\frac{1}{m}$. You should practise finding c using m and a point on the line too.

Warm-Up and Worked Exam Questions

On the day of the exam you'll have to know straight-line graphs like the back of your hand. If you struggle with any of the warm-up questions, go back over the section again before you go any further.

Warm-Up Questions

1) Without drawing them, state whether the lines passing through the following points form a horizontal line, a vertical line, the line $y = x$ or the line $y = -x$.
   a) (1, 1) to (5, 5)   b) (0, 4) to (-3, 4)   c) (-1, 3) to (-1, 7)   d) (4, -4) to (-3, 3).

2) a) Plot the line $y = 3x - 4$.
   b) How do the gradient and y-intercept of $y = 3x + 2$ compare with those of $y = 3x - 4$?

3) The equation of line S is $y = -5x + 1$.
   a) Find the equation of the line which is parallel to line S and passes through the point (0, 4).
   b) Find the gradient of a line which is perpendicular to S.

Worked Exam Questions

You know the routine by now — work carefully through this example and make sure you understand it. Then it's on to the real test of doing some exam questions for yourself.

1   Line **L** passes through the points A (0, -3) and B (5, 7), as shown below.

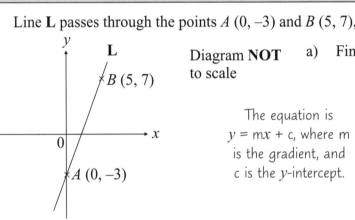

Diagram **NOT** to scale

The equation is $y = mx + c$, where m is the gradient, and c is the y-intercept.

a) Find the equation of line **L**. (**4**)

$$m = \frac{\text{change in } y}{\text{change in } x} = \frac{(7 - (-3))}{(5 - 0)}$$

$$m = 2$$

The line passes through (0, -3), so c = -3.

$$\underline{y = 2x - 3}$$

[3 marks]

b) Find the equation of the line which is parallel to line **L** (**6**) and passes through the point (2, 10).

A line which is parallel to line L will have the same gradient.

m = 2, so $y = 2x + c$

$10 = (2 \times 2) + c$ ◄——— Substitute in the x and y

$c = 10 - 4 = 6$ values of the point to find c.

So $y = 2x + 6$ $\underline{y = 2x + 6}$

[2 marks]

c) Find the equation of the line which is perpendicular to line **L** (**7**) and passes through the point (-2, 3).

The gradient of a line which is perpendicular to line L will be $-\frac{1}{m}$.

$$\text{Gradient} = -\frac{1}{2}$$

Use $y = mx + c$ to find c.   When $x = -2$, $y = 3$ so: $3 = -\frac{1}{2} \times -2 + c$

$c = 2$

$$\underline{y = -\frac{1}{2}x + 2}$$

[3 marks]

Exam Questions

2   Point P has coordinates $(6, 2)$ and point Q has coordinates $(-4, 1)$.

a)   Find the coordinates of the midpoint of PQ.

(................. , ...)
[2 marks]

b)   Point R has coordinates (a, b). The midpoint of PR is $(3, 5)$.
Find the values of a and b.

$a =$ ....

$b =$ ....
[3 marks]

3   The lines **K** and **L** are drawn on the axes on the right.

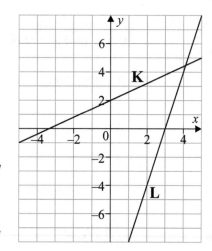

a)   Find the equation of **K** in the form $y = mx + c$.

....
[3 marks]

b)   A third line, **N**, has the equation $2y = 8x + 4$.
Draw **N** on the axes.

[2 marks]

c)   Find the coordinates of the point where **L** intersects the y-axis.

(................. , ...)
[2 marks]

4   The graph of $y = x^3 - 6x^2 + 10x$ is shown on the right.
Estimate the gradient of the graph at $x = 1$.

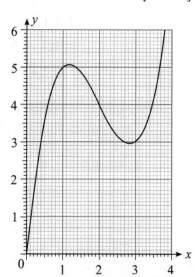

....
[3 marks]

Quadratic Graphs

Quadratic functions take the form $\underline{y = \text{anything with } x^2}$ (but no higher powers of x).
x^2 graphs all have the same symmetrical bucket shape.

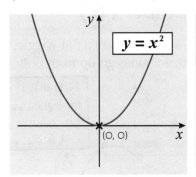

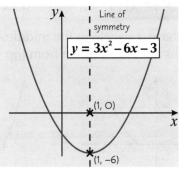

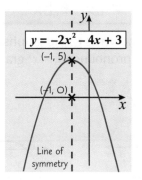

If the x^2 bit has a '−' in front of it then the bucket is upside down.

Plotting Quadratics

EXAMPLE: **Complete the table of values for the equation $y = x^2 + 2x − 3$ and then draw the graph.**

x	−5	−4	−3	−2	−1	0	1	2	3
y	12	5	0	3	−4	−3	0	5	12

1) Work out each y-value by substituting the corresponding x-value into the equation.

   To check you're doing it right, make sure you can reproduce the y-values they've already given you.

$y = (−5)^2 + (2 × −5) − 3$
$= 25 − 10 − 3 = 12$

$y = (2)^2 + (2 × 2) − 3$
$= 4 + 4 − 3 = 5$

2) Plot the points and join them with a completely smooth curve. Definitely DON'T use a ruler.

   NEVER EVER let one point drag your line off in some ridiculous direction. When a graph is generated from an equation, you never get spikes or lumps.

This point is obviously wrong.

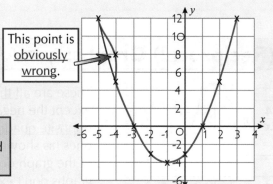

Solving Quadratic Equations

EXAMPLE: **Use the graph of $y = x^2 + 2x − 3$ to solve the equation $x^2 + 2x − 3 = 0$.**

The equation $x^2 + 2x − 3 = 0$ is what you get when you put $\underline{y = 0}$ into the graph's equation, $y = x^2 + 2x − 3$.

So to solve the equation, all you do is read the x-values where $y = 0$, i.e. where it crosses the x-axis.

So the solutions are $x = −3$ and $x = 1$.

Quadratic equations usually have 2 solutions.

Tables of values, plotting — easy marks, as long as you're accurate

Filling in tables of values and plotting graphs are easy questions, but too many people rush them and make silly errors. Take your time and get them right — if your curve isn't smooth, check the points in your table.

Harder Graphs

Graphs come in all sorts of shapes, sizes and wiggles — here are the first of 6 more types you need to know:

x³ Graphs: $y = ax^3 + bx^2 + cx + d$ (b, c and d can be zero)

All x^3 graphs (also known as <u>cubic</u> graphs) have a <u>wiggle</u> in the middle — sometimes it's a flat wiggle, sometimes it's more pronounced. $-x^3$ graphs always go down from <u>top left</u>, $+x^3$ ones go up from <u>bottom left</u>.

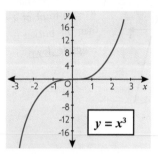

$y = x^3$

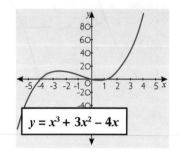

$y = x^3 + 3x^2 - 4x$

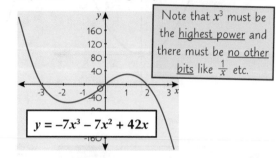

$y = -7x^3 - 7x^2 + 42x$

Note that x^3 must be the <u>highest power</u> and there must be <u>no other</u> <u>bits</u> like $\frac{1}{x}$ etc.

EXAMPLE: Draw the graph of $y = x^3 + 4x^2$ for values of x between –4 and +2.

Start by making a <u>table of values</u>.

x	–4	–3	–2	–1	0	1	2
$y = x^3 + 4x^2$	0	9	8	3	0	5	24

Plot the points and join them with a lovely <u>smooth curve</u>. <u>DON'T</u> use your ruler.

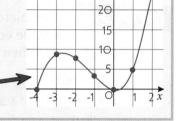

1/x (Reciprocal) Graphs: $y = A/x$ or $xy = A$

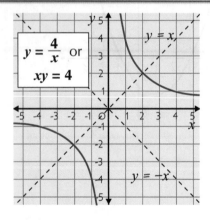

$y = \frac{4}{x}$ or $xy = 4$

These are <u>all the same basic shape</u>, except the negative ones are in <u>opposite quadrants</u> to the positive ones (as shown). The two halves of the graph don't touch. The graphs <u>don't exist</u> for <u>x = 0</u>.

They're all <u>symmetrical</u> about the lines <u>y = x</u> and <u>y = –x</u>.

(You get this type of graph with inverse proportion — see p.83.)

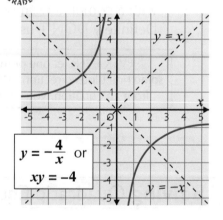

$y = -\frac{4}{x}$ or $xy = -4$

1/x² Graphs: $y = A/x^2$ or $x^2y = A$

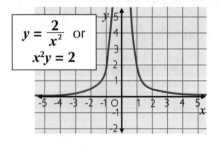

$y = \frac{2}{x^2}$ or $x^2y = 2$

These are a bit like the $y = \frac{A}{x}$ graphs — except the two bits are <u>next to each other</u>. The <u>positive</u> ones are <u>above</u> the x-axis and the <u>negative</u> ones are <u>below</u> the x-axis. They're all <u>symmetrical</u> about the <u>y-axis</u>.

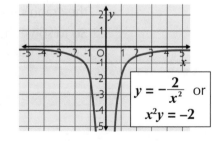

$y = -\frac{2}{x^2}$ or $x^2y = -2$

x³ graphs always have a wiggle in the middle
These graphs look nasty, but as long as you have the equation you can always make a table of values.

Harder Graphs

The graphs of cos, sine and tan all have a <u>different pattern</u>. Make sure you learn all <u>three</u>.

Sine 'Waves' and Cos 'Buckets'

1) The underlying shape of the sin and cos graphs is <u>identical</u> — they both bounce between <u>y-limits of exactly +1 and −1</u>.

2) The only difference is that the <u>sin graph</u> is <u>shifted right by 90°</u> compared to the cos graph.

3) <u>For 0° – 360°</u>, the shapes you get are a <u>Sine 'Wave'</u> (one peak, one trough) and a <u>Cos 'Bucket'</u> (starts at the top, dips, and finishes at the top).

4) Sine and cos repeat every 360° and they go on forever in <u>both directions</u> along the <u>x-axis</u>.

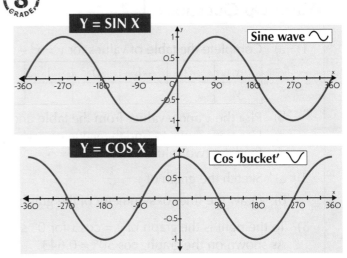

EXAMPLE: **Complete the table and draw the graph of y = cos x for values between −180° and 180°. Give all rounded numbers to 2 d.p.**

x	−180°	−150°	−120°	−90°	−60°	−30°	0°	30°	60°	90°	120°	150°	180°
cos x	−1	−0.87	−0.5	0	0.5	0.87	1	0.87	0.5	0	−0.5	−0.87	−1

Plot the points and join them up with a smooth curve.

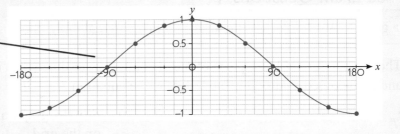

Tan x can be Any Value at all

tan x is <u>different</u> from sin x or cos x — it goes between −∞ and +∞. It also repeats every 180°.

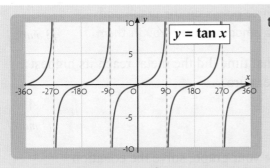

tan x is <u>undefined</u> at ±90°, ±270°,...

As you approach one of these undefined points from the left, tan x just shoots up to <u>infinity</u>.

As you approach from the right, it drops to <u>minus infinity</u>.

The graph never ever touches these lines. But it does get infinitely close, if you see what I mean...

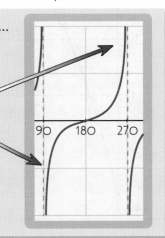

tan x goes from −∞ and +∞ every 180°.

So it repeats every 180° and takes every possible value in each 180° interval.

Do a quick sketch of each graph

sin x and cos x look pretty similar so they're easy to mix up. Remember that sin x passes through (0, 0) and cos x passes through (1, 0). tan x is the weird one that shoots off to −∞ and +∞ every 180°.

Warm-Up and Worked Exam Questions

The warm-up questions run quickly over the basic facts you'll need in the exam. The exam questions come later — but unless you've learnt the facts first you'll find the exams tougher than stale bread.

Warm-Up Questions

1) a) Complete the table of values for $y = x^2 - 2x - 1$.

x	−2	−1	0	1	2	3	4	5
y								

b) Plot the x and y values from the table and join the points up to form a smooth curve.
c) Use your curve to find the value of y when $x = 3.5$.
d) Find the two values of x when $y = 5$.

2) a) Sketch the graph of $y = \dfrac{3}{x}$.
b) Draw the lines of symmetry of the graph.

3) To the right is the graph of $y = \cos x$ for $0° \le x \le 360°$
As shown on the graph, $\cos 50° = 0.643$.
Give another value of x, found on this graph,
where $\cos x = 0.643$.

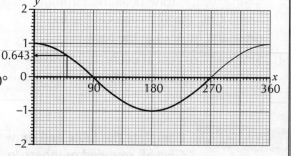

Worked Exam Questions

Take a good look at this exam question — unlike the real thing, the answers are helpfully written in.

1 The temperature (T) of a piece of metal changes over time (t) as it is rapidly heated and then cooled again. It is modelled by the equation $T = -5t^2 + 40t - 35$.

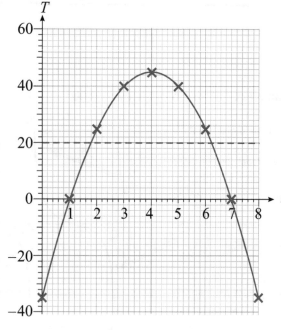

a) Plot the graph of $T = -5t^2 + 40t - 35$ on the grid.

Make a table of values:

t	O	1	2	3	4	5	6	7	8
T	−35	O	25	40	45	40	25	O	−35

Plot these points on the graph and draw a smooth curve through them. *[3 marks]*

b) At what time did the metal reach its highest temperature?

$t = \underline{\quad 4 \quad}$
[1 mark]

c) Using your graph, solve the equation $-5t^2 + 40t - 35 = 20$.

Draw the line $y = 20$ and read off where it crosses the curve.

$t = \underline{\quad 1.8 \quad}$ and $t = \underline{\quad 6.2 \quad}$
[2 marks]

Exam Questions

2   This question is about the equation $y = 2x^2 - 8x + 8$.

a)   Complete this table of values.

x	0	1	2	3	4	5
y	8	....	....	....	8	18

[1 mark]

b)   Draw the graph of $y = 2x^2 - 8x + 8$ for values of x between 0 and 5 on the axes on the left.

[2 marks]

c)   Use your graph to estimate the solutions to $4 = 2x^2 - 8x + 8$. Give your answers to 1 d.p.

$x = $ ....

$x = $ ....

[2 marks]

3   This question is about the equation $y = x + \dfrac{4}{x} - 3$.

a)   Complete this table of values.

x	0.2	0.5	1	2	3	4	5
y	....	5.5	2	1	1.333...	2	....

[1 mark]

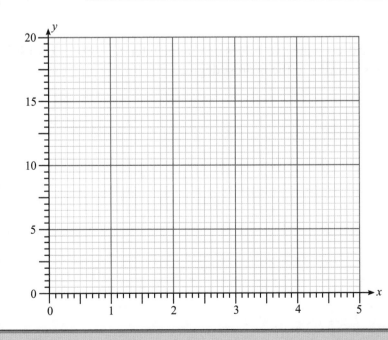

b)   On the axes on the left, draw the graph of $y = x + \dfrac{4}{x} - 3$ for $0.2 \le x \le 5$.

[2 marks]

c)   Draw a suitable straight line on your graph to estimate the solution to the equation $x + \dfrac{4}{x} - 3 = 5x + 5$ in the interval $0.2 \le x \le 5$. Give your answer to 1 d.p.

$x = $ ....

[3 marks]

Exam Questions

4   This question is about the equation $y = \sin x$.

a)   Complete the table below.

x	$-180°$	$-150°$	$-90°$	$-30°$	$0°$	$30°$	$90°$	$150°$	$180°$
y	0	-0.5	....	....	0	....	....	0.5	0

[2 marks]

b)   Use your table to draw the graph of $y = \sin x$ on the grid,
     for values of x in the range $-180° \le x \le 180°$.

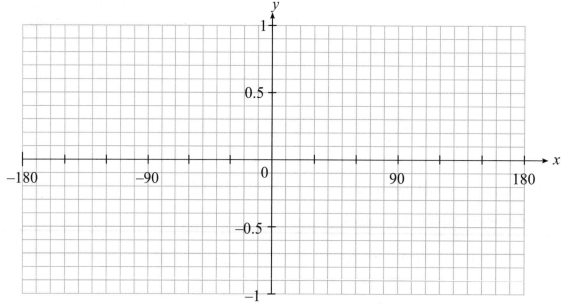

[2 marks]

c)   By drawing a straight line on the grid, estimate two values of x in the interval $-180° \le x \le 180°$
     that satisfy $\sin x = 0.3$. Give your answers to the nearest degree.

$x = $ ....$°$

$x = $ ....$°$

[2 marks]

Functions

Functions can seem tricky to start with, but all they do is take an input and give you an output.

Functions **Map** Numbers from **One Set to Another**

1) A function is a <u>rule</u> that <u>maps</u> each number from a set called the <u>domain</u> to <u>exactly one number</u> of a second set called the <u>range</u>.

   But different domain values <u>can</u> map to the <u>same value</u> in the range — see the e.g. on the right.

2) A function is really just another way of writing an equation.

   E.g. instead of writing an <u>equation</u> like $y = 5x + 2$, you can write a <u>function</u> like $f(x) = 5x + 2$ or $f : x \rightarrow 5x + 2$. The diagram on the right shows the function $f(x) = x^2$.

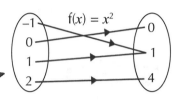

See page 37 for set notation.

> **EXAMPLE:** $f(x) = \sin x°$. **If the domain is $\{x : -180 \leq x \leq 180\}$, find the range of f(x).**
>
> Each x value in the <u>domain</u> maps to a value between <u>-1 and 1</u>. Range = $\{f(x) : -1 \leq f(x) \leq 1\}$

3) You might be given $\underline{x}$ and asked to find $\underline{f(x)}$, or vice versa:

> **EXAMPLES:** **1.** **If $f(x) = x^2 - x + 7$, find f(3).**
>
> Just substitute 3 for x and evaluate. — $f(x) = 3^2 - 3 + 7$
>
> $= 9 - 3 + 7 = 13$

> **2.** $f(x) = \dfrac{1 - 2x}{x + 4}$. **Given that $f(x) = -\dfrac{1}{2}$, find x.**
>
> $\dfrac{1 - 2x}{x + 4} = -\dfrac{1}{2} \Rightarrow 2(1 - 2x) = -1(x + 4)$
>
> Just solve this like an ordinary equation.
>
> $2 - 4x = -x - 4$
> $3x = 6$
> $x = 2$

Excluding Values from a **Domain**

Sometimes certain values <u>won't work</u> in a function. You have to <u>exclude</u> these from the domain. These <u>two rules</u> will help you decide <u>which values</u> must be excluded (if any).

> 1) Dividing by zero is undefined. | E.g. for $f(x) = \dfrac{12}{x}$ you'd have to exclude $\underline{x = 0}$.

> 2) You can't find the square root of a negative number. | E.g. for $f(x) = \sqrt{(x - 2)}$ you'd have to exclude $\underline{x < 2}$.

> **EXAMPLES:** **1.** **State which value of x cannot be included in the domain of $f : x \rightarrow \dfrac{1 - 2x}{x + 4}$.**
>
> Dividing by zero is <u>undefined</u>, so find the x-value which makes the <u>bottom</u> of the fraction <u>zero</u>.
>
> $x + 4 = 0 \Rightarrow x = -4$
> So $x = -4$ cannot be included.

> **2.** **State which values of x cannot be included in the domain of $g(x) = \sqrt{(x^2 - 9)}$.**
>
> You <u>can't</u> find the square root of a <u>negative number</u>, so find the values of x which make $(x^2 - 9)$ <u>negative</u>.
>
> $x^2 - 9 < 0 \Rightarrow x^2 < 9$
> $\Rightarrow -3 < x < 3$ cannot be included.

Function : Domain → Range

Function notation and the vocabulary 'domain' and 'range' are things which people often struggle with in the exams — but that doesn't stop the examiners asking about them. Remember that the domain is the set of numbers the function maps from and the range is the set of numbers it maps to.

Functions

Functions get a bit trickier on this page. But once you can see through all the f's, g's and (x)'s they're OK.

Composite Functions — fg(x) or gf(x)

You might get a question with two functions, e.g. f(x) and g(x).

- fg(x) means that you <u>replace</u> the <u>x</u> in f(x) with the <u>whole function</u> g(x).
- gf(x) means that you replace the <u>x</u> in g(x) with the <u>whole function</u> f(x).

fg(x) does <u>NOT</u> mean f(x) × g(x)

> **EXAMPLE:** If $f(x) = 2x - 10$ and $g(x) = -\frac{x}{2}$, find: a) fg(x) b) gf(x).
>
> a) Substitute g(x) in place of x in f(x).
>
> $fg(x) = f\left(-\frac{x}{2}\right)$
>
> $= 2\left(-\frac{x}{2}\right) - 10$
>
> $= -x - 10$
>
> b) Substitute f(x) in place of x in g(x).
>
> $gf(x) = g(2x - 10)$
>
> $= -\frac{(2x - 10)}{2}$
>
> $= -(x - 5) = 5 - x$

> **EXAMPLE:** If $f(x) = \frac{6}{x}$ and $g(x) = 4 - x$, find fg(-2).
>
> *You could also find fg(x), then substitute −2 for x.*
>
> 1) First find g(-2): $g(-2) = 4 - (-2) = 6$
>
> 2) Now substitute g(-2) = 6 into f(x) to find fg(-2): $fg(-2) = f(6) = \frac{6}{6} = 1$
>
> *Another way to think of this is that you have to do the function <u>closest to x</u> first. So for fg(x), you do <u>g first</u>, then f.*

Inverse Functions — f⁻¹(x)

The <u>inverse</u> of a function f(x) is another function, $f^{-1}(x)$, which <u>reverses</u> f(x). Here's the <u>method</u> to find it:

> 1) Write out the equation <u>x = f(y)</u>.
> 2) <u>Rearrange</u> the equation to <u>make y the subject</u>.
> 3) You've now got the equation $y = f^{-1}(x)$.

f(y) is just the expression f(x), but with y's instead of x's

See pages 56-57 for more on rearranging.

> **EXAMPLE:** If $f(x) = \frac{12 + x}{3}$, find $f^{-1}(x)$.
>
> 1) Write out x = f(y): $x = \frac{12 + y}{3}$
>
> 2) Rearrange to make y the subject: $3x = 12 + y \Rightarrow y = 3x - 12$
>
> 3) Now you've got $f^{-1}(x)$: $f^{-1}(x) = 3x - 12$

<u>Check</u> your answer by testing if the inverse function <u>does reverse</u> the original function:

E.g. for the example above, find $f(9) = \frac{12 + 9}{3} = 7$. Now find $f^{-1}(7) = 21 - 12 = 9$.

We're back to the <u>start number</u>, so the inverse function is likely to be <u>right</u>.

Remember — do the function closest to x first

When you're working with composite functions, order does matter. And if you learn the three-step method in the box above, you shouldn't have too much trouble finding inverse functions either.

Graph Transformations

The next two pages cover all the types of graph transformation you'll need to know for your exam — translations, reflections and stretches.

Translations on the **y-axis**: y = f(x) + a

This is where the whole graph is slid up or down the y-axis, and is achieved by simply adding a number onto the end of the equation: $y = f(x) + a$. This can be described as a translation by the vector $\begin{pmatrix} 0 \\ a \end{pmatrix}$.

EXAMPLE: **To the right is the graph of $y = f(x)$. Write down the coordinates of the minimum point of the graph with equation $y = f(x) + 5$.**

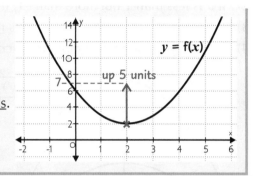

The minimum point of $y = f(x)$ has coordinates (2, 2).
$y = f(x) + 5$ is the same shape graph, translated 5 units upwards.

So, the graph has been translated by vector $\begin{pmatrix} 0 \\ 5 \end{pmatrix}$

So the minimum point of $y = f(x) + 5$ is at **(2, 7)**.

Translations on the **x-axis**: y = f(x – a)

1) This is where the whole graph slides left or right and it only happens when you replace 'x' everywhere in the equation with 'x – a'. These are tricky because they go 'the wrong way'. If you want to go from $y = f(x)$ to $y = f(x – a)$ you must move the whole graph a distance 'a' in the positive x-direction →.

2) The translation $f(x – a)$ can be described as a translation by the vector $\begin{pmatrix} a \\ 0 \end{pmatrix}$.

3) Be careful though — with the translation $f(x + a)$, a is negative. E.g. $f(x + 2) = f(x – (–2))$, which means it's a translation by the vector $\begin{pmatrix} -2 \\ 0 \end{pmatrix}$.

EXAMPLE: **The graph $y = \sin x$ is shown below, for $-360° \leq x \leq 360°$.**

a) **Sketch the graph of $\sin(x – 60)$.**
$y = \sin(x – 60)$ is $y = \sin x$ translated 60 units in the positive x-direction — it's translated by the vector $\begin{pmatrix} 60 \\ 0 \end{pmatrix}$

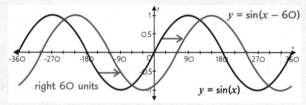

b) **Give the coordinates of a point where $y = \sin(x – 60)$ crosses the x-axis.**
$y = \sin x$ crosses the x-axis at (0, 0), so $y = \sin(x – 60)$ will cross at (60, 0)

Reflections: y = –f(x) and y = f(–x)

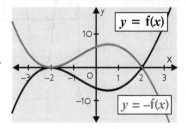 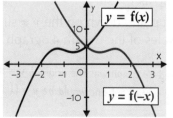

$y = –f(x)$ is the reflection in the x-axis of $y = f(x)$.

$y = f(–x)$ is the reflection in the y-axis of $y = f(x)$.

Remember f(x) just means an expression in x

Graphs can slide up or down by adding or subtracting a number to/from the whole function, and slide left or right when x is replaced with x ± a. (x + a) slides the graph left, (x – a) slides the graph right.

Graph Transformations

On the last page, you saw graphs sliding and flipping around.
On this page you'll see graphs being <u>stretched</u> and <u>squashed</u>.

Stretches in the y-direction: y = af(x)

1) This is where the original graph is <u>stretched parallel to the y-axis</u> by multiplying the whole function by a number (a <u>scale factor</u>), i.e. $y = f(x)$ becomes $y = af(x)$ (where a = 2 or 5 etc.).

2) If a is less than 1 but more than –1, then the graph is <u>squashed down</u> in the y-direction.

3) If a is less than –1, then the graph is <u>reflected and also stretched</u> in the y-direction.

4) For every point on the graph, the x-coordinate <u>stays the same</u>, and the y-coordinate is <u>multiplied by a</u>.

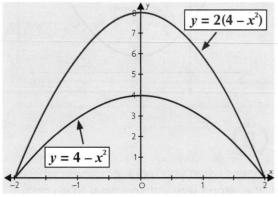

This graph shows $y = f(x)$ and $y = 2f(x)$
($y = 4 - x^2$ and $y = 2(4 - x^2)$).

EXAMPLE: **Graph R is a transformation of $y = \sin(x)$. Give the equation of Graph R.**

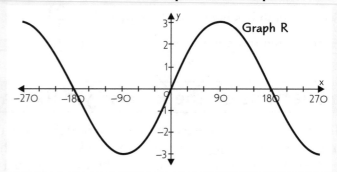

Graph R is $y = \sin x$ <u>stretched in the vertical direction</u>. You saw on p.97 that $y = \sin x$ 'bounces' between 1 and –1 on the y-axis. Graph R 'bounces' between 3 and –3, so the stretch has a <u>scale factor of 3</u>. So the equation of Graph R is $y = 3\sin x$.

Stretches in the x direction: y = f(ax)

1) This is where the graph is <u>stretched parallel to the x-axis</u> by a scale factor of $\frac{1}{a}$.

2) If a is more than 1 or less than –1 then the graph is <u>squashed</u>.
   If a is more than –1 but less than 1 the graph is <u>stretched</u>.

3) The y-coordinate of each point stays the same and the x-coordinate is multiplied by $\frac{1}{a}$.

 **EXAMPLE:** **The graph of $y = \sin x$ is shown to the right. Sketch the graph $y = \sin 4x$ for $0° \leq x \leq 360°$.**

$y = \sin 4x$ has a <u>scale factor</u> of $\frac{1}{4}$, so its graph will be <u>4 times as squashed up</u> as $y = \sin x$.

There is <u>one</u> cycle of up and down on the $y = \sin x$ graph, so you can fit <u>four</u> cycles of the $y = \sin 4x$ graph in the same space.

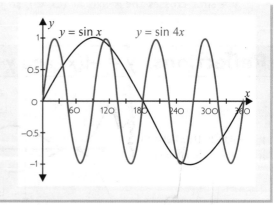

> If the squashed-up graph was the original, $y = f(x)$, then the more spread out one would be $y = f\left(\frac{1}{4}x\right)$.

Transformations in the x-direction do the opposite of what you'd expect

Pay attention to where a is in the function. If everything is multiplied by a (e.g. $6(x^2 + x + 1)$) then it's a stretch in the y-direction. If only the x's are multiplied by a (e.g. $(6x)^2 + 6x + 1$) then it's an x-direction stretch.

Warm-Up and Worked Exam Questions

Here's another batch of warm-up questions on graphs — they'll get your brain working,
ready for those exam practice questions.

Warm-Up Questions

1) If $f(x) = 5x - 1$, $g(x) = 8 - 2x$ and $h(x) = x^2 + 3$, find:
   a) $f(4)$ b) $h(-2)$ c) $gf(x)$
   d) $fh(x)$ e) $gh(-3)$ f) $f^{-1}(x)$

2) For each of the following functions determine which
   values of x are excluded from the domain of f:
   a) $f(x) = \sqrt{4-x}$ b) $f(x) = x^{-\frac{1}{2}}$ c) $f(x) = (x-1) \div x$
   d) $f(x) = \sqrt{2x+7}$ e) $f(x) = \dfrac{10}{4x+3}$

3) Graphs are drawn showing the functions $y = f(x)$ and $y = f(x) + 2$.
   Describe how the shape and position of the two graphs are related.

Worked Exam Questions

Exam questions don't tend to vary that wildly, the basic format is often pretty similar.
You'd be foolish not to spend a bit of time learning how to answer a common question, wouldn't you?

1   f and g are functions such that $f(x) = 2x^2 + 3$ and $g(x) = \sqrt{2x - 6}$.

a)   Find g(21). **(6)**

$$g(21) = \sqrt{(2 \times 21) - 6} = \sqrt{36} = 6$$

√ just means the
positive square root,
so you don't need −6.

...6...
[1 mark]

b)   Find gf(x). **(8)**

$$gf(x) = g(f(x)) = g(2x^2 + 3)$$
$$= \sqrt{2(2x^2 + 3) - 6}$$
$$= \sqrt{4x^2 + 6 - 6}$$
$$= \sqrt{4x^2}$$
$$= 2x$$

Remember to do the
function closest to x first.

$gf(x) = $ ...2x...
[2 marks]

c)   Solve fg(a) = 7. **(8)**

First find the
composite fg(a).

$$fg(a) = f(g(a)) = 2(\sqrt{2a - 6})^2 + 3$$
$$= 2(2a - 6) + 3$$
$$= 4a - 12 + 3$$
$$= 4a - 9$$

So when fg(a) = 7:   4a − 9 = 7

Then set it equal
to 7 and solve the
equation.

$$4a = 16$$
$$a = 4$$

$a = $ ...4...
[3 marks]

Section Three — Graphs, Functions and Calculus

Exam Questions

2   f is a function such that $f(x) = \sqrt{x^2 - 25}$.

a)   Find f(13). **(6)**

....
[1 mark]

b)   Which values of x must be excluded from the domain of f(x)? **(7)**

....
[2 marks]

c)   For what values of x does f(x) = 1? **(7)**

....
[3 marks]

The graph of $y = g(x)$ is drawn
on the grid on the right.

d)   Find the exact value of fg(1). **(8)**

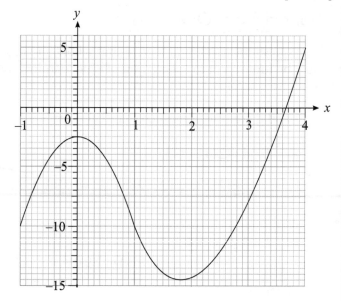

....
[2 marks]

3   The graph of $y = \sin x$ for $0° \le x \le 360°$ is shown on the grid below. **(9)**

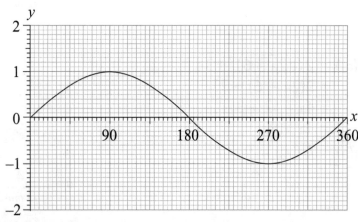

a)   Draw the graph of $y = 2 \sin x$
     on the grid.

[1 mark]

b)   Draw the graph of $y = \sin (2x)$
     on the grid.

[1 mark]

Differentiation

This page just shows you <u>how to do</u> differentiation. <u>Why you do it</u> is covered on the next pa

Use the Formula to **Differentiate Powers of x**

This means 'the result of differentiating the thing in the brackets'.

$$\frac{d}{dx}(x^n) = nx^{n-1}$$

If $y = x^n$, then you write: $\frac{dy}{dx}$

1. **Differentiate** y **when** $y = x^5$

n is just the power of x, so here $n = 5$

$$\frac{dy}{dx} = nx^{n-1} = 5x^4$$

2. **Differentiate** $6x^3$

Ignore the 6 and just differentiate the <u>x bit</u>...

... then simplify.

$$\frac{dy}{dx} = 6(3x^2)$$
$$= 18x^2$$

3. **Differentiate** y **when** $y = 24x$

$x = x^1$, so $n = 1$:

$$\frac{dy}{dx} = 24(1 \times x^0)$$
$$= 24$$

When you've only got an x-term you just end up with the <u>number in front of the x</u>.

4. **Differentiate** y **when** $y = 5$

You need every term to be a <u>power of x</u> to differentiate. $x^0 = 1$, so use this to make 5 a power of x:

$$y = 5 \Rightarrow y = 5x^0$$

$$\frac{dy}{dx} = 5(0 \times x^{-1}) = 0$$

Isolated numbers just <u>disappear</u> when you differentiate.

5. **Differentiate** $\frac{3}{x^2}$

If you get an x on the <u>bottom</u> of a fraction, move it to the <u>top</u> and make the power of x <u>negative</u> (see page 45).

$$\frac{3}{x^2} = 3 \times \frac{1}{x^2} = 3x^{-2} \qquad \frac{dy}{dx} = 3(-2 \times x^{-3}) = -6x^{-3} \text{ or } -\frac{6}{x^3}$$

Differentiate **Each Term** in an Equation **Separately**

Even if there are loads of terms in the equation, it doesn't matter. Differentiate each bit <u>separately</u> and you'll be fine.

1. Find $\frac{dy}{dx}$ for $y = 6x^4 + 4x^3 - 2x + 1$.

Think of this as four separate differentiations, i.e.

$$\frac{dy}{dx} = \frac{d}{dx}(6x^4) + \frac{d}{dx}(4x^3) - \frac{d}{dx}(2x) + \frac{d}{dx}(1)$$

$$\frac{dy}{dx} = 6(4x^3) + 4(3x^2) - 2(1x^0) + 0$$
$$= 24x^3 + 12x^2 - 2$$

2. **Differentiate** $\frac{3+x^2}{5}$

Dividing by 5 is the same as multiplying by $\frac{1}{5}$:

$$\frac{3+x^2}{5} = \frac{1}{5}(3 + x^2)$$

Now differentiate each term in the brackets:

$$\frac{dy}{dx} = \frac{1}{5}(0 + 2x^1) = \frac{2x}{5}$$

Differentiation: multiply by the power and reduce the power by one

If you can differentiate the basics then you should be ok with longer equations — they're just made up of a bunch of terms. Don't panic if a question uses letters other than x and y. Just differentiate in the same way.

Differentiation

As you saw on p.90, the gradient of a curve is <u>constantly changing</u>. You can draw a tangent to estimate what it is at a point, but differentiation means you can find it exactly.

Use **Differentiation** to Find a **Gradient**

<u>Differentiating</u> the equation of a curve gives you an <u>expression</u> for the curve's gradient. Then you can find the gradient of the curve at any point by <u>substituting the value for x</u> into the expression.

 **Find the gradient of the graph $y = x^2$ at $x = 1$ and $x = -2$.**

<u>Differentiate</u> to get the gradient expression:
$$y = x^2 \Rightarrow \frac{dy}{dx} = 2x$$

Now when $\underline{x = 1}$,
$$\frac{dy}{dx} = 2 \times 1 = 2$$
So the gradient at $x = 1$ is 2.

And when $\underline{x = -2}$,
$$\frac{dy}{dx} = 2 \times -2 = -4$$
So the gradient at $x = -2$ is -4.

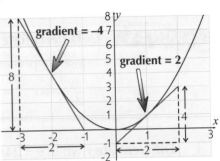

This graph shows how you'd find the gradients by drawing tangents. If your tangents were slightly off you'd get different gradients with this method though.

Differentiating Gives the **Rate of Change**

You can differentiate to find a <u>rate of change</u> — how fast something is decreasing or increasing <u>compared to something else</u>. <u>Velocity</u> (often called speed) and <u>acceleration</u> are rates of change:

> **<u>VELOCITY</u> = rate of change of <u>DISTANCE</u> (or displacement) compared to <u>TIME</u>**
> **<u>ACCELERATION</u> = rate of change of <u>VELOCITY</u> compared to <u>TIME</u>**

The letter 's' is commonly used for distance.

Now this is where it gets tricky:

Differentiating an expression for <u>distance in terms of time</u> gives <u>velocity</u>.
Differentiating an expression for <u>velocity in terms of time</u> gives <u>acceleration</u>.
An example will make this clearer:

If s = distance, t = time, v = velocity, a = acceleration:
$$v = \frac{ds}{dt} \quad \text{and} \quad a = \frac{dv}{dt}$$

 **An object's displacement, s metres, from a fixed point after t seconds is $s = 5t^3 + t^2$, $0 \le t \le 10$.**
a) Find expressions for the object's velocity and acceleration at time t seconds.
b) Find the velocity after 3 seconds.

a) Differentiate the <u>displacement</u> expression (s) to get the <u>velocity</u> expression.
$$\text{velocity} = \frac{ds}{dt} = 5(3t^2) + 2t \Rightarrow \text{velocity} = 15t^2 + 2t$$

Differentiate the <u>velocity</u> expression (v) to get the <u>acceleration</u> expression.
$$\text{acceleration} = \frac{dv}{dt} = 15(2t) + 2 \Rightarrow \text{acceleration} = 30t + 2$$
Remember to put the correct units.

b) Substitute <u>3 for t</u> in the <u>velocity</u> expression to find the velocity after this many seconds.
$$v = 15t^2 + 2t$$
When $t = 3$, $v = 15(3^2) + 2(3) = 135 + 6 = 141$ m/s

Substitute into dy/dx to find the gradient at a point

The examiners probably won't tell you to use differentiation in rates of change questions — you'll just have to know. Remember, distance/displacement differentiates to velocity, velocity differentiates to acceleration.

Differentiation

Some graphs have <u>stationary points</u> — places where the graph 'levels off'. You find them by <u>differentiating</u>.

Stationary Points are When the Gradient is Zero

1) A <u>stationary point</u> is a point on a curve where the <u>gradient equals zero</u>.

2) So to find the stationary points of a graph, you need to find the points where:

$$\frac{dy}{dx} = 0$$

3) A <u>turning point</u> is a type of stationary point which can be a <u>maximum</u> or a <u>minimum</u>.

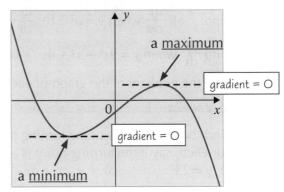

EXAMPLE: **Find the coordinates of the two turning points of the graph of $y = x + \frac{4}{x}$.**

① $y = x + \frac{4}{x} \Rightarrow y = x + 4x^{-1}$ $\frac{dy}{dx} = 1x^0 + 4(-1)x^{-2}$

$$= 1 - \frac{4}{x^2}$$

② $0 = 1 - \frac{4}{x^2} \Rightarrow 1 = \frac{4}{x^2} \Rightarrow x^2 = 4 \Rightarrow x = 2$ and -2

③ When $x = 2$, $y = 2 + \frac{4}{2} \Rightarrow y = 4$

When $x = -2$, $y = -2 + \frac{4}{-2} \Rightarrow y = -4$

So the turning points are at (2, 4) and (−2, −4).

1) First <u>differentiate</u> to find $\frac{dy}{dx}$.

2) Now set $\frac{dy}{dx}$ <u>equal to 0</u>, and solve for x.

3) Substitute the x-values into the <u>ORIGINAL</u> equation to find the <u>y-values</u> of the turning points.

Maximum or Minimum?

You <u>can't tell</u> if a turning point is a <u>maximum</u> or <u>minimum</u> from the coordinates. The easiest way of telling is to think about the <u>shape</u> of the graph (see p.95-97).

EXAMPLE: **Determine whether each turning point of the graph of $y = x + \frac{4}{x}$ identified above is a maximum or a minimum.**

This is a $y = \frac{A}{x}$ graph with a bit added on (see page 96). It's a nasty one, so you might be best sketching it using a table of values. If you did, you'd get a graph like this:

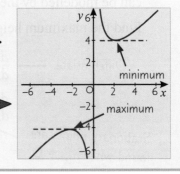

The turning point at (2, 4) is a minimum.
The turning point at (−2, −4) is a maximum.

A stationary point is where the graph is flat

'Maximum or minimum' questions are often set in a context — e.g. you might be asked to find the maximum volume, V, of a shape where $V = $ a function of x. Differentiate to find the value of x at which the maximum occurs and then substitute this into the equation to find the maximum value of V.

Warm-Up and Worked Exam Questions

That's another section wrapped up. Here's one last bundle of warm-up questions to see how you fared.

Warm-Up Questions

1) Find: a) $\frac{dy}{da}$ when $y = a^7$ b) $\frac{dy}{dt}$ when $y = 10t^5$ c) $\frac{dy}{ds}$ when $y = s$ d) $\frac{dy}{dw}$ when $y = -\frac{2}{3}w^6$

2) Find $\frac{dy}{dx}$ when $y = 9x^4 + x^3 + 4x^2 + 6x + 22$

3) Find the gradient of the graph of each of the following equations at $x = 2$.

    a) $y = -2x - 1$ b) $y = 2x^3 - 3$ c) $y = -\frac{1}{2}x^3 + 2$ d) $y = \frac{2}{x}$

4) Find the coordinates of the turning points of these graphs.
For each, say if the turning point is a maximum or minimum.

    a) $y = 2x^2$ b) $y = -x^2 + 4x - 8$ c) $y = x^3 + 6x^2 + 1$

Worked Exam Questions

Two worked exam questions coming up below all about differentiation. There are loads of places differentiation can sneak into the exam so get a good feel for these before moving on to the next page.

1   $F = \frac{13}{x^2} + x^3$. Find $\frac{dF}{dx}$.   **(6)**   Don't be put up off by the F. The method is the same as when it's y.

Write the fraction as a power of x. ——— $F = 13x^{-2} + x^3$

Differentiate each term using $\frac{d}{dx}(x^n) = nx^{n-1}$ ——— $\frac{dF}{dx} = 13(-2x^{-3}) + 3x^2$
$= -26x^{-3} + 3x^2$

Rewrite the power of x as a fraction. ——— $= -\frac{26}{x^3} + 3x^2$

$$\frac{dF}{dx} = \underline{-\frac{26}{x^3} + 3x^2}$$

[2 marks]

2   The height above ground level, h metres, of part of a roller coaster track   **(8)**   can be modelled by the equation $h = -2x^2 + 15x + 12$ for $0 \le x \le 8$.

Find the maximum height of this part of the roller coaster. Show your working.

Differentiate. ——— $\frac{dh}{dx} = -2(2x) + 15 = -4x + 15$

$\frac{dh}{dx} = 0 \Rightarrow -4x + 15 = 0$ Solve the equation to find x.
$4x = 15$
$x = 3.75$

Stationary points are found when $\frac{dh}{dx} = 0$.

At $x = 3.75$, $h = -2 \times 3.75^2 + 15 \times 3.75 + 12$
$= 40.125$

Substitute back into the original equation to find the corresponding value of h.

$\underline{40.125}$ m

[5 marks]

Exam Questions

3 A rectangular airfield has a length of $5x + 1$ km and a width of $5 - 2x$ km, where $-0.2 < x < 2.5$.

a) Write an equation for the area, A km², of the airfield.
Expand and simplify your final answer.

....
[2 marks]

b) Find $\frac{dA}{dx}$. ⑥

....
[2 marks]

c) Find the maximum area of the airfield. ⑧

.... km²
[3 marks]

4 Use differentiation to decide which of the graphs on the right is the graph of $y = x^3 + 6x^2 + 9x - 2$. Show your working.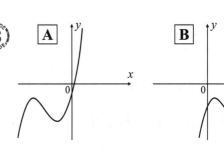

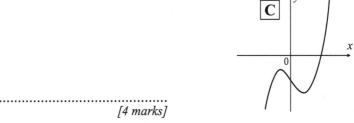

....
[4 marks]

5 The displacement, s metres, of an object from a fixed point after t seconds is given by $s = 2t^3 - 3t^2 + 8$ for $0 \le t \le 5$.

a) What is the velocity of the object after 4 seconds?

.... m/s
[3 marks]

b) After how many seconds was the acceleration of the object zero?

.... seconds
[3 marks]

Revision Questions for Section Three

<u>Section Three</u> is done and dusted — take a bash at these and see what knowledge you've soaked up.
- Try these questions and <u>tick off each one</u> when you <u>get it right</u>.
- When you've done <u>all the questions</u> for a topic and are <u>completely happy</u> with it, tick off the topic.

Coordinates (p.87) ☑

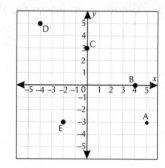

1) Give the coordinates of points A to E in the diagram on the right. ☑
2) Find the midpoint of a line segment with endpoints B and C. ☑
3) A parallelogram has vertices (2, 1), (6, 3) and (2, 7). Find the fourth vertex, given that it lies in the same quadrant as the other three. ☑

Straight-Line Graphs and Gradients (p.88-92) ☑

4) Sketch the lines a) $y = -x$, b) $y = -4$, c) $x = 2$ ☑
5) What does a straight-line equation look like? ☑
6) Use the 'table of three values' method to draw the graph $y = x + \frac{1}{10}x$ ☑
7) Use the '$x = 0$, $y = 0$' method to draw the graph $y = 3x + 5$. ☑

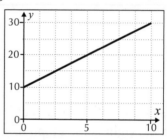

8) Find the gradient of the line on the right. ☑
9) What do 'm' and 'c' represent in $y = mx + c$? ☑
10) Draw the graph of $5x = 2 + y$ using the '$y = mx + c$' method. ☑
11) Find the equation of the graph on the right. ☑
12) Line A has a gradient of 5.
   a) Line B is parallel to Line A. What is the gradient of Line B?
   b) Line C is perpendicular to line A. What is the gradient of line C? ☑

Other Graphs (p.95-97) ☑

13) Describe the shapes of the graphs $y = x^2 + 2x - 8$ and $y = -x^2 + 2x - 8$. ☑
14) Plot the graph $y = x^2 + 2x - 8$ and: a) use it to estimate the solutions to $-2 = x^2 + 2x - 8$ (to 1 d.p.), b) estimate the gradient when $x = 1$ by drawing a tangent. ☑
15) Describe in words, and with a sketch, the shapes of these graphs:
   a) $y = ax^3 + bx^2 + cx + d$ b) $xy = a$ c) $y = \frac{a}{x^2}$ ☑

Functions (p.101-102) ☑

16) If f: $x \rightarrow 3x^2 - 2x$, find f(–1). ☑
17) State which values of x must be excluded from the domain of: a) $f(x) = \frac{2}{x^2 - 1}$ b) $f(x) = \sqrt{x + 2}$ ☑
18) If $f(x) = 6 - 2x$ and $g(x) = \frac{4}{x^2}$, find gf(–2). ☑
19) Explain how you can find the inverse of a function. ☑

Graphs Transformations (p.103-104) ☑

20) Describe how each of the following graphs differs from the graph of $y = x^3 + 1$.
   a) $y = (-x)^3 + 1$ b) $y = (x + 2)^3 + 1$ c) $y = (3x)^3 + 1$ d) $y = x^3 - 1$ ☑

Differentiation (p.107-109) ☑

21) Differentiate $3x^5 + 2x$, and then find the gradient of the graph of $y = 3x^5 + 2x$ at $x = 3$. ☑
22) An object's displacement, s metres, after t seconds is given by $s = t^2 - 2t$.
   Find the object's velocity and acceleration after 4 seconds. ☑
23) Find the coordinates of the turning point of each of these graphs.
   Say if each is a minimum or a maximum. a) $y = x^2 - 2x$ b) $y = -x^2 - 2x$. ☑

Maps and Scale Drawings

<u>Scales</u> tell you what a <u>distance</u> on a <u>map</u> or <u>drawing</u> represents in <u>real life</u>. They can be written in various ways, but they all boil down to something like "<u>1 cm represents 5 km</u>".

Map Scales

1 cm = 3 km — "1 cm represents 3 km"

1 : 2000 — 1 cm on the map means 2000 cm in real life.
Converting to m gives "1 cm represents 20 m".

 Use a ruler — the line's 2 cm long, so 2 cm means 1 km.
0   km   1   Dividing by 2 gives "1 cm represents 0.5 km".

Always make sure the scale is of the form "<u>1 cm = ...</u>" before you start working with it.

Converting from Map Distance to Real Life — Multiply

EXAMPLE: **This map shows a road between two cities, marked as P and W. Work out the length of the section of the road between P and W in km.**

1) Measure with a <u>ruler</u>: Distance on map = 2 cm

2) Read off the <u>scale</u>: Scale is 1 cm = 12 km

3) For <u>real life</u>, <u>multiply</u> by the <u>map scale</u>: Real distance is: 2 × 12 = 24 km

   This looks <u>sensible</u>. ✓

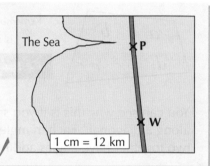

The Sea
×P
×W
1 cm = 12 km

Converting from Real Life to Map Distance — Divide

EXAMPLE: **Helmsley and Pickering are 18 km apart.**
How far apart would they be on a map with a scale of 1 cm = 6 km?

<u>Divide</u> by the <u>scale</u> to find the <u>map distance</u>.

Real-life distance = 18 km, Scale is 1 cm = 6 km
Distance on map = 18 ÷ 6 = 3 cm
This looks <u>sensible</u>. ✓

Scale Drawings

To convert between real life and <u>scale drawings</u>, just replace the word 'map' with 'drawing' in the <u>rules</u> above.

EXAMPLE: **1 cm represents 1.5 m on this scale drawing of a room in Clare's house. Her dining table is 0.9 m wide and 1.8 m long. Draw the table on the scale drawing.**

1) <u>Divide</u> to get scale drawing dimensions.

Width on drawing = 0.9 ÷ 1.5 = 0.6 cm
Length on drawing = 1.8 ÷ 1.5 = 1.2 cm

2) Draw with a <u>ruler</u> in any sensible position and label.

Table

Practise reading scales on any maps you can find

Map scales can be a bit confusing at first — but as long as you work through the examples on this page and make sure you understand them, you shouldn't have a problem in the exam.

Geometry

If you know <u>all</u> these rules <u>thoroughly</u>, you'll at least have a fighting chance of working out problems with lines and angles. If you don't — you've no chance. Sorry to break it to you like that.

6 Simple Rules — that's all

1) Angles in a triangle add up to 180°.

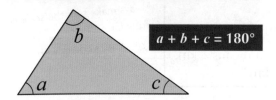

$$a + b + c = 180°$$

2) Angles on a straight line add up to 180°.

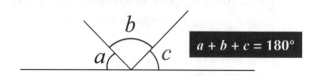

$$a + b + c = 180°$$

3) Angles in a quadrilateral add up to 360°.

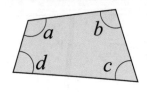

Remember that a quadrilateral is a 4-sided shape.

$$a + b + c + d = 360°$$

4) Angles round a point add up to 360°.

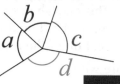

$$a + b + c + d = 360°$$

You can <u>see why</u> this is if you split the quadrilateral into <u>two triangles</u> along a <u>diagonal</u>. Each triangle has angles adding up to 180°, so the two together have angles adding up to 180° + 180° = 360°.

5) Exterior angle of a triangle = sum of opposite interior angles.

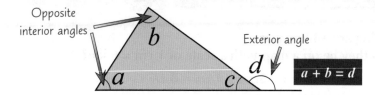

Opposite interior angles

Exterior angle

$$a + b = d$$

There's a nice easy <u>proof</u> of this:
$a + b + c = 180°$ (angles in a triangle) and
$c + d = 180°$ (angles on a straight line),
so $a + b = d$.

6) Isosceles triangles have 2 sides the same and 2 angles the same.

In an isosceles triangle, you only need to know <u>one angle</u> to be able to find the other two.

These dashes indicate two sides the same length.

These angles are the same.

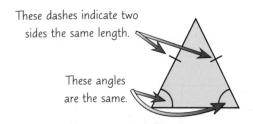

EXAMPLE: **Find the size of angle x.**

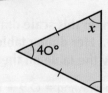

180° − 40° = 140°
<u>The two angles on the right are the same</u> (they're both x) and they must add up to 140°, so 2x = 140°, which means x = 70°.

Six simple rules, make sure you learn them

Scribble them down again and again until they're ingrained in your brain (or desk). The basic facts are pretty easy really, but examiners like to combine them in questions to confuse you — if you've learnt them all you've got a much better chance of spotting which ones you need.

Parallel Lines

Parallel lines are quite straightforward really. (They're also quite straight. And parallel.)
There are a few rules you need to learn — make sure you don't get them mixed up.

Angles Around Parallel Lines

When a line crosses two parallel lines, it forms special sets of angles.

1) The two bunches of angles formed at the points
   of intersection are the same.

2) There are only actually two different angles involved
   (labelled a and b here), and they add up to 180°
   (from rule 2 on the previous page).

3) Vertically opposite angles (ones opposite each other) are equal
   (in the diagram, a and a are vertically opposite, as are b and b).

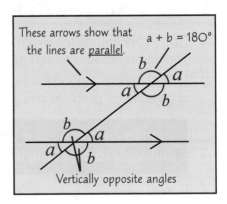

These arrows show that the lines are parallel.
$a + b = 180°$
Vertically opposite angles

Alternate, Allied and Corresponding Angles

The diagram above has some characteristic shapes to look out for — and each shape contains a
specific pair of angles. The angle pairs are known as alternate, allied and corresponding angles.

> You need to spot the characteristic Z, C, U and F shapes:

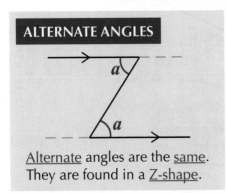

ALTERNATE ANGLES

Alternate angles are the same.
They are found in a Z-shape.

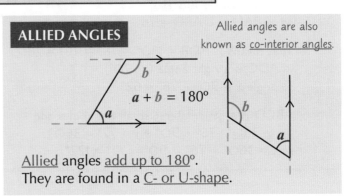

ALLIED ANGLES

Allied angles are also known as co-interior angles.

$a + b = 180°$

Allied angles add up to 180°.
They are found in a C- or U-shape.

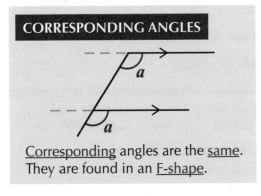

CORRESPONDING ANGLES

Corresponding angles are the same.
They are found in an F-shape.

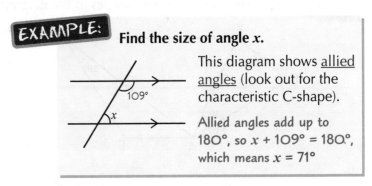

EXAMPLE: **Find the size of angle x.**

This diagram shows allied
angles (look out for the
characteristic C-shape).

Allied angles add up to
180°, so $x + 109° = 180°$,
which means $x = 71°$

Parallelograms are quadrilaterals made from two sets of parallel lines.
You can use the properties above to show that opposite angles in a
parallelogram are equal, and each pair of neighbouring angles add up to 180°.

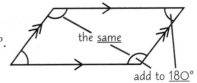

the same
add to 180°

Parallel lines are key things to look out for in geometry

Watch out for parallel lines and Z, C, U and F shapes — extending the lines can make spotting them easier.
Learn the proper names (alternate, allied and corresponding angles) as you'll have to use them in the exam.

Geometry Problems

Once you've learnt all the geometry rules on the last two pages, you can have a go at using them.

Try Out All The Rules One by One

1) Don't concentrate too much on the angle you have been asked to find.
The best method is to find ALL the angles in whatever order they become obvious.

2) Don't sit there waiting for inspiration to hit you. It's all too easy to find yourself staring at a geometry problem and getting nowhere. The method is this:

> GO THROUGH ALL THE RULES OF GEOMETRY (including PARALLEL LINES), ONE BY ONE, and apply each of them in turn in as many ways as possible — one of them is bound to work.

3) Before we get going, there's one bit of notation you need to be familiar with — three-letter angle notation. It's not hard — if you get an angle written as ∠ABC (or just ABC), it's the angle formed at letter B (it's always the middle letter).

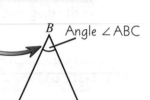

EXAMPLE: **Find the size of angles x and y.**

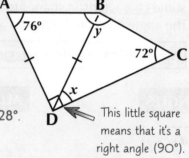

Write down everything you know (or can work out) about the shape:

Triangle ABD is isosceles,
so ∠ BAD = ∠ ABD = 76°.

That means ∠ ADB = 180° − 76° − 76° = 28°.
∠ ADC is a right angle (= 90°),
so angle x = 90° − 28° = 62°

This little square means that it's a right angle (90°).

ABCD is a quadrilateral, so all the angles add up to 360°. 76° + 90° + y + 72° = 360°, so y = 360° − 76° − 90° − 72° = 122°

You could have worked out angle y before angle x.

EXAMPLE: **Find all the missing angles in the diagram below.**

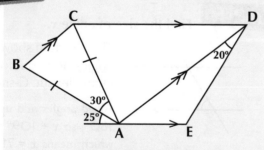

1) Triangle ABC is isosceles, so:
$$\angle ABC = \angle ACB = \frac{(180° - 30°)}{2} = 75°$$

2) BC and AD are parallel, BCAD is a Z-shape, so:
∠ ACB and ∠ CAD are alternate angles.
As ∠ ACB = 75° then ∠ CAD = 75° too.

3) Angles on a straight line means:
∠ EAD = 180° − 25° − 30° − 75° = 50°

4) AE and CD are parallel so ∠ ADC = ∠ EAD = 50° as well.

5) Angles in triangle ACD add up to 180° so ∠ ACD = 180° − 75° − 50° = 55°

6) Angles in triangle ADE add up to 180° so ∠ AED = 180° − 50° − 20° = 110°

The most important rule of all — don't panic

Geometry problems often look a lot worse than they are — don't panic, just write down everything you can work out. You'll need all the rules from the last two pages so make sure they're clear in your head.

Polygons

A <u>polygon</u> is a <u>many-sided shape</u>, and can be <u>regular</u> or <u>irregular</u>. A <u>regular</u> polygon is on[e]
all the <u>sides</u> and <u>angles</u> are the <u>same</u> (in an <u>irregular</u> polygon, the sides and angles are <u>diffe[rent]</u>

Regular Polygons

You need to be familiar with the first few <u>regular polygons</u> — ones with up to <u>10 sides</u>. You need to know their
<u>names</u> and how many <u>sides</u> they have (remember that all the <u>sides</u> and <u>angles</u> in a regular polygon are the <u>same</u>).

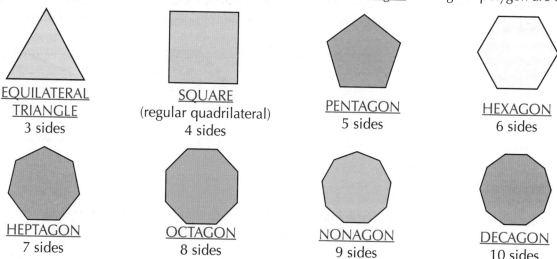

<u>EQUILATERAL
TRIANGLE</u>
3 sides

<u>SQUARE</u>
(regular quadrilateral)
4 sides

<u>PENTAGON</u>
5 sides

<u>HEXAGON</u>
6 sides

<u>HEPTAGON</u>
7 sides

<u>OCTAGON</u>
8 sides

<u>NONAGON</u>
9 sides

<u>DECAGON</u>
10 sides

Interior and Exterior Angles

Questions on <u>interior</u> and <u>exterior angles</u> often come up in exams — so you need to know <u>what</u> they are
and <u>how to find them</u>. There are a couple of <u>formulas</u> you need to learn as well.

For <u>ANY POLYGON</u> (regular or irregular):

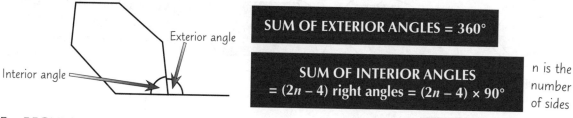

Exterior angle

Interior angle

SUM OF EXTERIOR ANGLES = 360°

SUM OF INTERIOR ANGLES
$= (2n - 4)$ right angles $= (2n - 4) \times 90°$

n is the
number
of sides

For <u>REGULAR POLYGONS</u> only:

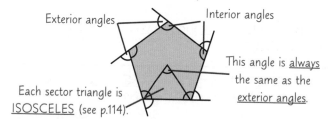

Exterior angles

Interior angles

This angle is <u>always</u>
the same as the
<u>exterior angles</u>.

Each sector triangle is
<u>ISOSCELES</u> (see p.114).

$$\text{EXTERIOR ANGLE} = \frac{360°}{n}$$

INTERIOR ANGLE = 180° − EXTERIOR ANGLE

> **EXAMPLE:** The interior angle of a regular polygon is 165°. How many sides does the polygon have?
>
> First, find the <u>exterior angle</u> of the shape: exterior angle = 180° − 165° = 15°
>
> Use this value to find the <u>number of sides</u>: exterior angle = $\frac{360°}{n}$ so n = $\frac{360°}{\text{exterior angle}}$ = $\frac{360°}{15°}$ = 24 sides

Four very simple and very important formulas

There are all sorts of questions they can ask on angles in polygons, but you can answer them all with the four
formulas here — check you've learnt them and you know which ones go with regular and irregular polygons.

Symmetry

This page is jam-packed with details about the <u>TWO types</u> of symmetry — and you need to learn them both.

Symmetry

Line Symmetry

This is where you can draw one or more <u>MIRROR LINES</u> across a shape and both sides <u>fold exactly</u> together.
A <u>regular polygon</u> (see previous page) has the same number of <u>lines of symmetry</u> as its number of <u>sides</u>.

Regular pentagon
— 5 lines of symmetry

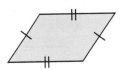

Parallelogram — no
lines of symmetry

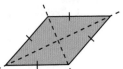

Rhombus — 2 lines
of symmetry

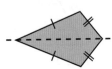

Kite — 1 line
of symmetry

Rotational Symmetry

This is where you can <u>rotate</u> the shape into different positions that <u>look exactly the same</u>.
Again, <u>regular polygons</u> have the same <u>order of rotational symmetry</u> as <u>number of sides</u>.

Square — order 4

Regular hexagon
— order 6

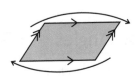

Parallelogram — order 2

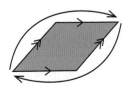

Rhombus — order 2

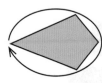

Kite — order 1

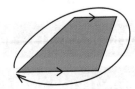

Trapezium — order 1

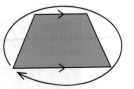

When a shape has <u>only 1 position</u>
you can <u>either</u> say that it has
'rotational symmetry of <u>order 1</u>' or that
it has '<u>NO rotational symmetry</u>'.

Symmetry of **Triangles**

Triangles crop up all the time in geometry questions, so it pays to learn <u>as much as you can</u> about them.
Take note of the <u>symmetry</u> properties of the <u>different types</u> of triangle:

EQUILATERAL Triangle	RIGHT-ANGLED Triangle	ISOSCELES Triangle 2 sides and 2 angles equal	SCALENE Triangle No sides or angles equal
			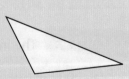
3 lines of symmetry. Rotational symmetry <u>order 3</u>.	<u>No lines</u> of symmetry (unless the angles are <u>45°</u> — then it's isosceles). Rotational symmetry <u>order 1</u>.	1 line of symmetry. Rotational symmetry <u>order 1</u>.	<u>No lines</u> of symmetry. Rotational symmetry <u>order 1</u>.

Make sure you learn the two different types of symmetry

You'll then be able to dazzle your friends by spotting symmetry in everyday shapes like road signs
and letters — and more importantly, you'll get some nice marks in your exam.

Warm-Up and Worked Exam Questions

Don't just look at those lovely big diagrams — you need to work through the examples in this section one by one to make sure that you've remembered all those rules...

Warm-Up Questions

1) The diagram on the right is a scale drawing of a flag, where 1 cm represents 20 cm. Calculate the actual length of the vertical side of the flag.

2) Find the missing angles *a*-*d* below. State any angle laws used.

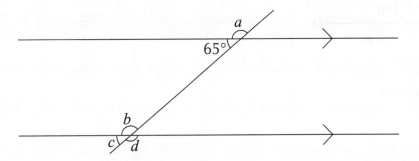

3) How many sides does a hexagon have?

4) Write down the name of the shape to the right:

5) What is the size of an exterior angle of a regular 15-sided polygon?

6) A quadrilateral has 1 line of symmetry and 2 pairs of equal sides. What is the name of the quadrilateral?

Worked Exam Questions

There'll probably be a question in the exam that asks you to find angles. That means you have to remember all the different angle rules and practise using them in the right places...

1   *DEF* and *BEC* are straight lines that cross at *E*.
      AFB and *AC* are perpendicular lines.

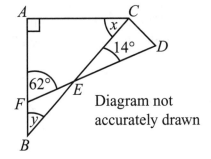

   a)   Find angle *x*.
       Give a reason for each stage of your working.

       Angles on a straight line add up to 180°,
       so angle FEC = 180° − 14° = 166°

       Angles in a quadrilateral add up to 360°,
       so *x* = 360° − 90° − 62° − 166° = 42°

Angle *x* is in quadrilateral ACEF, so find the other missing angle in ACEF, then you can find *x*.

$$x = \underline{\ \ 42\ \ }°$$
[2 marks]

   b)   Use your answer to part a) to show that *y* = 48°.

       Angles in a triangle add up to 180°, so *y* = 180° − 90° − 42° = 48°

Angle *y* and angle *x* are both in the triangle ABC.

[2 marks]

2   *AB* and *CD* are parallel lines. *EF* and *GH* are straight lines. Work out the size of angle *x*.

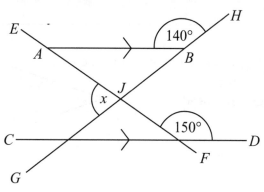

Diagram not accurately drawn

x = ... °

[4 marks]

3   Part of a regular polygon is shown below. Each interior angle is 150°.

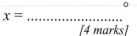   Diagram not
accurately drawn

Calculate the number of sides of the polygon.

....
[3 marks]

4   *A*, *B* and *C* are points on a circle, centre *O*. *OA*, *OB* and *OC* are radii of the circle.
OBD is a straight line and *EF* is the tangent to the circle at *A*.
Angle *OCB* = 27°, angle *FDB* = 142° and angle *OAD* is a right angle.

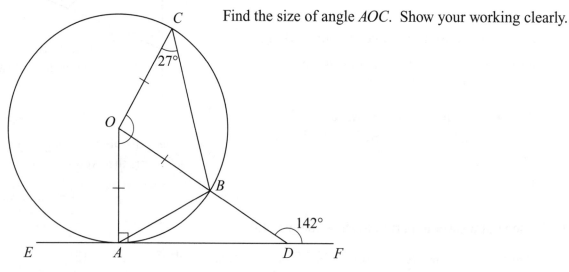

Find the size of angle *AOC*. Show your working clearly.

Diagram not accurately drawn

.... °
[4 marks]

Circle Geometry

It's time to plunge you into some pretty serious geometry now, with a 3-page extravaganza on <u>circle theorems</u>. There's a lot to learn on these pages, but it's all really useful stuff.

Parts of a Circle

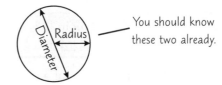

You should know these two already.

There are some wacky names for the <u>parts of a circle</u> — make sure you know what they all mean.

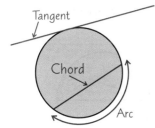

<u>A TANGENT</u> is a straight line that <u>just touches</u> the <u>outside</u> of a circle.
<u>A CHORD</u> is a line drawn <u>across the inside</u> of a circle.
The <u>CIRCUMFERENCE</u> of a circle is the <u>distance all the way around it</u>.
<u>AN ARC</u> is just <u>part of the circumference</u> of a circle.

<u>A SECTOR</u> is a wedge-shaped area (like a slice of cake) cut right from the centre.
<u>SEGMENTS</u> are the areas you get when you cut a circle with a chord.

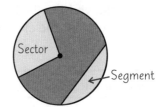

11 Rules to Learn — 4 Simple Ones to Start With...

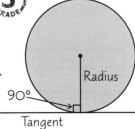

1) A <u>TANGENT</u> and a <u>RADIUS</u> meet at <u>90°</u>.

A <u>TANGENT</u> is a line that just touches a single point on the circumference of a circle.
A tangent always makes an angle of <u>exactly 90°</u> with the <u>radius</u> it meets at this point.

Radius

90°

Tangent

2) <u>TANGENTS</u> from the <u>SAME POINT</u> are the <u>SAME LENGTH</u>.

Two tangents drawn from an outside point are <u>always equal in length</u> (up to the point where they touch the circle), so creating an 'isosceles' situation, with <u>two congruent right-angled triangles</u>.

There's more about congruence on p.130.

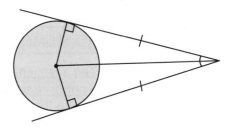

3) The <u>PERPENDICULAR BISECTOR</u> of a <u>CHORD</u> passes through the <u>CENTRE</u> of the circle.

A <u>CHORD</u> is any line <u>drawn across a circle</u>. And no matter where you draw a chord, the line that <u>cuts it exactly in half</u> (at 90°), will <u>go through the centre of the circle</u>.

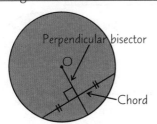

EXAMPLE:

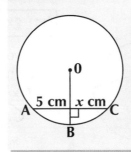

A, B and C are points on the circumference of the circle with centre O. Find x.

Line <u>AC is a chord</u>.

Line OB is at <u>right angles</u> to AC and goes through the <u>centre</u> of the circle.

This means that:

OB is the perpendicular bisector of AC, so x = 5.

4) <u>TWO RADII</u> form an <u>ISOSCELES TRIANGLE</u>.   Radii is the plural of radius.

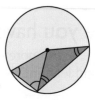

They <u>don't have the little tick marks on the sides</u> to remind you that they are the same — the fact that <u>they are both radii</u> is enough to make it an isosceles triangle.

Circle Geometry

5 Trickier Ones...

5) The angle at the <u>CENTRE</u> of a circle is <u>TWICE</u> the angle at the <u>CIRCUMFERENCE</u>.

The angle subtended at the <u>centre</u> of a circle is <u>EXACTLY DOUBLE</u> the angle subtended at the <u>circumference</u> of the circle from the <u>same two points</u> (two ends of the same <u>chord</u>).

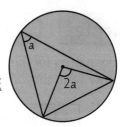

'Angle subtended at' is just a posh way of saying 'angle made at'.

6) The <u>ANGLE</u> in a <u>SEMICIRCLE</u> is <u>90°</u>.

A triangle drawn from the <u>two ends of a diameter</u> will <u>ALWAYS</u> make an <u>angle of 90° where it hits</u> the circumference of the circle, no matter where it hits.

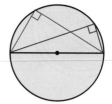

7) Angles in the <u>SAME SEGMENT</u> are <u>EQUAL</u>.

All triangles drawn from a chord will have <u>the same angle where they touch the circumference</u>. Also, the two angles on opposite sides of the chord <u>add up to 180°</u>.

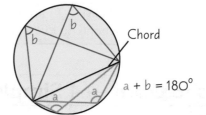

Chord

$a + b = 180°$

8) <u>OPPOSITE ANGLES</u> in a <u>CYCLIC QUADRILATERAL</u> add up to <u>180°</u>.

A <u>cyclic quadrilateral</u> is a <u>4-sided shape with every corner touching the circle</u>. Both pairs of opposite angles add up to 180°.

$\underline{a + c = 180°}$
$\underline{b + d = 180°}$

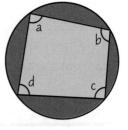

9) The <u>ALTERNATE SEGMENT THEOREM</u>.

The <u>angle between</u> a <u>tangent</u> and a <u>chord</u> is always <u>equal</u> to 'the angle in the opposite segment' (i.e. the angle made at the circumference by two lines drawn from ends of the chord).

This is probably the hardest rule, so take care.

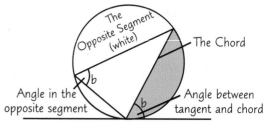

The Opposite Segment (white)

The Chord

Angle in the opposite segment

Angle between tangent and chord

...and 2 Intersecting Chord Properties

10) <u>INTERNAL INTERSECTION</u>.

For any two chords that intersect inside a circle:

$\underline{AE \times EB = CE \times ED}$

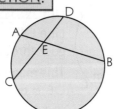

11) <u>EXTERNAL INTERSECTION</u>.

If two chords are extended and meet outside the circle:

$\underline{AE \times BE = CE \times DE}$

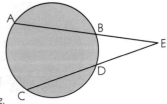

All these lengths are measured from the point outside the circle.

There you have it — eleven rules to learn

This page is just more of the same: some more rules to cram into your overcrowded brain. But there's no way round learning this stuff, and once you've learnt all eleven, circle geometry becomes much easier.

Circle Geometry

After learning all eleven of those rules you might wonder where you'll actually use them. Behold:

Using the Circle Theorems

EXAMPLE: **A, B, C and D are points on the circumference of the circle, and O is the centre of the circle. Angle ADC = 109°. Work out the size of angles ABC and AOC.**

You'll probably have to use more than one rule to solve circle theorem questions — here, ABCD is a <u>cyclic quadrilateral</u>, so use rule 8:

> 8) OPPOSITE ANGLES in a CYCLIC QUADRILATERAL add up to 180°.

Angles ADC and ABC are <u>opposite</u>, so angle ABC = 180° − 109° = 71°

Now, angles ABC (which you've just found) and AOC both come from chord AC, so you can use rule 5:

Remember three-letter angle notation from p.116 — angle ADC is the angle formed at D (it's always the middle letter).

> 5) The angle at the CENTRE of a circle is TWICE the angle at the CIRCUMFERENCE.

So angle AOC is <u>double</u> angle ABC, which means angle AOC = 71° × 2 = 142°

EXAMPLE: **Line ABC is a tangent to the circle with centre O, and points B, D and E are points on the circumference. Angle EOB = 88°. Work out the size of angles BEO and ABE.**

To find <u>angle BEO</u>, use rule 4:

> 4) TWO RADII form an ISOSCELES TRIANGLE.

Triangle <u>EOB</u> is an <u>isosceles triangle</u> with an angle of 88°.
So angle BEO = (180° − 88°) ÷ 2 = 46°

To find angle <u>ABE</u>, use rule 9:

> 9) The ALTERNATE SEGMENT THEOREM.

So angle <u>ABE</u> is the <u>same</u> as angle <u>EDB</u>, which we can find using rule 5:

> 5) The angle at the CENTRE of a circle is TWICE the angle at the CIRCUMFERENCE.

Angle EDB = 88° ÷ 2 = 44°, so angle ABE = 44°

EXAMPLE: **In the diagram, AE = 49 mm, BE = 22 mm and CE = 47 mm. Find the length of chord CD.**

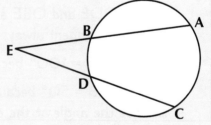

1) Use the <u>external intersection</u> formula: AE × BE = CE × DE
2) Put in the numbers to find <u>DE</u>:   49 × 22 = 47 × DE
   DE = 22.9 mm
3) <u>Subtract</u> DE from CE to find <u>CD</u>:   CE − DE = CD
   47 − 22.9 = 24.1 mm

Have you remembered those eleven rules?

If you find this page isn't making much sense, you need to go back for another look at pages 121 and 122. Sometimes you'll find there's more than one way of finding the angle you want.

Warm-Up and Worked Exam Questions

Time to have a go at using all those lovely circle theorems. The only way this stuff is going to sink in is if you practise answering questions — luckily you've got three pages of them here so you can do just that...

Warm-Up Questions

1) *PQR* and *RST* are tangents to the circle. Find the missing angles x, y and z.

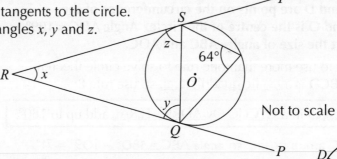

Not to scale

2) *AB* and *CD* are chords of the circle on the right. They intersect at *X*. $AX = 3$ cm, $CX = 2$ cm and $BX = 5$ cm. Find the length of *DX*.

Worked Exam Questions

Circle theorem questions can sometimes be a bit overwhelming, and it can be difficult to know where to start. The best approach is to keep finding any angles you can using the circle theorems and the angle rules from pages 114 and 115, until you have enough information to find the angle you want.

1   In the diagram, *O* is the centre of the circle. *A*, *B*, *C* and *D* are points on the circumference of the circle and *DE* and *BE* are tangents. Angle *DEB* is 80°.

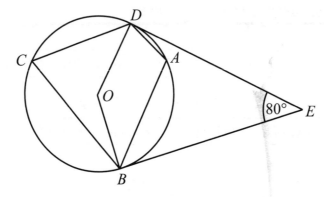

Not to scale

Work out the size of angle *DAB*.

Angles ODE and OBE are both 90°
because a tangent always meets a radius at 90°.

Angle DOB = 100° because angles in a quadrilateral add up to 360°.

Angle DCB = 50° because an angle at the centre
is twice the angle at the circumference.

This uses rules 1, 5 and 8
from pages 121-122.

Angle DAB = 130° because opposite angles of
a cyclic quadrilateral add up to 180°.

130 °

[4 marks]

Exam Questions

2   *B* and *C* are points on the circumference of a circle with centre *O*.
    AB and *AC* are tangents of the circle.

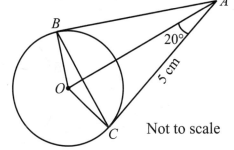

a)   State the length *AB*.

.... cm
[1 mark]

b)   Calculate the size of angle *BOC*.

Not to scale

○
....
[3 marks]

c)   Calculate the size of angle *OBC*.

○
....
[2 marks]

3   The diagram shows a circle, centre *O*. *A*, *B*, *C* and *D* are points on the circumference.

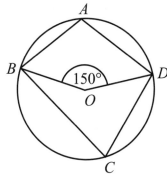

Not to scale

a)   Work out the size of angle *BCD*.
     Give a reason for your answer.

....

....
[2 marks]

b)   Explain why angle *BAD* = 105°.

....

....
[1 mark]

4   The diagram below shows a circle with centre *O*. *A*, *B*, *C* and *D* are
    points on the circumference of the circle and *AOC* is a straight line.

Work out the size of the angle marked *x*.

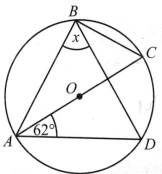

Not to scale

○
x = ...
[3 marks]

Exam Questions

5 Points B, C, D and E lie on the circumference of a circle.
  $AB = 6$ cm, $BC = 10$ cm, $AE = 8$ cm and $ED = x$.

Find the length of x.

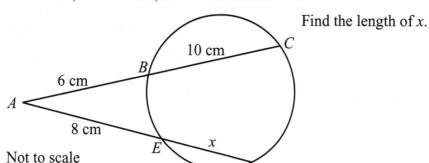

Not to scale

.... cm

[2 marks]

6 Points A, B, C, D and E lie on the circumference of a circle with centre O.
  AFD and CFE are chords of the circle. $AF = 6$ cm and $EF = 9$ cm.

Find the length of CF.

Not to scale

.... cm

[3 marks]

7 A, B, C and D are points on the circumference of
  a circle with centre O. Angle $BCD = 53°$.
  The line AE is a tangent to the circle, touching it at A.
  Angle $DAE = 32°$. Find the size of angle OBA.

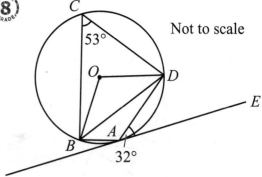

Not to scale

.... °

[4 marks]

The Four Transformations

There are four <u>transformations</u> you need to know — <u>translation</u>, <u>rotation</u>, <u>reflection</u> and <u>enlargement</u>.

1) Translations

In a <u>translation</u>, the <u>amount</u> the shape moves by is given as a <u>vector</u> (see p.165-166) written $\begin{pmatrix} x \\ y \end{pmatrix}$ — where x is the <u>horizontal movement</u> (i.e. to the <u>right</u>) and y is the <u>vertical movement</u> (i.e. <u>up</u>). If the shape moves <u>left and down</u>, x and y will be <u>negative</u>.

EXAMPLE:
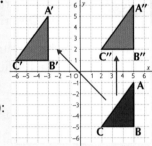

a) Describe the transformation that maps triangle ABC onto A'B'C'.

The transformation from ABC to A'B'C' is a translation of 8 units left and 6 units up.

b) Describe the transformation that maps triangle ABC onto A"B"C". Give your answer as a vector.

To get from A to A", you need to move 7 units up (and no units horizontally):

The transformation from ABC to A"B"C" is a **translation by the vector** $\begin{pmatrix} 0 \\ 7 \end{pmatrix}$.

2) Rotations

To describe a <u>rotation</u>, you must give <u>3 details</u>:

1) The <u>angle of rotation</u> (usually 90° or 180°).
2) The <u>direction of rotation</u> (clockwise or anticlockwise).
3) The <u>centre of rotation</u> (often, but not always, the origin).

<u>+ and − signs</u> are sometimes used to show whether a rotation is <u>clockwise (−)</u> or <u>anticlockwise (+)</u>.
+90° means 90° anticlockwise
and −90° means 90° clockwise.

EXAMPLE:

a) Describe the transformation that maps triangle ABC onto A'B'C'.

If it helps, you can use tracing paper to help you find the centre of rotation.

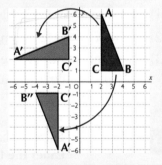

The transformation from ABC to A'B'C' is a rotation of 90° anticlockwise about the origin.

The transformation from ABC to A"B"C" is a **rotation of 180° clockwise (or anticlockwise) about the origin.**

3) Reflections

For a <u>reflection</u>, you must give the <u>equation</u> of the <u>mirror line</u>.

EXAMPLE:

a) Describe the transformation that maps shape A onto shape B.
b) Describe the transformation that maps shape A onto shape C.

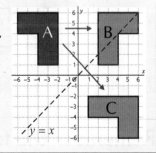

a) The transformation from A to B is a reflection in the *y*-axis.

b) The transformation from A to C is a reflection in the line *y* = *x*.

The most common mirror lines that come up are the
x-axis, the *y*-axis, the line *y* = *x* and the line *y* = −*x*.

The Four Transformations

One more transformation coming up — <u>enlargements</u>. Unfortunately, they're probably the trickiest.

4) Enlargements

For an <u>enlargement</u>, you must specify:

1) The <u>scale factor</u>. ⟵

2) The <u>centre of enlargement</u>.

$$\text{scale factor} = \frac{\text{new length}}{\text{old length}}$$

EXAMPLE: a) **Describe the transformation that maps triangle A onto triangle B.**
  b) **Describe the transformation that maps triangle B onto triangle A.**

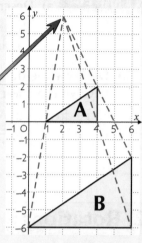

a) Use the formula above to find the <u>scale factor</u> (just choose one side):

$$\text{scale factor} = \frac{6}{3} = 2$$

For the <u>centre of enlargement</u>, draw <u>lines</u> that go through <u>corresponding vertices</u> of both shapes and see where they <u>cross</u>.

So the transformation from A to B is an <u>enlargement of scale factor 2</u>, centre (2, 6).

b) Using a similar method, $\text{scale factor} = \frac{3}{6} = \frac{1}{2}$ and the centre of enlargement is the same as before, so the transformation from B to A is an enlargement of scale factor $\frac{1}{2}$, centre (2, 6).

If the scale factor is less than 1, the shape will get smaller (A is smaller than B). There's more on this below.

Scale Factors — Three Key Facts

1) If the scale factor is <u>bigger than 1</u> the <u>shape gets bigger</u>.

2) If the scale factor is <u>smaller than 1</u> (e.g. $\frac{1}{2}$) it <u>gets smaller</u>.

3) The scale factor also tells you the <u>relative distance</u> of old points and new points from the <u>centre of enlargement</u> — this is very useful for <u>drawing an enlargement</u>, because you can use it to trace out the positions of the new points.

EXAMPLE: **Enlarge shape A below by a scale factor of 3, centre (–4, 1). Label the transformed shape B.**

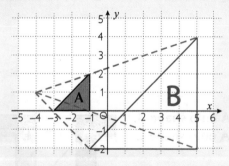

1) First, <u>draw lines</u> from <u>(–4, 1)</u> going through each <u>vertex</u> of shape A.

2) Then, <u>multiply</u> the distance from the centre of enlargement to each vertex by 3, and measure this distance from the centre of enlargement along each of the lines you've drawn.

So on shape A, vertex (–1, 2) is 3 right and 1 up from (–4, 1) — so the corresponding point on shape B will be 3 × 3 = 9 right and 3 × 1 = 3 up from (–4, 1). Do this for every point.

3) <u>Join</u> the points you've drawn to form shape B.

Remember the four types of transformation

Shapes are <u>congruent</u> under translation, rotation and reflection, and <u>similar</u> under enlargement — more on congruence and similarity on p.130. You'll also need to learn the three key facts about scale factors.

More Transformation Stuff

Just one more page on transformations, and then you're done. With transformations anyway, not with maths.

Combinations of Transformations

If they're feeling really mean, the examiners might make you do <u>two transformations</u> to the <u>same shape</u>, then ask you to <u>describe</u> the <u>single transformation</u> that would get you to the <u>final shape</u>. It's not as bad as it looks.

a) **Reflect shape A in the x-axis. Label this shape B.**
b) **Reflect shape B in the y-axis. Label this shape C.**
c) **Describe the single transformation that will map shape A onto shape C.**

For a) and b), just draw the reflections.

For c), you can ignore shape B and just work out how to get from A to C. You can see it's a <u>rotation</u>, but the tricky bit is working out the <u>centre of rotation</u>. Use <u>tracing paper</u> if you need to.

The transformation from A to C is a **rotation of 180° clockwise** (or anticlockwise) **about the origin**.

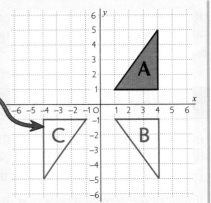

How Enlargement Affects Area and Volume

If a shape is enlarged by a <u>scale factor</u> (see previous page), its <u>area</u>, or <u>surface area</u> and <u>volume</u> (if it's a 3D shape), will change too. However, they <u>don't</u> change by the <u>same value</u> as the scale factor:

For a SCALE FACTOR n:		AS RATIOS:	
The <u>SIDES</u> are	n times bigger		
The <u>AREAS</u> are	n^2 times bigger	Lengths	$a:b$
The <u>VOLUMES</u> are	n^3 times bigger	Areas	$a^2:b^2$
		Volumes	$a^3:b^3$

$$n = \frac{\text{new length}}{\text{old length}} \qquad n^2 = \frac{\text{new area}}{\text{old area}}$$

$$n^3 = \frac{\text{new volume}}{\text{old volume}}$$

So if the <u>scale factor</u> is <u>2</u>, the lengths are <u>2 times</u> as long, the area is $2^2 =$ <u>4 times</u> as big, and the volume is $2^3 =$ <u>8 times</u> as big. As <u>ratios</u>, these enlargements are <u>1:2</u> (length), $1^2:2^2 =$ <u>1:4</u> (area) and $1^3:2^3 =$ <u>1:8</u> (volume).

There's more on areas on p.133-135 and volumes on p.136-137.

Cylinder A has surface area 6π cm², and cylinder B has surface area 54π cm². The volume of cylinder A is 2π cm³. Find the volume of cylinder B, given that B is an enlargement of A.

First, work out the <u>scale factor</u>, n: $n^2 = \dfrac{\text{Area B}}{\text{Area A}} = \dfrac{54\pi}{6\pi} = 9$, so <u>$n = 3$</u>

Use this in the volume formula: $n^3 = \dfrac{\text{Volume B}}{\text{Volume A}} \Rightarrow 3^3 = \dfrac{\text{Volume B}}{2\pi}$

$\Rightarrow$ Volume of B = $2\pi \times 27 = 54\pi$ cm³

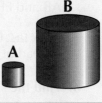

This shows that if the scale factor is <u>3</u>, lengths are <u>3 times as long</u>, the surface area is <u>9 times as big</u> and the volume is <u>27 times as big</u>.

For combinations of transformations, just do one after the other

You need to be really specific when <u>describing</u> transformations — write down <u>all</u> of the details that you know (look back over these pages to see what you need for each transformation). Remember that you have to square or cube the scale factor n when dealing with areas or volumes — that always catches people out.

Congruence and Similarity

Shapes can be <u>similar</u> or <u>congruent</u>. This page will tell you all you need to know about what that means.

Congruent Shapes — Same Shape, Same Size

<u>Congruence</u> is another ridiculous maths word which sounds really complicated when it's not. If two shapes are congruent, they are simply <u>the same</u> — the <u>same size</u> and the <u>same shape</u>. That's all it is.

It doesn't matter which way round the shape is, so <u>translations</u>, <u>reflections</u> and <u>rotations</u> all produce a shape that's congruent to the original shape.

Similar Shapes Have the Same Angles

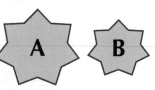

<u>Similar</u> shapes are <u>exactly the same shape</u>, but can be <u>different sizes</u> (they can also be <u>rotated</u> or <u>reflected</u>).

For two shapes to be <u>similar</u>, all the <u>angles</u> must match and the <u>sides</u> must be <u>proportional</u>.

If one shape is an <u>enlargement</u> of another shape then they're similar — this applies to 3D shapes too. Exam questions often <u>tell you</u> that two shapes are similar, then ask you to find the <u>length</u> of a <u>missing side</u>. You need to find the <u>scale factor</u> to get from one shape to the other.

EXAMPLE: **Triangles ABC and DEF are similar. Calculate the length of side EF.**

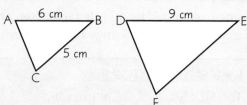

The first thing to do is to work out the <u>scale factor</u>. AB and DE are <u>corresponding sides</u>:

$$\text{scale factor} = \frac{DE}{AB} = \frac{9}{6} = 1.5$$

Now <u>use</u> the scale factor to work out the length of EF:

$$EF = BC \times 1.5 = 5 \times 1.5 = 7.5 \text{ cm}$$

EXAMPLE: **Quadrilaterals ABCD and EFGH are similar.**

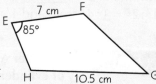

a) **Calculate the length of side CD.**

First, work out the <u>scale factor</u>.

AB and EF are <u>corresponding sides</u>, so the scale factor is $\frac{EF}{AB} = \frac{7}{4} = 1.75$.

Now <u>use</u> the scale factor to work out the length of CD (this time, instead of multiplying by the scale factor, you need to <u>divide</u> by it):
$$CD = GH \div 1.75$$
$$= 10.5 \div 1.75 = 6 \text{ cm}$$

b) **Find the size of angle EFG.**

All the angles must match, so angle EFG must equal angle ABC: Angle EFG = Angle ABC = 111°

Similar means the same shape but a different size

Make sure you really know the difference between congruent and similar shapes. To help you remember, think '<u>similar siblings</u>, <u>congruent clones</u>' — siblings are alike but not the same, clones are identical.

Warm-Up and Worked Exam Questions

These warm-up questions cover some of the basics you'll need for the exam — use them to make sure you've learnt all the key information properly before you move on to tackling some exam questions.

Warm-Up Questions

1) What translation would map the point (1, 3) onto (–2, 6)?

2) Point A is reflected in the *y*-axis to give point B. Given that point A is found at (3, 5), write down the coordinates of point B.

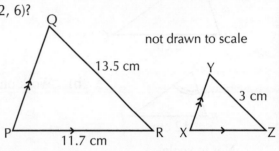

not drawn to scale

3) Triangles PQR and XYZ are similar.
   a) Triangle XYZ is an enlargement of triangle PQR. What is the scale factor of the enlargement?
   b) What is the length of XZ?

4) From the diagram to the right, pick out:
   a) a pair of congruent shapes
   b) a pair of similar shapes

Worked Exam Questions

I'm afraid this helpful blue writing won't be there in the exam, so if I were you I'd make the most of it and make sure you fully understand it now.

1 The quadrilateral *ABCD* is made up of two similar triangles, *ABC* and *ACD*. *AB* = 5.25 cm, *AD* = 20 cm and *AC* = 15 cm. Angle *ABC* = angle *ACD* and angle *ACB* = angle *CAD*.

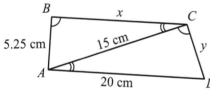

Not to scale

a) Find the length of sides *x* and *y*.

The side AD in ACD corresponds to AC in ABC.

scale factor from ACD to ABC
$= 15 \div 20 = \frac{3}{4}$

Multiply to go from ACD to ABC: $x = 15 \times \frac{3}{4}$ $x = \underline{11.25}$ cm

Divide to go from ABC to ACD: $y = 5.25 \div \frac{3}{4}$ $y = \underline{7}$ cm

[3 marks]

b) The area of triangle *ACD* is 42 cm². What is the area of quadrilateral *ABCD*?

For areas, use (scale factor)²   Area of ABC $= 42 \times \left(\frac{3}{4}\right)^2 = 23.625$

So area of ABCD $= 42 + 23.625 = 65.625$ cm²

$\underline{65.625}$ cm²

[2 marks]

2 The radius of a tennis ball and the radius of a basketball are in the ratio 1 : 7. Assuming both balls are spheres, work out the ratio of the volume of a tennis ball to the volume of a basketball.

Lengths are in the ratio 1 : 7. So volumes are $1^3 : 7^3 = 1 : 343$

$\underline{1:343}$

[1 mark]

Exam Questions

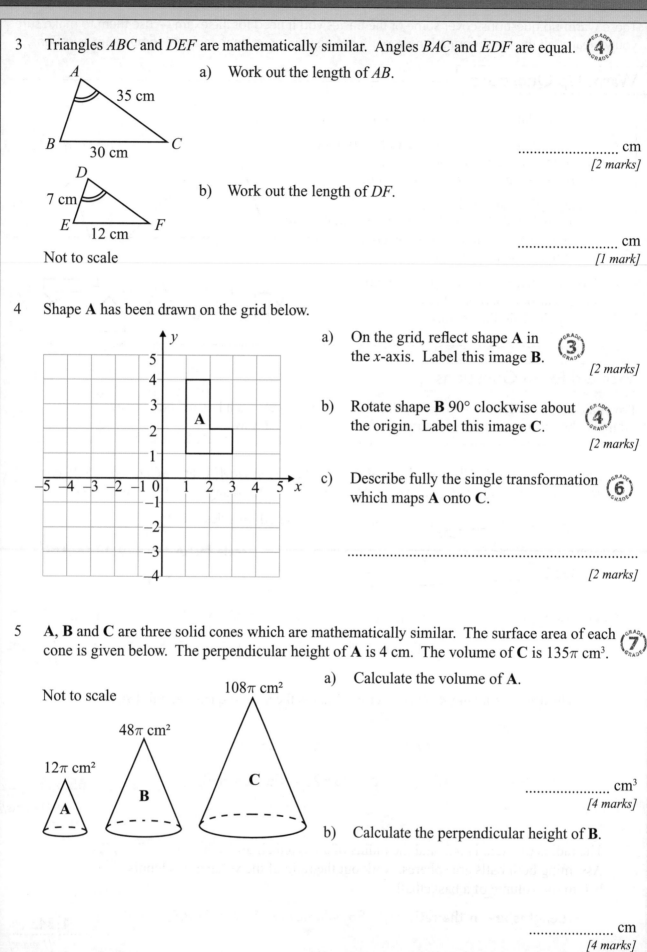

3   Triangles *ABC* and *DEF* are mathematically similar. Angles *BAC* and *EDF* are equal. **(4)**

a)   Work out the length of *AB*.

A

35 cm

B   30 cm   *C*

.... cm
[2 marks]

D

7 cm

b)   Work out the length of *DF*.

E   12 cm   *F*

Not to scale

.... cm
[1 mark]

4   Shape **A** has been drawn on the grid below.

a)   On the grid, reflect shape **A** in the *x*-axis. Label this image **B**. **(3)**
[2 marks]

b)   Rotate shape **B** 90° clockwise about the origin. Label this image **C**. **(4)**
[2 marks]

c)   Describe fully the single transformation which maps **A** onto **C**. **(6)**

....

[2 marks]

5   **A**, **B** and **C** are three solid cones which are mathematically similar. The surface area of each **(7)** cone is given below. The perpendicular height of **A** is 4 cm. The volume of **C** is 135π cm³.

a)   Calculate the volume of **A**.

Not to scale

108π cm²

48π cm²

12π cm²

C

B

A

.... cm³
[4 marks]

b)   Calculate the perpendicular height of **B**.

.... cm
[4 marks]

Areas

Be warned — there are lots of <u>area formulas</u> coming up on the next two pages for you to <u>learn</u>.
You should remember the formulas for the area of a <u>rectangle</u> ($A = l \times w$) and the area of a <u>square</u> ($A = l^2$).

Areas of **Triangles** and **Quadrilaterals**

Note that for each of the three formulas below, the <u>height</u>
must be the <u>vertical height</u> – not the sloping height.

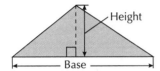

<u>Area of triangle</u> = $\frac{1}{2}$ × base × vertical height

$$A = \frac{1}{2} \times b \times h_v$$

The alternative formula is:
<u>Area of triangle</u> = $\frac{1}{2}ab\sin C$
This is covered on p.160.

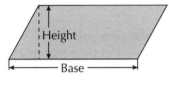

$\dfrac{\text{Area of}}{\text{parallelogram}}$ = base × vertical height $A = b \times h_v$

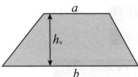

$\dfrac{\text{Area of}}{\text{trapezium}}$ = $\dfrac{\text{average of}}{\text{parallel sides}}$ × $\dfrac{\text{distance}}{\text{between them}}$ $A = \frac{1}{2}(a + b) \times h_v$
(vertical height)

(This one's on the formula sheet —
but you should learn it anyway.)

Split **Composite Shapes** into **Easier Shapes**

<u>Composite shapes</u> are made up of different shapes <u>stuck together</u>. Finding their area is actually fairly
easy — just <u>split them up</u> into <u>separate shapes</u>, work out the area of each bit, then add them up.

EXAMPLE: **Lotte is painting one wall of her loft bedroom, with
dimensions as shown on the diagram. One pot of paint
will cover 1.9 m². How many pots of paint will she need?**

You need to work out the <u>area</u> of the wall — so split
it into two shapes (a <u>rectangle</u> and a <u>trapezium</u>):

1) Find the area of the rectangle:
   Area = l × w = 6 × 0.75 = 4.5 m²

2) Find the area of the trapezium (using the formula above):
   Area = $\frac{1}{2}$(a + b) × h = $\frac{1}{2}$(6 + 2) × 1.25 = 5 m²

So the <u>total area</u> of the wall is 4.5 m² + 5 m² = 9.5 m²
Each pot covers 1.9 m², so Lotte will need 9.5 ÷ 1.9 = **5 pots of paint**

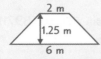

Did I say already — you must learn these formulas
Not much to say about this page really — LEARN the formulas and practise using them.

Areas

Some more <u>formulas</u> to learn — this time all about the different parts of <u>circles</u>.

Area and Circumference of Circles

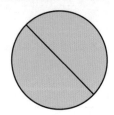

<u>Area of circle</u> = π × (radius)²
Remember that the <u>radius</u> is <u>half</u> the <u>diameter</u>.

$A = \pi r^2$

For these formulas, use the π button on your calculator (unless the question tells you otherwise).

<u>Circumference</u> = π × diameter
= 2 × π × radius

$C = \pi D = 2\pi r$

Remember, a <u>semicircle</u> is <u>half</u> a circle, so the <u>area</u> of a semicircle is just <u>half the area</u> of the <u>whole circle</u>.

Areas of Sectors and Segments

These next ones are a bit more tricky — before you try and <u>learn</u> the <u>formulas</u>, make sure you know what a <u>sector</u>, an <u>arc</u> and a <u>segment</u> are (I've helpfully labelled the diagrams below — I'm nice like that).

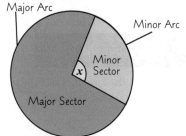

Area of sector $= \dfrac{x}{360} \times$ **Area of full Circle**

Length of arc $= \dfrac{x}{360} \times$ **Circumference of full Circle**

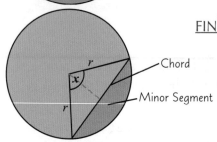

<u>FINDING THE AREA OF A SEGMENT</u> is OK if you know the formulas.

1) Find the <u>area of the sector</u> using the above formula.

2) Find the area of the triangle, then <u>subtract it</u> from the sector's area. You can do this using the $\frac{1}{2}ab\sin C$ formula for the area of the triangle (see previous page), which becomes: $\frac{1}{2}r^2\sin x$.

EXAMPLE: **Find the area of the shaded segment in the diagram on the right. The circle has radius 3 cm and the sector angle is 60°. Give your answer to 3 significant figures.**

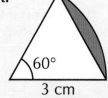

First, find the area of the <u>whole sector</u>:

area of sector $= \dfrac{x}{360} \times \pi r^2 = \dfrac{60}{360} \times \pi \times 3^2 = \dfrac{1}{6} \times \pi \times 9 = \dfrac{3}{2}\pi$ cm²

Then find the area of the <u>triangle</u>: area of triangle $= \frac{1}{2}r^2\sin x = \frac{1}{2} \times 3^2 \times \sin 60° = 3.897114...$ cm²

Finally, <u>subtract</u> the area of the triangle from the area of the sector:

$\frac{3}{2}\pi - 3.897114... = 0.815274... = 0.815$ cm² (3 s.f.)

Four more lovely formulas for you to learn

One more thing — if you're asked to find the perimeter of a semicircle or quarter circle, don't forget to add on the straight edges too. It's an easy mistake to make, and it'll cost you marks.

Surface Area and Nets

It's time now to move on to the next <u>dimension</u> — yep, that's right, <u>3D shapes</u>.

Nets

A <u>net</u> is just a hollow <u>3D shape</u> folded out flat.
Here are the nets of some <u>common shapes</u> — make sure you can recognise them.

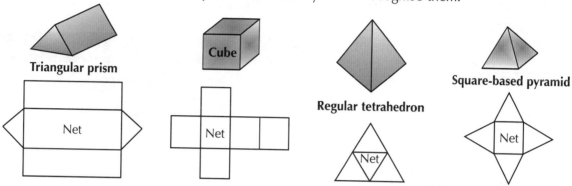

Triangular prism

Net

Cube

Net

Regular tetrahedron

Net

Square-based pyramid

Net

Note that these are just <u>some</u> of the nets for these shapes — there are <u>many other nets</u>
that will produce the <u>same shapes</u> (particularly for a cube).

Surface Area

1) <u>SURFACE AREA</u> only applies to solid 3D objects — it's simply the <u>total area</u> of all the <u>faces</u> added together.
2) <u>SURFACE AREA OF SOLID = AREA OF NET</u>. So if it helps, imagine the net and add up the area of <u>each bit</u>.
3) There's a formula for the surface area of a <u>CYLINDER</u>:

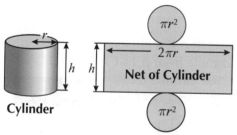

πr^2

$2\pi r$

Net of Cylinder

πr^2

Cylinder

Surface area of a CYLINDER $= 2\pi rh + 2\pi r^2$

Note that the <u>length of the rectangle</u> is equal
to the <u>circumference</u> of the circular ends.

4) <u>SPHERES</u> and <u>CONES</u> have their own surface area formulas too:

Surface area of a SPHERE $= 4\pi r^2$

curved area of cone
(*l* is the slant height)

area of
circular base

Surface area of a CONE $= \pi rl + \pi r^2$

EXAMPLE: **Find the exact surface area of a hemisphere with radius 4 cm.**

A hemisphere is <u>half a sphere</u> — so the surface area of the
<u>curved face</u> is $4\pi r^2 \div 2 = 2\pi r^2 = 2 \times \pi \times 4^2 = 32\pi$ cm^2.

Don't forget the area of the <u>flat face</u> though — this is just
the area of a <u>circle</u> with radius 4 cm: $\pi r^2 = 16\pi$ cm^2.

So the <u>total surface area</u> is $32\pi + 16\pi = 48\pi$ cm^2.

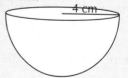

4 cm

You're asked for the exact value, so
leave your answer in terms of π.

To find the surface area of a solid, just add up the areas of each face

In a net all the faces are folded out flat — which makes it easier to see the shapes you're dealing with.

Volume

...whole pages on the volumes of 3D shapes. You might see the ...d CAPACITY used in exam questions — it just means the same as volume.

Volumes of Cuboids

A cuboid is a rectangular block. Finding its volume is easy:

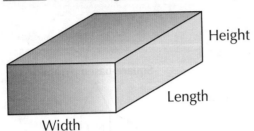

Height
Length
Width

Volume of Cuboid = Length × Width × Height

$$V = L \times W \times H$$

Volumes of Prisms

A PRISM is a solid (3D) object which is the same shape all the way through — i.e. it has a CONSTANT AREA OF CROSS-SECTION.

The cross-section is the shape you get if you slice a solid along its length.

VOLUME OF PRISM = CROSS-SECTIONAL AREA × LENGTH

$$V = A \times L$$

Triangular Prism

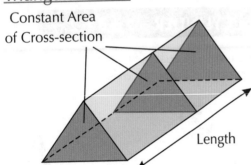

Constant Area of Cross-section

Length

Cylinder

Here the cross-section is a circle. So, using the formula from p.134 to find its area, the formula for the volume of a cylinder becomes:

$$V = \pi r^2 h$$

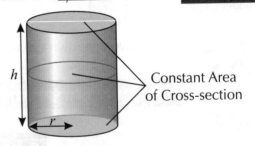

h

r

Constant Area of Cross-section

EXAMPLE: Honey comes in cylindrical jars with radius 4.5 cm and height 12 cm. 1 cm³ of honey weighs 1.4 g. Work out the mass of honey in this jar to 3 s.f.

First, work out the volume of the jar — just use the formula above:

$V = \pi r^2 h = \pi \times 4.5^2 \times 12 = 763.41$ cm³

1 cm³ of honey weighs 1.4 g, so multiply the volume by 1.4:

mass of honey = 1.4 × 763.41 = 1068.8 = **1070 g** (3 s.f.)

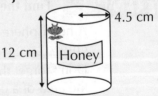

4.5 cm
12 cm
Honey

You have to remember what a prism is

It's the constant cross-section which is important — that's what makes a prism a prism.
If you remember that, it makes perfect sense that to get the volume you just multiply that area by the length.

Volume

Another page on volumes — this time it's <u>spheres</u> and <u>cones</u>.

Volumes of **Spheres**

VOLUME OF SPHERE $= \frac{4}{3}\pi r^3$

A <u>hemisphere</u> is half a sphere. So the volume of a hemisphere is just half the volume of a full sphere: $\boxed{V = \frac{2}{3}\pi r^3}$

 A sphere has radius 7 cm. Calculate its volume.

1) Write down the <u>formula</u>: $\text{Volume} = \frac{4}{3} \times \pi r^3$

2) Put in the <u>numbers</u>: $= \frac{4}{3} \times \pi \times 7^3 = 1436.8 \text{ cm}^3 \text{ (to 1 d.p.)}$

Volumes of **Cones**

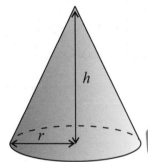

VOLUME OF CONE $= \frac{1}{3} \times \pi r^2 \times h_v$

Make sure you use the <u>vertical</u> (<u>perpendicular</u>) <u>height</u> — don't get confused with the <u>slant height</u>, which you used to find the <u>surface area</u> of a cone.

 A cone has a vertical height of 20 cm. Its volume is 170 cm³. Find the radius of the cone.

1) Write down the <u>formula</u>: $\text{Volume} = \frac{1}{3} \times \pi r^2 \times h_v$

2) Put in the <u>numbers</u>: $170 = \frac{1}{3} \times \pi r^2 \times 20$

3) <u>Rearrange</u> to find r: $r = \sqrt{\dfrac{170 \times 3}{20\pi}}$

$= 2.8 \text{ cm (to 1 d.p.)}$

 A cone and a sphere both have a radius of 9 cm. Their volumes are the same. Find the vertical height, h, of the cone.

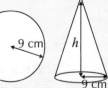

1) Substitute into the formula for the <u>sphere</u>: $\frac{4}{3}\pi r^3 = \frac{4}{3} \times \pi \times 9^3 = 972\pi$

2) Substitute into the formula for the <u>cone</u>: $\frac{1}{3}\pi r^2 h = \frac{1}{3} \times \pi \times 9^2 \times h = 27\pi h$

3) The volumes are the same so <u>set them equal</u> to each other: $972\pi = 27\pi h$

4) <u>Rearrange</u> to find h. $h = \frac{972\pi}{27\pi} = 36 \text{ cm}$

It's vertical height for the volume of a cone — not the slant height

These formulas are pretty tricky but thankfully you don't need to memorise them — they'll be given to you on your formula sheet. You just need to make sure you know how to substitute into them.

Warm-Up and Worked Exam Questions

There are lots of formulas in this section. The best way to see what you know is to practise these questions.

Warm-Up Questions

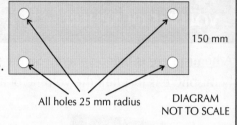

300 mm

150 mm

All holes 25 mm radius

DIAGRAM NOT TO SCALE

1) A woodworking template has the shape shown here.
   a) Calculate the exact area of one of the round holes.
   b) Use this to calculate the exact area of the template.
   c) If the template is 4 mm thick, calculate its exact volume.

2) a) The net of a regular tetrahedron consists of
      four equilateral triangles. Which of the shapes
      below could be this net?

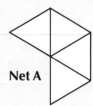

Net A

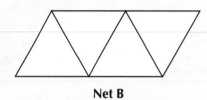

Net B

   b) Each triangle has base *b* and perpendicular height *h*. Find a simplified
      expression for the surface area of the tetrahedron in terms of *b* and *h*.

3) Calculate the volume of the triangular prism on the right.

4) Calculate the volume of a sphere with a radius of 7 metres.
   Give your answer to 3 s.f.

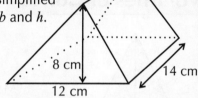

8 cm

12 cm

14 cm

Worked Exam Questions

Take a look at this worked exam question — it'll help you to prepare for the real exam:

1   Look at the sector shown in the diagram below.

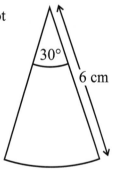

Diagram not
accurately
drawn

30°

6 cm

Find the perimeter and the area of the sector.
Give your answers to 3 significant figures.

Circumference of full circle = 2 × π × 6
                             = 12π cm

Length of arc = (30° ÷ 360°) × circumference of circle
              = (30° ÷ 360°) × 12π = π cm

Perimeter of sector = π + 6 + 6 = 15.1 cm (3 s.f.)

Area of full circle = π × 6² = 36π cm²
Area of sector = (30° ÷ 360°) × area of circle
               = (30° ÷ 360°) × 36π = 3π cm²
               = 9.42 cm² (3 s.f.)

Perimeter = ...15.1........ cm

Area = ...9.42........ cm²

[5 marks]

Exam Questions

2   The triangle and rectangle shown on the right have the same area. Find the value of x.

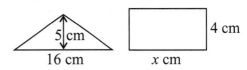

x = ...
[4 marks]

3   The diagram shows Amy's new paddling pool. It has a diameter of 2 metres, and is 40 cm high.

The instructions that came with the pool say that it should only be filled three-quarters full.

What is the maximum volume of water that Amy can put in the pool? Give your answer to 2 decimal places.

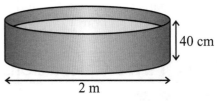

Diagram not accurately drawn

.... m³
[3 marks]

4   The circle below has a radius of 12 cm. The sector S has a central angle of 50°. Find the area of the sector S of the circle. Give your answer to 3 significant figures.

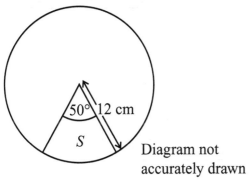

Diagram not accurately drawn

.... cm²
[3 marks]

5   The curved surface of a cone is made from the net below. The cone has a circular base. Calculate the total surface area of the cone. Give your answer in terms of π.

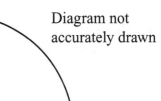

Diagram not accurately drawn

16 cm

.... cm²
[5 marks]

Time

Make sure you can handle <u>time questions</u> — they're <u>simple</u> and might grab you a mark or two in the exam.

<u>am</u> means <u>morning</u>

<u>pm</u> means <u>afternoon or evening</u>

<u>12 am</u> (<u>00:00</u>) means <u>midnight</u>

<u>12 pm</u> (<u>12:00</u>) means <u>noon</u>

12-hour clock	24-hour clock
12.00 am	00:00
1.12 am	01:12
12.15 pm	12:15
1.47 pm	13:47
11.32 pm	23:32

The hour parts of times on 12- and 24-hour clocks are <u>different after 1 pm</u>:
<u>add 12 hours</u> to go from <u>12-hour to 24-hour</u>, and subtract 12 to go the other way.

3.24 pm $\xrightarrow{+ 12\ h}$ 15:24 $\xleftarrow{- 12\ h}$

Break **Time** Calculations into **Simple Stages**

GRADE 1

EXAMPLE:

Angela watched a film that started at 7.20 pm and finished at 10.05 pm. How long was the film in minutes?

1) Split the time between 7.20 pm and 10.05 pm into <u>simple stages</u>.

7.20 pm $\xrightarrow{+ 2\ hours}$ 9.20 pm $\xrightarrow{+ 40\ minutes}$ 10.00 pm $\xrightarrow{+ 5\ minutes}$ 10.05 pm

2) <u>Convert</u> the hours to minutes.   2 hours = 2 × 60 = 120 minutes

3) <u>Add</u> to get the total minutes.   120 + 40 + 5 = 165 minutes

<u>Avoid calculators</u> — the decimal answers they give are confusing, e.g. <u>2.5 hours = 2 hours 30 mins</u>, NOT 2 hours 50 mins.

Timetable Exam Questions

GRADE 2

EXAMPLE:

Use the timetable to answer these questions:

a) How long does it take for the bus to get from Market Street to the hospital?

Bus Timetable					
Bus Station	18 45	19 00	19 15	19 30
Market Street	18 52	19 07	19 22	19 37
Long Lane Shops	19 01	19 16	19 31	19 46
Train Station	19 11	19 26	19 41	19 56
Hospital	19 23	19 38	19 53	20 08

Read times from the <u>same column</u> (I've used the 1st) — break the <u>time</u> into <u>stages</u>.

Market Street   Hospital

18 52 $\xrightarrow{+ 8\ mins}$ 19 00 $\xrightarrow{+ 23\ mins}$ 19 23

8 + 23 = 31 minutes

b) Henriette wants to get a bus from the bus station to the train station in time for a train that leaves at 19:30. What is the latest bus that she can catch?

1) Read along the <u>train station</u> row.   19 11   (19 26)   19 41   19 56

This is the latest time she could arrive before 19 30.

2) Move up this column to the <u>bus station</u> row and read off the entry.

The bus that gets to the train station at 19 26 leaves the bus station at **19 00**.

This page might look easy, but make sure you learn it all

It's easy to go wrong when you're using your calculator for time questions, so be extra careful. Always try to split questions down into easier stages — that way you'll make fewer mistakes.

Speed, Density and Pressure

Speed, density and pressure. Just a matter of <u>learning the formulas</u>, plugging in the <u>numbers</u> and watching <u>units</u>.

Speed = Distance ÷ Time

Speed is the <u>distance travelled per unit time</u>, e.g. the number of <u>km per hour</u> or <u>metres per second</u>.

$$\text{SPEED} = \frac{\text{DISTANCE}}{\text{TIME}} \qquad \text{TIME} = \frac{\text{DISTANCE}}{\text{SPEED}} \qquad \text{DISTANCE} = \text{SPEED} \times \text{TIME}$$

<u>Formula triangles</u> are a handy tool for remembering formulas like these. The speed one is shown below.

How do you use formula triangles?
1) <u>COVER UP</u> the thing you want to find and <u>WRITE DOWN</u> what's left showing.
2) Now <u>PUT IN THE VALUES</u> and <u>CALCULATE</u> — check the <u>UNITS</u> in your answer.

EXAMPLE: A tractor travels 9 kilometres at 36 kilometres per hour. How many minutes does it take?

Write down the <u>formula</u>, put in the values and <u>calculate</u>:
$$\text{time} = \frac{\text{distance}}{\text{speed}} = \frac{9 \text{ kilometres}}{36 \text{ kph}} = 0.25 \text{ hours} = 15 \text{ minutes}$$

Density = Mass ÷ Volume

Density is the <u>mass per unit volume</u> of a substance. It's usually measured in <u>kg/m³</u> or <u>g/cm³</u>.

$$\text{DENSITY} = \frac{\text{MASS}}{\text{VOLUME}} \qquad \text{VOLUME} = \frac{\text{MASS}}{\text{DENSITY}} \qquad \text{MASS} = \text{DENSITY} \times \text{VOLUME}$$

EXAMPLE: A giant 'Wunda-Choc' bar has a density of 1.3 g/cm³. If the bar's volume is 1800 cm³, what is the mass of the bar in kg?

Write down the <u>formula</u>, put in the values and <u>calculate</u>:
mass = density × volume
= 1.3 g/cm³ × 1800 cm³ = 2340 g
= 2.34 kg

Check your units match — if the density is in g/cm³, the volume must be in cm³ and you'll get a mass in g.

Pressure = Force ÷ Area

'N' stands for 'Newtons'.

Pressure is the amount of <u>force acting per unit area</u>. It's usually measured in <u>N/m²</u>, or pascals (Pa).

$$\text{PRESSURE} = \frac{\text{FORCE}}{\text{AREA}} \qquad \text{AREA} = \frac{\text{FORCE}}{\text{PRESSURE}} \qquad \text{FORCE} = \text{PRESSURE} \times \text{AREA}$$

EXAMPLE: A cylindrical barrel with a weight of 200 N rests on horizontal ground. The radius of the circular face resting on the ground is 0.4 m. Calculate the pressure exerted by the barrel on the ground to 1 d.p.

Work out the area of the circular face: $\pi \times 0.4^2 = 0.5026... \text{ m}^2$

Write down the pressure <u>formula</u>, put in the values and <u>calculate</u>:
$$\text{pressure} = \frac{\text{force}}{\text{area}} = \frac{200 \text{ N}}{0.5026... \text{ m}^2} = 397.8873... \text{ N/m}^2$$
$$= 397.9 \text{ N/m}^2 \text{ (1 d.p.)}$$

Formula triangles are really useful

Cover up the thing you want to find, then write down what's left on show. Put in the values and out pops your answer. Make sure that the units make sense — you won't get a distance in ms².

Distance-Time Graphs

Distance-time graphs just show how <u>distance changes over time</u>.

Distance-Time Graphs

Distance-time graphs are pretty common in exams.
They're not too bad once you get your head around them.

Just remember these 4 important points:

1) At any point, <u>GRADIENT = SPEED</u>, but watch out for the UNITS.

2) The <u>STEEPER</u> the graph, the <u>FASTER</u> it's going.

3) <u>FLAT SECTIONS</u> are where it is <u>STOPPED</u>.

4) If the gradient's negative, it's <u>COMING BACK</u>.

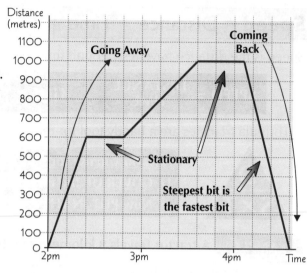

EXAMPLE: Hoshi went out for a ride on her bike. After a while she got a puncture and stopped to fix it. This graph shows the first part of Hoshi's journey.

a) **What time did Hoshi leave home?**

She left home at the point where the line <u>starts</u>.   At 8:15

b) **How far did Hoshi cycle before getting a puncture?**

The <u>horizontal</u> part of the graph is where Hoshi <u>stopped</u>.

12 km

c) **What was Hoshi's speed before getting a puncture?**

Using the speed formula is the same as finding the <u>gradient</u>.

$$\text{speed} = \frac{\text{distance}}{\text{time}} = \frac{12 \text{ km}}{0.5 \text{ hours}}$$
$$= 24 \text{ km/h}$$

d) **At 9:30 Hoshi turns round and cycles home at 24 km/h. Complete the graph to show this.**

You have to work out how long it will take Hoshi to cycle the 18 km home:

$$\text{time} = \frac{\text{distance}}{\text{speed}} = \frac{18 \text{ km}}{24 \text{ km/h}} = 0.75 \text{ hours}$$

$0.75 \times 60 \text{ mins} = 45 \text{ mins}$

It's usually best to avoid decimal times. In this case, convert it to <u>minutes</u>.

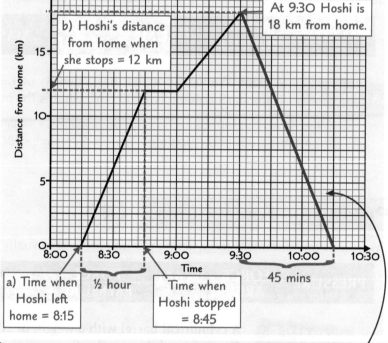

45 minutes after 9:30 is 10:15, so that's the time Hoshi gets home. Now you can complete the graph.

The gradient of a distance-time graph = speed

Have a quick look at the axes before starting questions like this. Once you notice that it's a plain old distance-time graph, use the 4 key points from the blue box. Practise that speed formula too — see p.141.

Speed-Time Graphs

This page <u>looks</u> pretty much the same as the last page — but there are some huge differences.

Speed-Time Graphs

1) At any point, <u>GRADIENT = ACCELERATION</u>.
2) <u>NEGATIVE SLOPE</u> is <u>DECELERATION</u> (slowing down).
3) <u>FLAT SECTIONS</u> are <u>STEADY SPEED</u>.
4) <u>AREA UNDER GRAPH = DISTANCE TRAVELLED</u>.

The <u>units of acceleration</u> equal the <u>speed units per the time units</u>.

For speed in m/s and time in seconds the units of acceleration are m/s per s — this is written as <u>m/s^2</u>.

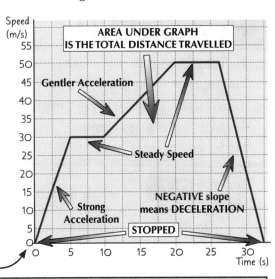

This graph is exactly the same shape as the one on page 142, but it means something completely different. The D/T graph showed something <u>moving away</u> and then <u>back again</u> with <u>steady speeds</u> and <u>long stops</u>, rather like an ocean liner. The <u>S/T graph</u> on the other hand shows something that sets off from <u>rest</u>, <u>accelerates strongly</u>, <u>holds its speed</u>, then <u>accelerates</u> again up to a <u>maximum speed</u> which it holds for a while, and then comes to a <u>dramatic halt</u> at the end. It's more like a <u>sports car</u> than an ocean liner.

EXAMPLE: The graph below shows the speed of a car as it travelled between two sets of traffic lights.

a) **What was the car's initial acceleration?**

The <u>gradient</u> of the first section of the graph gives the initial <u>acceleration</u>.

$$\text{gradient} = \frac{\text{change in speed}}{\text{change in time}}$$

$$= \frac{10 \text{ m/s}}{2.5 \text{ s}}$$

$$= 4 \text{ m/s}^2$$

b) **After how many seconds did the car stop accelerating?**

The <u>horizontal</u> part of the graph shows the car travelling at a <u>constant speed</u>.

7.5 s

c) **How far did the car travel at a constant speed?**

The <u>area</u> under the horizontal section of the graph gives the <u>distance</u> travelled at constant speed.

area = 2.5 × 12.5 = 31.25 m

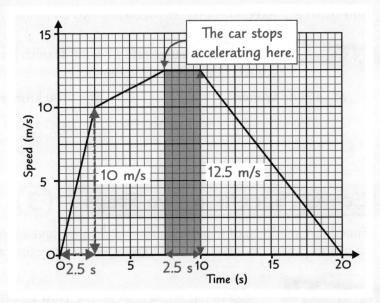

d) **For how long was the car decelerating?**

The car's speed starts to <u>decrease</u> after 10 s, and it comes to a stop after 20s.

deceleration time = 20 − 10 = 10 s

The gradient of a speed-time graph = acceleration

It's easy to get these mixed up with distance-time graphs, so make sure you check the axes. Here the area under the graph is the distance travelled, and the gradient at any point is the acceleration.

Unit Conversions

A nice easy page for a change — just some <u>facts</u> to learn. Oh, and you need to know how to <u>use them</u>.

Metric Units

1) <u>Length</u>   mm, cm, m, km
2) <u>Area</u> mm^2, cm^2, m^2, km^2,
3) <u>Volume</u> mm^3, cm^3, m^3, ml, litres
4) <u>Mass</u>   g, kg, tonnes
5) <u>Speed</u>   km/h, m/s

COMMON UNIT CONVERSIONS

1 cm = 10 mm	1 tonne = 1000 kg
1 m = 100 cm	1 litre = 1000 ml
1 km = 1000 m	1 litre = 1000 cm^3
1 kg = 1000 g	1 cm^3 = 1 ml

EXAMPLE: **A whale is 18.6 m in length. How long is this in mm?**

Do this conversion in two steps — metres to cm then cm to mm.

1) Write down the <u>first conversion factor</u>.   1 m = 100 cm

2) <u>Multiply</u> the number of metres by 100.   18.6 × 100 = 1860 cm

3) Write down the <u>second conversion factor</u>.   1 cm = 10 mm

4) <u>Multiply</u> the number of cm by 10.   1860 × 10 = 18 600 mm

> Always check your answer is sensible. E.g. 1 m = 100 cm, so when you convert from m to cm you should get a bigger number.

Currency Conversions

You could get asked to convert between any two currencies, but you'll be given the conversion factor.

EXAMPLE: **Using the exchange rate £1 = 8.8 Danish kroner, convert the following amounts:**

a) £75 to kroner.

£75 = 75 × 8.8 = 660 kroner

b) 1100 kroner to pounds.

1100 kroner = 1100 ÷ 8.8 = £125

> Check your answers — £1 = 8.8 kroner, so the number of kroner should always be bigger than the equivalent number of pounds.

Convert Speeds in Two Steps

Speeds are made up of <u>two measures</u> — a <u>distance</u> and a <u>time</u>. To convert from, say, km per hour to metres per second, you have to convert the distance unit and the time unit <u>separately</u>.

EXAMPLE: **A rabbit's top speed is 56 km/h. How fast is this in m/s?**

First convert from km/h to m/h: 56 km/h = (56 × 1000) m/h = 56 000 m/h

Now convert from m/h to m/s: 56 000 m/h = (56 000 ÷ 3600) m/s
                                 = 15.6 m/s (1 d.p.)

> 1 minute = 60 seconds and 1 hour = 60 minutes. So 1 hour = 60 × 60 = <u>3600</u> seconds.

There's no way round it — you'll have to learn some conversions

There are a lot of conversions here, and you'll need to remember all of those metric unit conversions (you'll be given currency conversion factors so don't worry about that). Keep going until you've learned them all.

Unit Conversions

Converting areas and volumes from one unit to another is an exam disaster that you have to know how to avoid. 1 m² definitely does <u>NOT</u> equal 100 cm². Remember this and read on for why.

Converting **Area** and **Volume** Measurements

$$1 \text{ m}^2 = 100 \text{ cm} \times 100 \text{ cm} = 10\ 000 \text{ cm}^2$$
$$1 \text{ cm}^2 = 10 \text{ mm} \times 10 \text{ mm} = 100 \text{ mm}^2$$

$$1 \text{ m}^3 = 100 \text{ cm} \times 100 \text{ cm} \times 100 \text{ cm} = 1\ 000\ 000 \text{ cm}^3$$
$$1 \text{ cm}^3 = 10 \text{ mm} \times 10 \text{ mm} \times 10 \text{ mm} = 1000 \text{ mm}^3$$

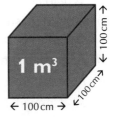

EXAMPLES:

1. Convert 9 m² to cm².

To change area measurements from m² to cm² multiply by 100 twice.

$$9 \times 100 \times 100 = 90\ 000 \text{ cm}^2$$

2. Convert 60 000 mm³ to cm³.

To change volume measurements from mm³ to cm³ divide by 10 three times.

$$60\ 000 \div (10 \times 10 \times 10) = 60 \text{ cm}^3$$

Conversion Graphs

Conversion graphs themselves are <u>easy</u> to use.

EXAMPLES:

1. Lucas goes to Florida and spends \$36 on a toy alligator. Use the graph to find what this is in pounds.

1) <u>Draw a line</u> from a value on <u>one axis.</u>
   Start from \$36 on the horizontal axis.

2) Keep going until you <u>hit the LINE.</u>

3) Then <u>change direction</u> and go straight to <u>the other axis.</u>

4) <u>Read off the value</u> from this axis. The two values are <u>equivalent.</u>

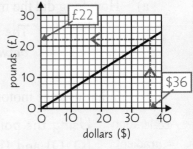

You end up at £22 on the vertical axis, so \$36 is equivalent to £22.

2. Draw a graph to convert between pounds and Russian roubles, given that £1 = 45 roubles.

1) Work out <u>3 pairs of values.</u>

You're told £1 = 45 roubles. It's easy to work out that £2 = 90 roubles, and £4 = 180 roubles.

2) <u>Plot</u> these points <u>accurately</u> and <u>draw a line</u> through them.

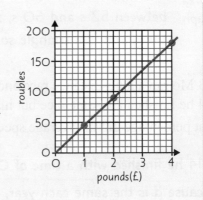

Conversion graphs are always straight lines

It's easy to make mistakes when converting the units for area or volume. You need to convert <u>all</u> of the dimensions, so multiply or divide by the length conversion factor twice for areas and three times for volumes.

Warm-Up and Worked Exam Questions

Time to check all that lovely revision has sunk in. Try these first to make sure you've learnt the key stuff:

Warm-Up Questions

1) A train leaves at 9.37 am and arrives at 11.16 am. How long is the train journey in minutes?

2) A lump of lead weighing 374 g has a volume of 33 cm³.
   What is the approximate density of the lead (to 3 s.f.)?

3) A solid plastic building block measures 5 cm × 4 cm × 6 cm.
   The density of the plastic is 0.8 g/cm³. What is the mass of the block?

4) A cheetah runs 100 m in 4 seconds. What is its average speed in km per hour?

5) A cyclist travels for 0.75 hours at a speed of 12 km per hour. What distance does he travel?

6) a) Convert 12.7 kg into grams.   b) Convert 1430 cm into metres.

7) Change 3 m³ to mm³.

Worked Exam Questions

Make sure you really take this stuff in — read it thoroughly and then have a go yourself to check you've understood. You'll kick yourself if this comes up in the exam and you only gave it a quick glance.

1   The speed of a motorcycle is recorded over a minute.
    The speed-time graph on the right shows the results.

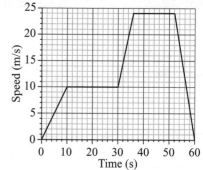

   a)   How long did the motorbike travel at a constant speed
        of 10 m/s?   The speed is 10 m/s
                      between 10 s and 30 s.   ....20.... s
                                                    [1 mark]

   b)   What was the motorbike's initial acceleration?

Acceleration   Using the points
= gradient   (0, 0) and (10, 10):   Gradient = $\frac{\text{change in } y}{\text{change in } x} = \frac{10 - 0}{10 - 0} = 1$ ....1.... m/s²
                                                                                                                    [2 marks]

   c)   How far did the motorbike travel while it was decelerating at the end of the journey?

Distance = area   The motorbike is decelerating from a speed of 24 m/s to 0 m/s
under the graph   between 52 s and 60 s, so for 8 s. The area beneath this part of
                   the graph is a triangle so: distance = area = $\frac{1}{2}$ × 8 × 24 = 96 m   ....96.... m
                                                                                                   [2 marks]

2   In 2013 Mo ran a long-distance race and finished with time t.
    In 2014 he finished the same race but his time was 10% quicker.

    By what percentage did his average speed for the race increase? Give your answer to 2 d.p.

In 2014 he finished with a time of 0.9t, so $s_1 = \frac{d}{t}$ and $s_2 = \frac{d}{0.9t}$ s_1 is Mo's
                                                                                                      speed in 2013
So, because d is the same each year, $s_1 t = 0.9 s_2 t \rightarrow s_2 = \frac{s_1}{0.9} = 1.11... \times s_1$ and s_2 is Mo's
                                                                                                      speed in 2014
So s_2 is 111.11... % of s_1.

His percentage increase was 11.11% (2 d.p.)   ....11.11.... %
                                                                                                      [4 marks]

Exam Questions

3   The distance-time graphs shows Selby's bike ride from **(3)** his house (**A**) to the zoo, which is 25 km away.

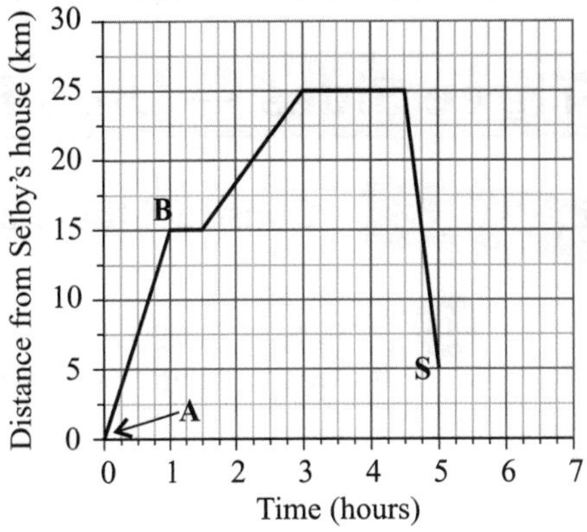

a)   After one hour Selby stops at a bench (**B**) to get his breath back. Find the gradient of the line between point **A** and point **B**.

....

[2 marks]

b)   What does the gradient of the line between point **A** and point **B** represent?

....

[1 mark]

c)   After the zoo, Selby stopped at the shops (**S**) for 30 minutes before cycling straight home. Given that he arrived home 7 hours after he first left, complete the graph above.

[2 marks]

4   The mass of a metal statue is 360 kg. **(4)**
The density of the metal alloy from which it is made is 1800 kg/m^3.

a)   Calculate the volume of the statue.

.... m^3

[2 marks]

b)   A new statue is made that has the same mass as the old one but a volume of 80 000 cm^3. Calculate the density of the new statue in kg/m^3.

.... kg/m^3

[3 marks]

5   The cone below has a base diameter of $20x$ cm. When the base of **(6)** the cone rests on horizontal ground it exerts a pressure of 650 N/m^2.

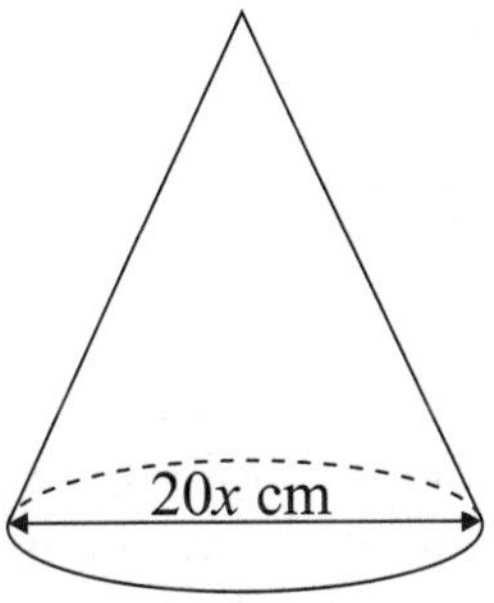

a)   Calculate the weight of the cone in terms of x and π.

.... N

[4 marks]

b)   The diameter of the cone is halved but the weight is kept the same. What effect will this have on the pressure exerted on the ground?

....

[2 marks]

Triangle Construction

How you construct a triangle depends on <u>what info you're given</u> about the triangle...

Three Sides — Use a **Ruler and Compasses**

EXAMPLE: **Construct the triangle ABC where AB = 6 cm, BC = 4 cm, AC = 5 cm.**

① First, <u>sketch and label</u> a triangle so you know roughly what's needed. It doesn't matter which line you make the baseline.

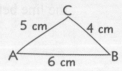

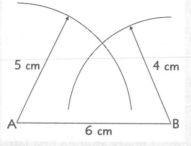

② Draw the <u>baseline</u>. <u>Label</u> the ends A and B.

③ For AC, set the <u>compasses</u> to <u>5 cm</u>, put the point at A and <u>draw an arc</u>. For BC, set the compasses to <u>4 cm</u>, put the point at B and <u>draw an arc</u>.

④ Where the <u>arcs cross</u> is <u>point C</u>. Now you can finish your triangle.

Sides and Angles — Use a **Ruler and Protractor**

EXAMPLE: **Construct triangle DEF, where DE = 5 cm, DF = 3 cm and angle EDF = 40°.**

① <u>Roughly sketch and label</u> the triangle.

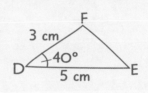

See p.116 if you're unsure how this notation works.

② Draw the <u>baseline</u>.

③ Draw <u>angle EDF</u> (the angle at D) — place the centre of the protractor over D, measure <u>40°</u> and put a dot.

④ Measure <u>3 cm</u> towards the dot and label it F. Join up <u>D and F</u>. Now you've drawn the <u>two sides</u> and the <u>angle</u>. Just join up F and E to <u>complete</u> the triangle.

Don't forget your compasses and protractor for the exam

Constructing a triangle isn't difficult, so long as you learn the methods on this page — and remember to take your ruler, compasses and protractor with you into the exam. You won't get far without them.

Constructions

Don't put your compasses away just yet. There's another page on constructions coming up.
The only way to master them is to practise lots and lots.

Constructing Accurate 90° Angles

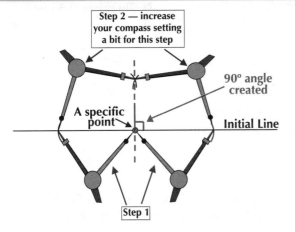

Step 2 — increase your compass setting a bit for this step

A specific point

90° angle created

Initial Line

Step 1

1) Being able to draw <u>accurate 90° angles</u> comes in handy for drawing squares or rectangles.

2) Make sure you can <u>follow the method</u> shown in this diagram.

> The examiners <u>WON'T</u> accept any of these constructions done 'by eye' or with a protractor. You've got to do them the <u>PROPER WAY</u>, with <u>compasses</u>.
> <u>DON'T</u> rub out your compass marks, or the examiner won't know you used the proper method.

Constructing Angle Bisectors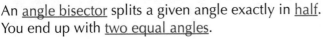

An <u>angle bisector</u> splits a given angle exactly in <u>half</u>. You end up with <u>two equal angles</u>.

1) Keep the compass setting <u>THE SAME</u> while you make <u>all four marks</u>.

2) Make sure you <u>leave</u> your compass marks <u>showing</u>.

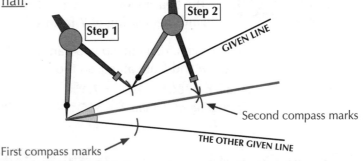

Step 1

Step 2

GIVEN LINE

Second compass marks

First compass marks

THE OTHER GIVEN LINE

Constructing Perpendicular Bisectors of Line Segments

<u>Bisecting</u> a line segment means dividing it into <u>two equal sections</u>. A <u>perpendicular</u> bisector is one that's at <u>right angles</u> to the line segment.

Here's how to draw the perpendicular bisector of <u>line segment AB</u>:

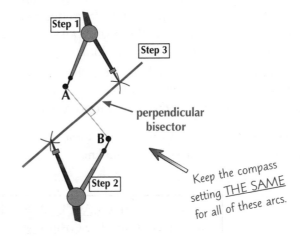

Step 1

Step 3

A

perpendicular bisector

B

Step 2

Keep the compass setting <u>THE SAME</u> for all of these arcs.

Constructions are basically tricks for maths drawings

There's nothing too 'mathsy' about this page. It's just a few simple tricks to use to draw different things accurately — it's almost art. So get it learnt quick-smart so you can get back to the maths.

Bearings

Bearings. They'll be useful next time you're off sailing. Or in your Maths exam.

Bearings

To find or plot a bearing you must remember <u>the three key words</u>:

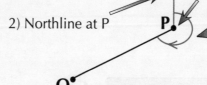

The bearing of A from B

1) 'FROM' <u>Find the word 'FROM' in the question</u>, and put your pencil on the diagram at the point you are going '<u>from</u>'.

2) NORTHLINE At the point you are going <u>FROM</u>, <u>draw in a NORTHLINE</u>. (There'll often be one drawn for you in exam questions.)

3) CLOCKWISE Now draw in the angle <u>CLOCKWISE from the northline to the line joining the two points</u>. This angle is the required bearing.

EXAMPLE: **Find the bearing of Q from P.**

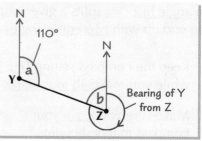

ALL BEARINGS SHOULD BE GIVEN AS 3 FIGURES
e.g. 176°, 034° (not 34°), 005° (not 5°), 018° etc.

1) 'From P'

2) Northline at P

3) <u>Clockwise</u>, from the N-line. This angle is the bearing of <u>Q from P</u>. Measure it with your protractor — 245°.

EXAMPLE: **The bearing of Z from Y is 110°. Find the bearing of Y from Z.**

See page 115 for allied angles.

First sketch a diagram so you can see what's going on. Angles *a* and *b* are <u>allied</u>, so they add up to <u>180°</u>.

Angle b = 180° − 110° = 70°
So bearing of Y from Z = 360° − 70° = 290°.

110°

N

Y *a*

b Bearing of Y from Z

Z

Bearings Questions and **Scale Drawings**

EXAMPLE: **A hiker walks 2 km from point A, on a bearing of 036°. If the scale of the map below is 2 cm to 1 km, how far is the hiker now from his car?**

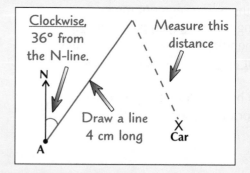

First, draw a line at a <u>bearing of 036°</u> from point A. <u>1 km</u> is <u>2 cm</u> on the map and the hiker walks <u>2 km</u>, so make the line from A <u>4 cm</u> long.

You want the distance of the hiker from the car, so use a ruler to measure it on the map, then use the scale to work out the <u>real distance</u> it represents.

Distance to car on map = 3 cm. 2 cm = 1 km, so 1 cm = 0.5 km, therefore 3 cm = 1.5 km.

Clockwise, 36° from the N-line.

N

Draw a line 4 cm long

A

Measure this distance

X Car

If you are asked to <u>CALCULATE</u> a distance or an angle, you'll need to use the <u>cosine or sine rule</u> (see p.160).

FROM a point draw a NORTHLINE then draw the angle CLOCKWISE

Make sure you've learnt the three key words above and the method for using them — scribble them out from memory to check you've got them spot on, then have a go at some questions to practise <u>using</u> them.

Warm-Up and Worked Exam Questions

You need to work through these one by one and make sure you really know what you're doing with your ruler and compasses. Look back over the last three pages if you get stuck.

Warm-Up Questions

1) Using a ruler and compasses, construct an equilateral triangle with sides of length 4 cm.
2) Construct a triangle with sides 3 cm, 4 cm and 5 cm. Check it by measuring the angles.
3) Construct four 90° angles to form a square with side length 5.5 cm.
4) Measure the bearing of T from H.

Worked Exam Questions

Two worked examples, and then it's over to you.

1 EFG is an isosceles triangle. Sides EG and FG are both 4.5 cm long.
   Side EF has been drawn here.

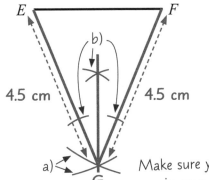

Make sure you remember to leave in your construction lines.

a) Complete the construction of triangle EFG by drawing sides EG and FG.

Use the 'three sides' method from p.148.

[2 marks]

b) Construct the bisector of angle EGF.

[2 marks]

2 A ship sails 12 km from Port P to Port Q on a bearing of 050°, then 20 km from Port Q to Port R on a bearing of 100°. It then sails directly back to Port P. Calculate the distance between Ports P and R to 1 d.p.

Start by making a sketch and labelling it.

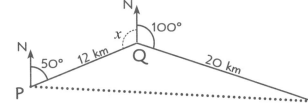

The question says 'calculate' so use one of the rules from p.160. In this case, you're interested in all three sides so use the cosine rule:
$$a^2 = b^2 + c^2 - 2bc \cos A$$

You want to know PR so you need the angle opposite this side — that's ∠PQR.

Using allied angles, angle $x = 180° - 50° = 130°$. Then, since angles around a point add up to 360°, ∠PQR = 360° - 130° - 100° = 130°.

Now use the cosine rule: $PR^2 = 12^2 + 20^2 - 2 \times 12 \times 20 \times \cos 130°$
$$= 852.538...$$

So $PR = \sqrt{852.538...} = 29.19... = 29.2$ km (1 d.p.)

............29.2.......... km
[5 marks]

Exam Questions

3   A coastguard spots a boat on a bearing of 040° and at a distance of 350 m. **(3)**
    She can also see a tree due east of her. The tree is due south of the boat.
    The coastguard's position, C, has been marked below.

a)   Draw a scale diagram of the boat and tree in relation to the coastguard.
     Label the diagram with the scale used.

[4 marks]

b)   Measure accurately the distance between:

     (i) the boat and the tree,

     .... m
     [1 mark]

N

     (ii) the coastguard and the tree.

C ●
     .... m
     [1 mark]

4   In the space below, construct a triangle which has one right angle and two angles of 45°. **(4)**
    Leave your construction marks visible.

[3 marks]

5   In kite *ABCD*, sides *AB* and *CB* are both 3 cm long and sides *AD* and *CD* are both 5 cm long.
    The shorter diagonal of the kite, *AC*, has a length of 4 cm. **(4)**
    Construct an accurate, full-size drawing of the kite and label the corners.
    Show all your construction lines.

A ——————————— *C*

[3 marks]

Revision Questions for Section Four

There are lots of opportunities to show off your artistic skills here (as long as you use them to answer the questions).
- Try these questions and <u>tick off each one</u> when you <u>get it right</u>.
- When you've done <u>all the questions</u> for a topic and are <u>completely happy</u> with it, tick off the topic.

Maps and Scale Drawings (p.113) ☑

1) How do you use a map scale to go from a real-life distance to a distance on a map, and vice versa? ☑

2) Bobby is planning the layout of a new car park for his local supermarket,
   shown on the right. Draw a plan of the car park using a scale of 1 cm = 5 m. ☑

   60 m | **Car Park**
   100 m

Angles and Polygons (p.114-118) ☑

3) What do angles in a quadrilateral add up to? ☑

4) Find the missing angles in the diagrams below. ☑

a) 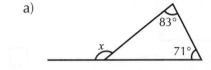   b) 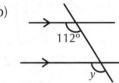   c)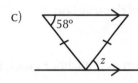

5) Find the exterior angle of a regular hexagon. ☑

6) a) How many lines of symmetry does an equilateral triangle have?
   b) What is its order of rotational symmetry? ☑

Circle Geometry (p.121-123) ☑

7) What angle is formed when a tangent meets a radius? ☑

8) Find the missing angle in each of the diagrams below. ☑

a) 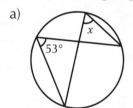   b) 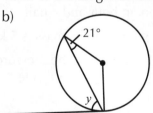   c)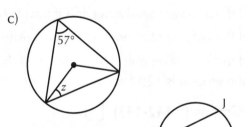

9) In the diagram, JN = 12 cm, LN = 10 cm and MN = 6 cm.
   Find the length of KN. ☑

Transformations (p.127-129) ☑

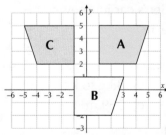

10) Describe the transformation that maps:
    a) Shape A onto Shape B
    b) Shape A onto shape C ☑

11) Carry out the following transformations on the triangle X, which has vertices (1, 1), (4, 1) and (2, 3):
    a) a rotation of 90° clockwise about (1, 1)   b) a translation by the vector $\binom{-3}{-4}$
    c) an enlargement of scale factor 2, centre (1, 1) ☑

12) A shape with area 5 cm² is enlarged by a scale factor of 4. What is the area of the enlarged shape? ☑

Congruence and Similarity (p.130) ☑

13) What are congruent and similar shapes? ☑

14) The shapes on the right are similar.
    What is the length of side x? ☑

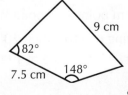

Revision Questions for Section Four

Area, Surface Area and Volume (p.133-137) ☑

15) What is the formula for finding the area of a trapezium?

16) Find the area of the shape on the right.

17) A circle has diameter 16 cm. Find its exact circumference and area.

18) Find the area of the sector with radius 10 cm and angle 45° to 2 d.p.

19) What is the formula for finding the surface area of a sphere?

20) The shape on the right is made from a cylinder and a hemisphere. Find its exact surface area.

21) Find the volume of a hexagonal prism with a cross-sectional area of 36 cm² and a length of 11 cm.

22) Find the volume of the solid on the right to 2 d.p.

Time (p.140) ☑

23) Write: a) 4.20 pm as a 24-hour clock time,   b) 07:52 as a 12-hour clock time.

24) Using the timetable, how many minutes does the journey from Edinburgh to York last for?

25) Jane lives in Berwick and needs to be in Durham by 1.30 pm.   a) What is the latest train she can catch? She lives 20 minutes' walk from the train station.
   b) What is the latest time she should leave the house?

Train Timetable	Edinburgh	11 14	11 37	12 04
	Berwick	11 55	12 18	12 45
	Newcastle	12 43	13 06	13 33
	Durham	12 57	13 20	13 47
	Darlington	13 15	13 38	14 05
	York	13 45	14 08	14 35

Speed, Density and Pressure (p.141) ☑

26) Find the average speed of a car if it travels 63 km in an hour and a half.

27) Find the volume of a snowman if its density is 0.4 g/cm³ and its mass is 5 kg.

28) Find the area of an object in contact with horizontal ground, if the pressure it exerts on the ground is 120 N/m² and the force acting on the object is 1320 N.

Travel Graphs (p.142-143) ☑

29) a) What does a horizontal line mean on a distance-time graph?
   b) What does it mean on a speed-time graph?

30) The graph on the right shows Ben's car journey. What speed did he drive home at?

Unit Conversions (p.144-145) ☑

31) Convert: a) 5.6 litres to cm³   b) 83 g to kg
            c) 3 m/s to km/h   d) 569 m² to cm²

Constructions (p.148-149) ☑

32) Construct triangle XYZ, where XY = 5.6 cm, XZ = 7.2 cm and angle YXZ = 55°.

33) Construct an accurate 90° angle. Bisect it to form two 45° angles.

34) Draw a line 6 cm long. Construct the perpendicular bisector of the line.

Bearings (p.150) ☑

35) Describe how to find a bearing from point A to point B.

36) A helicopter flies 25 km on a bearing of 210°, then 20 km on a bearing of 040°.
   Draw a scale diagram to show this. Use a scale of 1 cm = 5 km.

Pythagoras' Theorem

Pythagoras' theorem sounds hard but it's actually <u>pretty simple</u>.
It's also really important, so make sure you really get your teeth into it.

Pythagoras' Theorem — $a^2 + b^2 = c^2$

1) <u>PYTHAGORAS' THEOREM</u> only works for <u>RIGHT-ANGLED TRIANGLES</u>.

2) Pythagoras uses <u>two sides</u> to find the <u>third side</u>.

3) The <u>BASIC FORMULA</u> for Pythagoras is $a^2 + b^2 = c^2$

4) Make sure you get the numbers in the <u>RIGHT PLACE</u>. c is the <u>longest side</u> (called the hypotenuse) and it's always <u>opposite</u> the right angle.

5) Always <u>CHECK</u> that your answer is <u>SENSIBLE</u>.

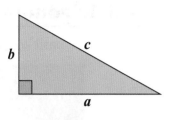

$$a^2 + b^2 = c^2$$

EXAMPLE: **ABC is a right-angled triangle. AB = 6 m and AC = 3 m. Find the exact length of BC.**

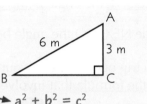

1) Write down the <u>formula</u>.

2) Put in the <u>numbers</u>.

3) <u>Rearrange</u> the equation.

4) Take <u>square roots</u> to find BC.

5) '<u>Exact length</u>' means you should give your answer as a <u>surd</u> (see p.51) — <u>simplified</u> if possible.

$a^2 + b^2 = c^2$

$BC^2 + 3^2 = 6^2$

$BC^2 = 6^2 - 3^2 = 36 - 9 = 27$

$BC = \sqrt{27} = 3\sqrt{3}$ m

It's <u>not always c</u> you need to find — loads of people go wrong here.

Remember to check the answer's <u>sensible</u> — here it's about <u>5.2</u>, which is between <u>3 and 6</u>, so that seems about right.

Use **Pythagoras** to Find the **Distance Between Points**

You need to know how to find the straight-line <u>distance</u> between <u>two points</u> on a <u>graph</u>.
If you get a question like this, follow these rules and it'll all become simple:

> 1) Draw a sketch to show the <u>right-angled triangle</u>.
> 2) Find the <u>lengths of the shorter sides</u> of the triangle.
> 3) <u>Use Pythagoras</u> to find the <u>length of the hypotenuse</u>. (That's your answer.)

EXAMPLE: **Point P has coordinates (8, 3) and point Q has coordinates (–4, 8). Find the length of the line PQ.**

1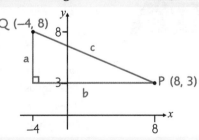

2 Length of side a = 8 – 3 = 5
Length of side b = 8 – (–4) = 12

3 Use Pythagoras to find side c:
$c^2 = a^2 + b^2 = 5^2 + 12^2 = 25 + 144 = 169$
So: $c = \sqrt{169} = 13$

Finding lengths in a right-angled triangle? Pythagoras is your man

This is probably one of the most famous of all maths formulas. It will most likely be in your exam at some point, so don't risk losing important marks — learn the formula and practise some questions.

Trigonometry — Sin, Cos and Tan

Trigonometry — it's a big scary word. It's _important_ and _always cropping up_ in exams, but if you just follow the method below it won't be a big scary topic.

The 3 Trigonometry Formulas

There are three basic _trig formulas_ — each one links _two sides and an angle_ of a _right-angled triangle_.

$$\text{Sin } x = \frac{\text{Opposite}}{\text{Hypotenuse}}$$

$$\text{Cos } x = \frac{\text{Adjacent}}{\text{Hypotenuse}}$$

$$\text{Tan } x = \frac{\text{Opposite}}{\text{Adjacent}}$$

- The _Hypotenuse_ is the _LONGEST SIDE_.

- The _Opposite_ is the side _OPPOSITE_ the angle _being used_ (x).

- The _Adjacent_ is the (other) side _NEXT TO_ the angle _being used_.

1) Whenever you come across a trig question, work out which _two sides_ of the triangle are involved in that question — then _pick the formula_ that involves those sides.

2) _To find the angle — use the inverse_, i.e. press **SHIFT** or **2ndF**, followed by _sin_, _cos_ or _tan_ (and make sure your calculator is in DEG mode) — your calculator will display $\sin^{-1}$, $\cos^{-1}$ or $\tan^{-1}$.

3) Remember, you can only use sin, cos and tan on _right-angled triangles_ — you may have to add lines to the diagram to create one.

Formula Triangles Make Things Simple

There's more about formula triangles on p.141 if you need to jog your memory.

A handy way to tackle trig questions is to convert the formulas into _formula triangles_. Then you can use the _same method every time_, no matter which side or angle is being asked for.

1) _Label_ the three sides _O, A and H_ (Opposite, Adjacent and Hypotenuse).

2) Write down _from memory_ 'SOH CAH TOA'.

3) Decide which _two sides_ are _involved_: O,H A,H or O,A and select _SOH_, _CAH_ or _TOA_ accordingly.

4) Turn the one you choose into a _FORMULA TRIANGLE_:

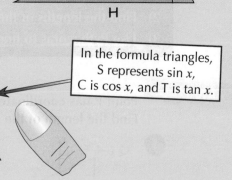

In the formula triangles, S represents sin x, C is cos x, and T is tan x.

5) _Cover up_ the thing you want to find (with your finger), and write down whatever is left showing.

6) _Translate into numbers_ and work it out.

7) Finally, _check_ that your answer is _sensible_.

If you can't make SOH CAH TOA stick, try using a mnemonic like 'Strange Orange Hamsters Creep Around Houses Tripping Over Ants'.

H = longest, O = opposite, A = next to, and remember SOH CAH TOA

You need to know this stuff off by heart — so go over this page a few times until you've got those formulas firmly lodged and all ready to reel off in the exam. All set? Good.

Trigonometry — Sin, Cos and Tan

Here are some lovely examples using the method from the previous page to help you through the trials of trig.

Examples:

1 Find the length of x in the triangle shown to 3 s.f.

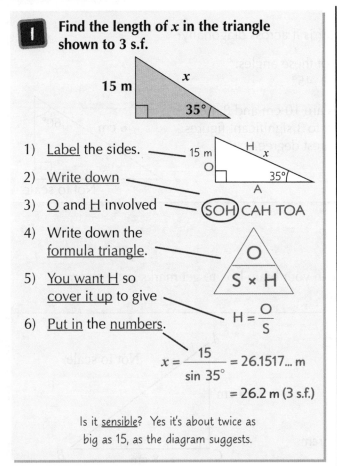

1) <u>Label</u> the sides.
2) <u>Write down</u>
3) <u>O</u> and <u>H</u> involved — (SOH) CAH TOA
4) Write down the <u>formula triangle</u>.
5) You want <u>H</u> so <u>cover it up</u> to give
6) <u>Put in</u> the <u>numbers</u>.

$$H = \frac{O}{S}$$

$$x = \frac{15}{\sin 35°} = 26.1517...\,m$$

$$= 26.2\,m\ (3\ s.f.)$$

Is it <u>sensible</u>? Yes it's about twice as big as 15, as the diagram suggests.

2 Find the angle x in this triangle to 1 d.p.

It's an <u>isosceles</u> triangle so <u>split</u> it <u>down the middle</u> to get a <u>right-angled triangle</u>.

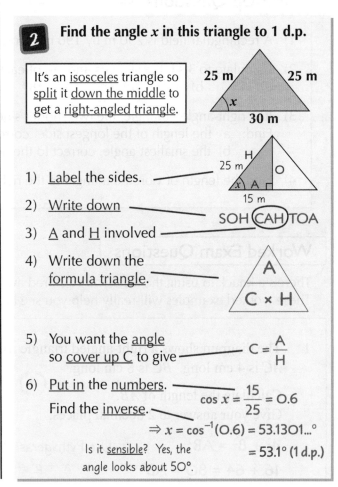

1) <u>Label</u> the sides.
2) <u>Write down</u>
3) <u>A</u> and <u>H</u> involved — SOH (CAH) TOA
4) Write down the <u>formula triangle</u>.
5) You want the <u>angle</u> so <u>cover up C</u> to give

$$C = \frac{A}{H}$$

6) <u>Put in</u> the <u>numbers</u>. Find the <u>inverse</u>.

$$\cos x = \frac{15}{25} = 0.6$$

$$\Rightarrow x = \cos^{-1}(0.6) = 53.1301...°$$

$$= 53.1°\ (1\ d.p.)$$

Is it <u>sensible</u>? Yes, the angle looks about 50°.

Angles of **Elevation** and **Depression**

1) The <u>angle of depression</u> is the angle <u>downwards</u> from the horizontal.
2) The <u>angle of elevation</u> is the angle <u>upwards</u> from the horizontal.
3) The angles of elevation and depression are <u>equal</u>.

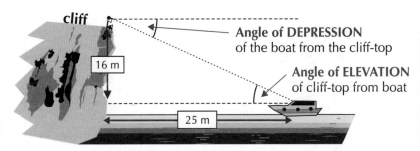

Angle of DEPRESSION of the boat from the cliff-top

Angle of ELEVATION of cliff-top from boat

3 Find the angle of elevation of the cliff-top from the boat in the diagram to the nearest degree.

Just use <u>trigonometry</u>. Call the angle of elevation x.

SOH CAH (TOA)

$$\tan x = \frac{O}{A} = \frac{16}{25} = 0.64$$

$$x = \tan^{-1}(0.64)$$

$$= 32.61...°$$

$$= 33°\ (nearest\ degree)$$

Looking at the diagram, this seems <u>sensible</u>.

You need to have learnt all seven steps on page 156

Here you can see the seven steps from the last page being put into action. It's easy to apply those steps, but only if you can remember them and practise using them — so practise.

Warm-Up and Worked Exam Questions

Learning facts and practising exam questions is the only recipe for success.
That's what the questions on these pages are all about. All you have to do... is do them.

Warm-Up Questions

1) A rectangular field is 250 m by 190 m. How far is it across diagonally?

2) Calculate to 3 s.f. the sin, cos and tan of each of these angles:
   a) 17°   b) 83°   c) 5°   d) 28°   e) 45°

3) In a right-angled triangle, the two shorter sides are 10 cm and 8.4 cm.
   Find: a) the length of the longest side, correct to 3 significant figures.
          b) the smallest angle, correct to the nearest degree.

4) Find the length of x on the triangle to the right.

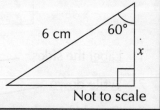

6 cm   60° x

Not to scale

Worked Exam Questions

There's a knack to using the facts you've stored away in your brain box to get marks in the exam.
These worked examples will really help you see how...

1   The diagram shows a right-angled triangle ABC.
    AC is 4 cm long. BC is 8 cm long.

    Calculate the length of AB.
    Give your answer to 2 decimal places.

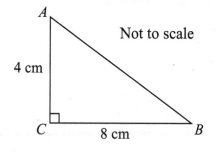

A Not to scale

4 cm

C 8 cm B

$4^2 + 8^2 = AB^2$ Use Pythagoras' Theorem:
$16 + 64 = 80 = AB^2$ $a^2 + b^2 = c^2$
$\sqrt{80} = AB$, so $AB = 8.94427... = 8.94$ cm (to 2 d.p.)

..........8.94.......... cm
[3 marks]

2   The diagram shows a right-angled triangle.
    Find the size of the angle marked x.
    Give your answer to 1 decimal place.

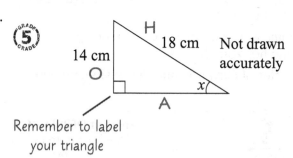

H 18 cm   Not drawn
14 cm   accurately
O
        x
    A

Remember to label
your triangle

(SOH) CAH TOA

O
$S \times H$

$S = \dfrac{O}{H}$

$\sin x = \dfrac{14}{18}$, so $x = \sin^{-1}(14 \div 18) = 51.05755... = 51.1°$ (to 1 d.p.)

..........51.1.......... °
[3 marks]

Exam Questions

3   A ladder is 3.5 m long. For safety, when the ladder is leant against a wall, the base should never be less than 2.1 m away from the wall.
   What is the maximum vertical height that the top of the ladder can safely reach to?

.... m

[3 marks]

4   The diagram shows a kite *ABCD*. *AB* is 28.3 cm long. *BC* is 54.3 cm long. *BE* is 20 cm long.
   Work out the perimeter of triangle *ABC*. Give your answer to 1 decimal place.

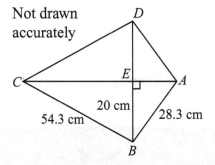

.... cm

[5 marks]

5   In the triangle on the right, *AB* = *BC* = 10 m and angle *C* = 34°.

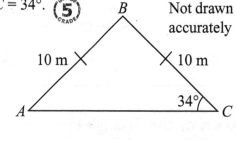

   a)   Calculate the height of the triangle.
       Give your answer to 2 decimal places.

.... m

[3 marks]

   b)   Calculate the length *AC*. Give your answer to 2 decimal places.

.... m

[3 marks]

6   A regular hexagon is drawn such that all of its vertices are on the circumference
   of a circle of radius 8.5 cm. Calculate the distance from the centre of the circle to
   the midpoint of one edge of the hexagon. Give your answer to 2 decimal places.

   The sum of internal angles in a polygon
   = ((2 × number of sides) − 4) × 90°.

.... cm

[5 marks]

The Sine and Cosine Rules

Normal trigonometry using SOH CAH TOA can only be applied to <u>right-angled</u> triangles. Which leaves us with the question of what to do with other-angled triangles. Step forward the <u>sine and cosine rules</u>...

Labelling the Triangle

This is very important. You must label the sides and angles properly so that the letters for the sides and angles correspond with each other. Use <u>lower case letters</u> for the <u>sides</u> and <u>capitals</u> for the <u>angles</u>.

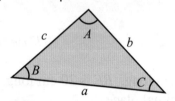

Remember, <u>side *a* is opposite angle *A*</u> etc.

It doesn't matter which sides you decide to call *a*, *b* and *c*, just as long as the angles are then labelled properly.

Three Formulas to Learn:

The Sine Rule

$$\frac{a}{\sin A} = \frac{b}{\sin B} = \frac{c}{\sin C}$$

You don't use the whole thing with both '=' signs of course, so it's not half as bad as it looks — you just <u>choose the two bits</u> that you want:

e.g. $\dfrac{b}{\sin B} = \dfrac{c}{\sin C}$ or $\dfrac{a}{\sin A} = \dfrac{b}{\sin B}$

The Cosine Rule

The 'normal' form is...

$$a^2 = b^2 + c^2 - 2bc \cos A$$

...or this form is good for finding an angle (you get it by rearranging the 'normal' version):

or $\cos A = \dfrac{b^2 + c^2 - a^2}{2bc}$

Area of the Triangle

This formula comes in handy when you know <u>two sides</u> and the <u>angle between them</u>:

$$\text{Area of triangle} = \tfrac{1}{2} ab \sin C$$

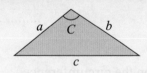

Of course, you already know a <u>simple formula</u> for calculating the area using the <u>base length</u> and <u>height</u> (see p.133). The formula here is for when you don't know those values.

EXAMPLE:

Triangle XYZ has XZ = 18 cm, YZ = 13 cm and angle XZY = 58°. Find the area of the triangle, giving your answer correct to 3 significant figures.

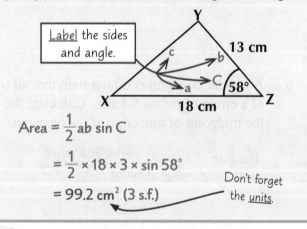

Label the sides and angle.

Area = $\dfrac{1}{2} ab \sin C$

$= \dfrac{1}{2} \times 18 \times 3 \times \sin 58°$

$= 99.2 \text{ cm}^2$ (3 s.f.)

Don't forget the <u>units</u>.

Make sure you label each side and angle of the triangle correctly

The formulas won't work if your labels don't match up. They'll be on the formula sheet so you don't need to know them off by heart — but you do need to know how to use them. Check out the next page for some examples.

The Sine and Cosine Rules

There are four main question types where the <u>sine</u> and <u>cosine</u> rules would be applied.
So learn the exact details of these four examples and you'll be laughing.

The Four **Examples**

1 | **TWO ANGLES given plus <u>ANY SIDE</u> — <u>SINE RULE</u> needed.**

Find the length of AB for the triangle below.

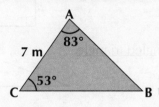

1) Don't forget the obvious... $B = 180° - 83° - 53° = 44°$

2) Put the <u>numbers</u> into the <u>sine rule</u>. $\dfrac{b}{\sin B} = \dfrac{c}{\sin C} \Rightarrow \dfrac{7}{\sin 44°} = \dfrac{c}{\sin 53°}$

3) <u>Rearrange</u> to find c. $\Rightarrow c = \dfrac{7 \times \sin 53°}{\sin 44°} = 8.05 \text{ m (3 s.f.)}$

2 | **TWO SIDES given plus an <u>ANGLE NOT ENCLOSED</u> by them — <u>SINE RULE</u> needed.**

Find angle ABC for the triangle shown below.

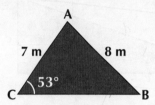

1) Put the <u>numbers</u> into the <u>sine rule</u>. $\dfrac{b}{\sin B} = \dfrac{c}{\sin C} \Rightarrow \dfrac{7}{\sin B} = \dfrac{8}{\sin 53°}$

2) <u>Rearrange</u> to find sin B. $\Rightarrow \sin B = \dfrac{7 \times \sin 53°}{8} = 0.6988...$

3) Find the <u>inverse</u>. $\Rightarrow B = \sin^{-1}(0.6988...) = 44.3°$ (1 d.p.)

The sine rule will always give you an <u>acute angle</u> — if the angle you're finding is <u>obtuse</u>, <u>subtract</u> the acute angle from 180° (see p.164).

3 | **TWO SIDES given plus the <u>ANGLE ENCLOSED</u> by them — <u>COSINE RULE</u> needed.**

Find the length CB for the triangle shown below.

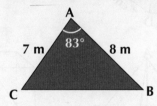

1) Put the <u>numbers</u> into the <u>cosine rule</u>.
$a^2 = b^2 + c^2 - 2bc \cos A$
$= 7^2 + 8^2 - 2 \times 7 \times 8 \times \cos 83°$
$= 99.3506...$

2) Take <u>square roots</u> to find a.
$a = \sqrt{99.3506...}$
$= 9.97 \text{ m (3 s.f.)}$

> You might come across a triangle that isn't labelled ABC — just <u>relabel it</u> yourself to match the sine and cosine rules.

4 | **<u>ALL THREE SIDES</u> given but <u>NO ANGLES</u> — <u>COSINE RULE</u> needed.**

Find angle CAB for the triangle shown.

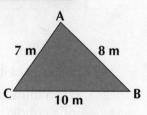

1) Use this version of the <u>cosine rule</u>. $\cos A = \dfrac{b^2 + c^2 - a^2}{2bc}$

2) <u>Put in</u> the <u>numbers</u>. $= \dfrac{49 + 64 - 100}{2 \times 7 \times 8}$

3) <u>Take the inverse</u> to find A. $= \dfrac{13}{112} = 0.11607...$

$\Rightarrow A = \cos^{-1}(0.11607...)$
$= 83.3°$ (1 d.p.)

Learn which rule you need for each question type

Rather than fret about which equation to use and how to do it, you just need to learn these four basic question types and practise them. It'll save you loads of time and stress on the big day.

3D Pythagoras

This is a 3D version of the 2D Pythagoras' theorem you saw on page 155.
There's just <u>one simple formula</u> — learn it and the world's your oyster...

3D Pythagoras for Cuboids — $a^2 + b^2 + c^2 = d^2$

<u>Cuboids</u> have their own formula for calculating
the length of their <u>longest diagonal</u>:

$$a^2 + b^2 + c^2 = d^2$$

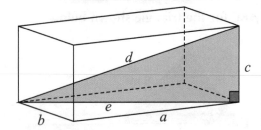

In reality it's nothing you haven't seen before
— it's just <u>2D Pythagoras' theorem</u> being used <u>twice</u>:

1) *a, b* and *e* make a <u>right-angled triangle</u> so
$$e^2 = a^2 + b^2$$

2) Now look at the <u>right-angled triangle</u>
formed by *e, c* and *d*:
$$d^2 = e^2 + c^2 = a^2 + b^2 + c^2$$

EXAMPLE:

Find the exact length of the diagonal BH for the cube in the diagram.

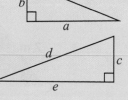

1) Write down the <u>formula</u>. $a^2 + b^2 + c^2 = d^2$

2) Put in the <u>numbers</u>. $4^2 + 4^2 + 4^2 = BH^2$

3) Take the <u>square root</u> to find BH. $\Rightarrow BH = \sqrt{48} = 4\sqrt{3}$ cm

The Cuboid Formula Can be Used in **Other 3D Shapes**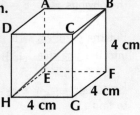

EXAMPLE:

**In the square-based pyramid shown, M is the midpoint of the base.
Find the vertical height AM.**

1) <u>Label N</u> as the midpoint of ED.

Then think of <u>EN, NM and AM</u> as three <u>sides</u> of a <u>cuboid</u>, and <u>AE</u> as the <u>longest diagonal</u> in the cuboid (like *d* in the section above).

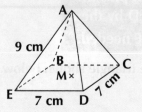 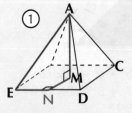

2) Sketch the <u>full cuboid</u>.

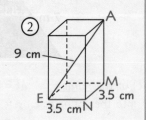

3) Write down the <u>3D Pythagoras formula</u>. $a^2 + b^2 + c^2 = d^2$

4) <u>Rewrite</u> it using <u>side labels</u>. $EN^2 + NM^2 + AM^2 = AE^2$

5) Put in the <u>numbers</u> and <u>solve for AM</u>. $\Rightarrow 3.5^2 + 3.5^2 + AM^2 = 9^2$

$\Rightarrow AM = \sqrt{81 - 2 \times 12.25} = 7.52$ cm (3 s.f.)

$a^2 + b^2 + c^2 = d^2$ gives you the longest diagonal from the 3 edge lengths

Finding the length of the longest diagonal of a cuboid is pretty easy as long as you learn the formula.
Other 3D shapes can be a little more tricky, but really you just need to work out where the formula fits.

3D Trigonometry

3D trig may sound tricky, and I suppose it is a bit... but it's actually just using the <u>same old rules</u>.

Angle Between Line and Plane — Use a Diagram

Learn the 3-Step Method

1) Make a <u>right-angled triangle</u> between the line and the plane.

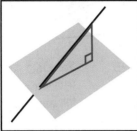

2) Draw a <u>simple 2D sketch</u> of this triangle and mark on the lengths of two sides (you might have to use <u>Pythagoras</u> to find one).

3) Use <u>trig</u> to find the angle.

Have a look at p.155-160 to jog your memory about Pythagoras and trig.

EXAMPLE:

ABCDE is a square-based pyramid with M as the midpoint of its base. Find the angle the edge AE makes with the base.

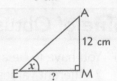

1) Draw a <u>right-angled triangle</u> using <u>AE</u>, the <u>base</u> and <u>a line between the two</u> (here it's the vertical height).

Label the <u>angle</u> you need to find.

2) Now sketch this triangle in 2D and <u>label</u> it.

Use <u>Pythagoras</u> (on the <u>base</u> triangle) to <u>find EM</u>.

$$EM^2 = 4^2 + 4^2 = 32$$
$$\Rightarrow EM = \sqrt{32}\text{ cm}$$

3) Finally, use <u>trigonometry</u> to find x — you know the <u>opposite</u> and <u>adjacent</u> sides so use <u>tan</u>.

$$\tan x = \frac{12}{\sqrt{32}} = 2.1213...$$
$$x = \tan^{-1}(2.1213...)$$
$$= 64.8° \text{ (1 d.p.)}$$

The Sine Rule and Cosine Rule Can Also be Used in 3D

For <u>triangles</u> inside 3D shapes that <u>aren't right-angled</u> you can use the <u>sine and cosine rules</u>. This sounds mildly terrifying but it's actually OK — just use the <u>same formulas</u> as before (see p.160-161).

EXAMPLE:

Find the size of angle AEH in the cuboid shown below.

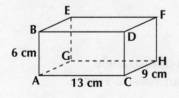

You could just use the rearranged version of the cosine rule at step 3 if you'd remembered it.

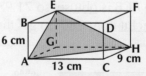 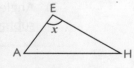

1) <u>Draw the triangle</u> AEH and label angle AEH as x.

2) Use <u>Pythagoras'</u> theorem to find the lengths of <u>AH, AE and EH</u>.

$$AH^2 = 13^2 + 9^2 = 250 \Rightarrow AH = \sqrt{250}$$
$$AE^2 = 6^2 + 9^2 = 117 \Rightarrow AE = \sqrt{117}$$
$$EH^2 = 6^2 + 13^2 = 205 \Rightarrow EH = \sqrt{205}$$

3) <u>Find x using the <u>cosine rule</u>:
<u>Put in</u> the <u>numbers</u>.
<u>Rearrange</u> and take the <u>inverse</u> to find x.

$$AH^2 = AE^2 + EH^2 - 2 \times AE \times EH \times \cos x$$
$$250 = 117 + 205 - 2\sqrt{117}\sqrt{205}\cos x$$
$$x = \cos^{-1}\left(\frac{117 + 205 - 250}{2\sqrt{117 \times 205}}\right) = 76.6° \text{ (1 d.p.)}$$

You can use the 2D trigonometry rules in 3D shapes too

The hard part is working out where to apply the rules you already know. Look for where you can make a triangle, then see which lengths and angles you've got, and which ones you need to find.

Sin, Cos and Tan for Larger Angles

You need to know about sin, cos and tan of <u>obtuse angles</u> (they're the ones between 90° and 180°).

Cosine of Obtuse Angles

Values of cos x for obtuse angles are <u>negative</u>, but the cosine rule works just the same as for acute angles.

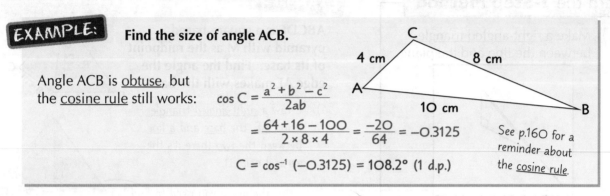

EXAMPLE: **Find the size of angle ACB.**

Angle ACB is obtuse, but the <u>cosine rule</u> still works:

$$\cos C = \frac{a^2 + b^2 - c^2}{2ab}$$

$$= \frac{64 + 16 - 100}{2 \times 8 \times 4} = \frac{-20}{64} = -0.3125$$

$$C = \cos^{-1}(-0.3125) = 108.2° \text{ (1 d.p.)}$$

See p.160 for a reminder about the <u>cosine rule</u>.

4 cm, 8 cm, 10 cm (triangle with C at top, A at left, B at right)

Sine of Obtuse Angles

1) You have to be a bit more careful with sine. Each value of <u>sin x</u> between 0 and 1 corresponds to <u>2 different values</u> of x between 0° and 180°.

2) When you use your calculator's $\sin^{-1}$ function to find the size of the angle, it gives you the answer between <u>0° and 90°</u>. If you know the angle is <u>obtuse</u>, you then have to <u>subtract</u> the calculator's answer from <u>180°</u>.

EXAMPLE: **Find the size of angle ACB.**

1) Use the <u>sine rule</u> (see p.160):

$$\frac{a}{\sin A} = \frac{c}{\sin C}$$

$$\frac{8}{\sin 49.5°} = \frac{10}{\sin C}$$

$$\sin C = \frac{10 \times \sin 49.5°}{8} = 0.9505...$$

2) Angle ACB is <u>obtuse</u>, so 71.9° is <u>too small</u> — $\sin^{-1}(0.9505...) = 71.8984...$ <u>subtract it from 180°</u> to get the answer. $180° - 71.8984°... = 108.1°$ (1 d.p.)

49.5°, 8 cm, 10 cm (triangle with C at top, A at left, B at right)

Tan of Obtuse Angles

1) When you use your calculator's $\tan^{-1}$ function to find the size of an angle, it gives you an answer between <u>–90° and 90°</u>.

2) If you know the angle is <u>obtuse</u>, you then have to <u>add 180°</u>.

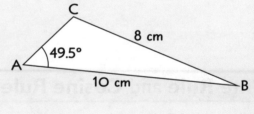

EXAMPLE: x is an obtuse angle with $\tan x = -1$. Find x.

$$\tan^{-1}(-1) = -45°$$

It's an <u>obtuse</u> angle, so <u>add 180°</u>:

$$-45° + 180° = 135°$$

Always check your answer's sensible — don't just copy your calculator

Remember the method for the three different trig functions: cos just works the same, sin is '180 minus' and tan is '180 plus'. Keep in mind roughly what size you'd expect your angle to be to spot if you've messed up.

Vectors

Vectors represent a movement of a certain <u>size</u> in a certain <u>direction</u>.
They might seem a bit weird at first, but there are really just a few facts to get to grips with...

Vector **Notations**

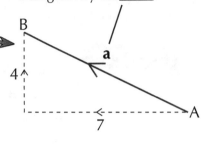

They're represented on
a diagram by an <u>arrow</u>.

There are several ways to <u>write</u> vectors...

1) <u>Column</u> vectors: $\begin{pmatrix} 2 \\ -5 \end{pmatrix}$ — 2 units right / 5 units down $\begin{pmatrix} -7 \\ 4 \end{pmatrix}$ — 7 units left / 4 units up

2) **a** —— <u>exam questions</u> often use <u>bold</u> like this

3) $\underline{a}$ or $\underset{\sim}{a}$ — <u>you</u> should always <u>underline</u> them

4) $\overrightarrow{AB}$ —— this means the vector <u>from point A to point B</u>

Magnitude — $|\overrightarrow{AB}|$

The <u>magnitude</u> (or <u>modulus</u>) of a vector is just its <u>length</u>.
You find it using <u>Pythagoras</u> (see p.155) — e.g. for the vector above:

$$|\overrightarrow{AB}| = \left|\begin{pmatrix} -7 \\ 4 \end{pmatrix}\right| = \sqrt{(-7)^2 + 4^2} = \sqrt{65} = 8.1 \text{ (1 d.p.)}$$

Multiplying by a **Scalar, Adding** and **Subtracting**

Multiplying a vector by a <u>positive</u> number <u>changes</u> the
vector's <u>size</u> but <u>not its direction</u> — it <u>scales</u> the vector.
If the number's <u>negative</u> then the <u>direction gets switched</u>.

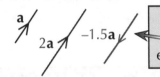

Vectors that are
<u>scalar multiples</u> of
each other are <u>parallel</u>.

You can describe movements between points by <u>adding and subtracting known vectors</u>.
The <u>sum</u> of two or more vectors is sometimes called the <u>resultant</u> vector.

> "$\underline{a} + \underline{b}$" means 'go along $\underline{a}$ then $\underline{b}$'.

To add column vectors, add the top to the top and the
bottom to the bottom. Then same goes when subtracting. $\begin{pmatrix} 3 \\ -1 \end{pmatrix} + \begin{pmatrix} 5 \\ 3 \end{pmatrix} = \begin{pmatrix} 8 \\ 2 \end{pmatrix}$

In the diagrams,
$\overrightarrow{PR} = \underline{a} + \underline{b}$ and
$\overrightarrow{XZ} = \underline{c} - \underline{d}$.

> "$\underline{c} - \underline{d}$" means 'go along $\underline{c}$ then backwards along $\underline{d}$'
> (the <u>minus</u> sign means go the <u>opposite</u> way).

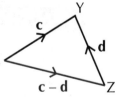

EXAMPLE:

In the diagram below, M is the midpoint of BC.
Find vectors $\overrightarrow{AM}$, $\overrightarrow{OC}$ and $\overrightarrow{AC}$ in terms of **a**, **b** and **m**.

To obtain the <u>unknown vector</u>,
just 'get there' by any route
<u>made up of known vectors</u>.

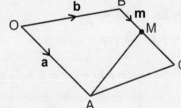

$\overrightarrow{AM} = -\underline{a} + \underline{b} + \underline{m}$ —— A to M via O and B

$\overrightarrow{OC} = \underline{b} + 2\underline{m}$ —— O to C via B and M — M's halfway
between B and C, so $\overrightarrow{BC} = 2\underline{m}$

$\overrightarrow{AC} = -\underline{a} + \underline{b} + 2\underline{m}$ —— A to C via O, B and M

That's four vital vector facts done

But they're only really 'done' if you've learnt them. So be sure you know how vectors can be written, how
to find the magnitude, what multiplying by a scalar does and how to add/subtract them — then you're done.

Vectors

Extra bits and pieces can crop up in vector questions — these examples will show you how to tackle them...

Vectors Along a Straight Line

1) You can use <u>vectors</u> to <u>show</u> that <u>points lie on a straight line</u>.
2) You need to show that the <u>vectors</u> along <u>each part of the line</u> point in the <u>same direction</u> — i.e. they're <u>scalar multiples</u> of each other.

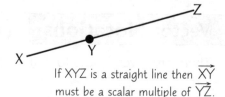

If XYZ is a straight line then $\overrightarrow{XY}$ must be a scalar multiple of $\overrightarrow{YZ}$.

EXAMPLE:

In the diagram,

$\overrightarrow{OB} = \mathbf{a}$, $\overrightarrow{AB} = 2\mathbf{b}$, $\overrightarrow{BD} = \mathbf{a} - \mathbf{b}$ and $\overrightarrow{DC} = \frac{1}{2}\mathbf{a} - 4\mathbf{b}$.

Show that OAC is a straight line.

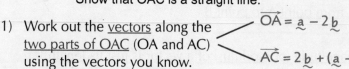

1) Work out the <u>vectors</u> along the <u>two parts of OAC</u> (OA and AC) using the vectors you know.

$\overrightarrow{OA} = \mathbf{a} - 2\mathbf{b}$

$\overrightarrow{AC} = 2\mathbf{b} + (\mathbf{a} - \mathbf{b}) + \left(\frac{1}{2}\mathbf{a} - 4\mathbf{b}\right)$

$= \frac{3}{2}\mathbf{a} - 3\mathbf{b} = \frac{3}{2}(\mathbf{a} - 2\mathbf{b})$

2) Check that $\overrightarrow{AC}$ is a <u>scalar multiple</u> of $\overrightarrow{OA}$.

So, $\overrightarrow{AC} = \frac{3}{2}\overrightarrow{OA}$.

3) <u>Explain</u> why this means OAC is a <u>straight line</u>.

Therefore, $\overrightarrow{AC}$ is a scalar multiple of $\overrightarrow{OA}$, so OAC must be a straight line.

Vector Questions Can Involve Ratios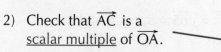

<u>Ratios</u> are used in vector questions to tell you the <u>lengths</u> of different <u>sections of a straight line</u>. If you know the vector along part of that line, you can use this information to <u>find other vectors along the line</u>.

E.g. $\underline{XY:YZ = 2:3}$ tells you that $\overrightarrow{XY} = \frac{2}{5}\overrightarrow{XZ}$ and $\overrightarrow{YZ} = \frac{3}{5}\overrightarrow{XZ}$.

EXAMPLE:

ABCD is a parallelogram, with AB parallel to DC and AD parallel to BC.

Point E lies on DC, such that DE:EC = 3:1.

$\overrightarrow{BC} = \mathbf{a}$ and $\overrightarrow{BA} = \mathbf{b}$.

Find $\overrightarrow{AE}$ in terms of $\mathbf{a}$ and $\mathbf{b}$.

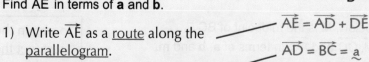

1) Write $\overrightarrow{AE}$ as a <u>route</u> along the <u>parallelogram</u>.

$\overrightarrow{AE} = \overrightarrow{AD} + \overrightarrow{DE}$

2) Use the <u>parallel sides</u> to find $\overrightarrow{AD}$ and $\overrightarrow{DC}$.

$\overrightarrow{AD} = \overrightarrow{BC} = \mathbf{a}$

$\overrightarrow{DC} = \overrightarrow{AB} = -\mathbf{b}$

3) Use the <u>ratio</u> to find $\overrightarrow{DE}$.

$\overrightarrow{DE} = \frac{3}{4}\overrightarrow{DC}$

4) Now use $\overrightarrow{AD}$ and $\overrightarrow{DE}$ to find $\overrightarrow{AE}$.

So $\overrightarrow{AE} = \overrightarrow{AD} + \overrightarrow{DE} = \mathbf{a} - \frac{3}{4}\mathbf{b}$

Remember — parallel vectors are scalar multiples of each other

For these types of questions, just use the vectors you're given to find what you're asked for. It's worth learning how to do these questions, because you could get very similar ones in the exam.

Warm-Up and Worked Exam Questions

Trigonometry and vector questions can be pretty tricky until you get your head around the basics. That's what these warm-up questions are all about — work through them carefully and check any bits you don't know.

Warm-Up Questions

1) In the triangle on the right, find the length of AC, correct to 1 decimal place.

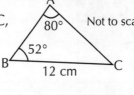

2) A triangle has sides of 4 cm, 6 cm and 8 cm. Calculate the largest angle, correct to 1 d.p.

3) In the cuboid on the right, FG = 5 cm, CD = 2 cm and CG = 8 cm. Calculate the size of the angle FDG to the nearest degree.

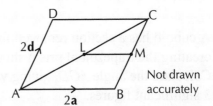

4) If $90° < x < 180°$, find x to 1 d.p. when:
   a) $\sin x = 0.84$ b) $\sin x = 0.173$ c) $\tan x = -1$ d) $\tan x = -14.3$

5) If $\mathbf{f} = \begin{pmatrix} -2 \\ 1 \end{pmatrix}$ and $\mathbf{g} = \begin{pmatrix} 7 \\ -3 \end{pmatrix}$, find the magnitude of $\mathbf{f} + \mathbf{g}$.

6) ABCD is a parallelogram. $\overrightarrow{AB} = 2\mathbf{a}$ and $\overrightarrow{AD} = 2\mathbf{d}$. L is the midpoint of AC, and M is the midpoint of BC. Write each of the following in terms of $\mathbf{a}$ and $\mathbf{d}$.
   a) $\overrightarrow{CD}$ b) $\overrightarrow{AC}$ c) $\overrightarrow{BL}$

Worked Exam Questions

Take the time to go through this example and make sure you understand it all.
If any of the facts are baffling you, it's not too late to take another peek over the section.

1   In the triangle on the right, $AB = 10$ cm, $BC = 7$ cm and angle $ABC = 85°$.

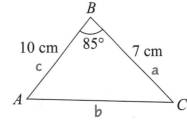

Diagram not accurately drawn

Label the sides of the triangle.

a)   Calculate the length of AC.
     Give your answer to 3 significant figures.

     Use the cosine rule to find b:

     $b^2 = a^2 + c^2 - 2ac \cos B,$
     $AC^2 = 7^2 + 10^2 - (2 \times 7 \times 10 \times \cos 85°)$
     $AC = \sqrt{149 - 140 \times \cos 85°} = 11.69607... = 11.7$ cm (to 3 s.f.)   ....11.7.... cm

     [3 marks]

b)   Calculate the area of triangle ABC.
     Give your answer to 3 significant figures.

     Area $= \frac{1}{2} ac \sin B$

     You know the length of two sides and the angle between them, so use the area formula from p.160.

     $= \frac{1}{2} \times 7 \times 10 \times \sin 85°$

     $= 34.86681... = 34.9$ cm^2 (to 3 s.f)   ....34.9.... cm^2

     [2 marks]

Exam Questions

2   A castle drawbridge is supported by two chains, AB and AC. Using the information on the diagram below, calculate the total length of the drawbridge, BD, correct to 3 s.f.

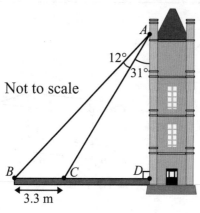

.... m

[6 marks]

3   A cuboid has a section removed from its top, creating the trapezoidal prism shown in the diagram. Calculate the angle AGD, giving your answer to 3 significant figures.

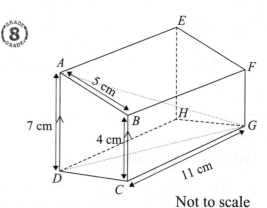

Not to scale

.... °

[5 marks]

4   $ABCD$ is a parallelogram. $\overrightarrow{AB} = 3\mathbf{a}$ and $\overrightarrow{BW} = \mathbf{b}$.
M is the midpoint of CD and $AX = 2XC$.
$BW : WC = 1 : 5$

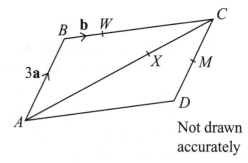

Not drawn accurately

a)   Find $\overrightarrow{BX}$ in terms of $\mathbf{a}$ and $\mathbf{b}$.

....

[3 marks]

b)   Hence show that B, X and M are three points on a straight line.

[2 marks]

Revision Questions for Section Five

There are a good few facts and formulas in this section, so use this page to check you've got them all sorted.

- Try these questions and <u>tick off each one</u> when you <u>get it right</u>.
- When you've done <u>all the questions</u> for a topic and are <u>completely happy</u> with it, tick off the topic.

Pythagoras' Theorem (p.155) ☐

1) What is the formula for Pythagoras' theorem? What do you use it for?

2) A museum has a flight of stairs up to its front door (see diagram). A ramp is to be put over the top of the steps for wheelchair users. Calculate the length that the ramp would need to be, to 3 s.f.

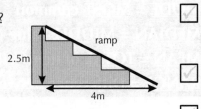

3) Point P has coordinates (–3, –2) and point Q has coordinates (2, 4). Calculate the length of the line PQ to 1 d.p.

Trigonometry — Sin, Cos, Tan (p.156-157) ☐

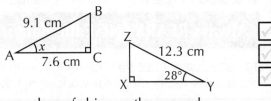

4) Write down the three trigonometry formula triangles.

5) Find the size of angle x in triangle ABC to 1 d.p.

6) Find the length of side XZ of triangle XYZ to 3 s.f.

7) A seagull is sitting on top of a 2.8 m high lamp-post. It sees a bag of chips on the ground, 7.1 m away from the base of the lamp-post. Calculate the angle of depression of the chips from the top of the lamp-post, correct to 1 d.p.

The Sine and Cosine Rules (p.160-161) ☐

8) Write down the sine and cosine rules and the formula (involving sin) for the area of any triangle.

9) List the 4 different types of sine/cosine rule questions and which rule you need for each.

10) In triangle FGH, side FH = 8 cm, side GH = 9 cm and angle FHG = 47°. Find the length of side FG.

11) Triangle PQR has side PQ = 12 cm, side QR = 9 cm and angle PQR = 63°. Find its area.

3D Pythagoras and Trigonometry (p.162-163) ☐

12) What is the formula for finding the length of the longest diagonal in a cuboid?

13) Find the length of the longest diagonal in the cuboid measuring 5 m × 6 m × 9 m.

14) Find the angle between the line BH and the plane ABCD in this cuboid.

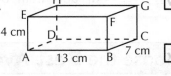

15) Find the size of angle WPU in the cuboid shown, to the nearest degree.

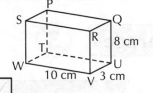

Sin, Cos and Tan for Larger Angles (p.164) ☐

16) Triangle JKL has side JK = 6 cm, side JL = 11 cm and angle JLK = 28°. Find the size of the obtuse angle JKL.

Vectors (p.165-166) ☐

17) What is the effect of multiplying a vector by a scalar?

18) What is the magnitude of $\begin{pmatrix} 5 \\ -2 \end{pmatrix}$?

19) ABCD is a quadrilateral.
   AXC is a straight line with AX : XC = 1 : 3.
   a) Find $\vec{AX}$.   b) Find $\vec{DX}$ and $\vec{XB}$.
   c) Is DXB a straight line? Explain your answer.

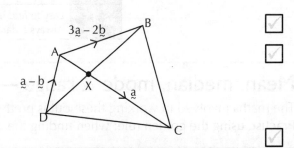

Mean, Median, Mode and Range

Mean, median, mode and range pop up all the time in statistics questions — make sure you know what they are.

The **Four Definitions**

MODE = MOST common
MEDIAN = MIDDLE value (when values are in order of size)
MEAN = TOTAL of items ÷ NUMBER of items
RANGE = Difference between highest and lowest

REMEMBER:
Mode = most (emphasise the 'mo' in each when you say them)
Median = mid (emphasise the m*d in each when you say them)
Mean is just the average, but it's mean 'cos you have to work it out.

The Golden Rule   There's one vital step for finding the median that lots of people forget:

Always REARRANGE the data in ASCENDING ORDER   (and check you have the same number of entries!)

You absolutely must do this when finding the median,
but it's also really useful for working out the mode too.

EXAMPLE: **Find the median, mode, mean, and range of these numbers:**
2, 5, 3, 2, 6, –4, 0, 9, –3, 1, 6, 3, –2, 3

> Check that you still have the same number of entries after you've rearranged them.

The MEDIAN is the middle value, so rearrange the numbers in order of size.
When there are two middle numbers, the median is halfway between the two.

–4, –3, –2, 0, 1, 2, (2, 3) 3, 3, 5, 6, 6, 9
← seven numbers this side   seven numbers this side →

An even number of values means there will be two middle numbers.

Median = 2.5

MODE (or modal value) is the most common value. ⟶ Mode = 3
Data sets can have more than one mode.

$$\text{MEAN} = \frac{\text{total of items}}{\text{number of items}} \longrightarrow \frac{-4-3-2+0+1+2+2+3+3+3+5+6+6+9}{14}$$

$$= 31 \div 14 = 2.214... = 2.21 \text{ (3 s.f.)}$$

RANGE = distance from lowest to highest value, i.e. from –4 up to 9. ⟶ 9 – (–4) = 13

Choose the **Best Average**

The mean, median and mode all have their advantages and disadvantages — LEARN THEM:

	Advantages	Disadvantages
Mean	Uses all the data. Usually most representative.	Isn't always a data value. May be distorted by extreme data values.
Median	Easy to find in ordered data. Not distorted by extreme data values.	Isn't always a data value. Not always a good representation of the data.
Mode	Easy to find in tallied data. Always a data value.	Sometimes there's more than one. Not always a good representation of the data.

Mean, median, mode & range — easy marks for learning four words

The maths involved in working these out is pretty simple — as long as you learn the definitions.
Practise using the golden rule: when finding the median, always arrange the data from smallest to largest.

Quartiles and Comparing Distributions

Measures of <u>spread</u> tell you <u>how spread out</u> data is. The <u>range</u> (see the previous page) is a measure of spread over all the data values. The <u>interquartile range</u> tells you the <u>spread</u> of the <u>middle 50%</u> of values.

Quartiles Divide the Data into Four Equal Groups

1) The quartiles are the <u>lower quartile</u> Q_1, the <u>median</u> Q_2 and the <u>upper quartile</u> Q_3.

2) If you put the data in <u>ascending order</u>, the quartiles are <u>25%</u> (¼), <u>50%</u> (½) and <u>75%</u> (¾) of the way through the list. So if a data set has n values, you work out the <u>positions</u> of the quartiles using these <u>formulas</u>:

$$Q_1 \text{ position number} = (n+1)/4$$
$$Q_2 \text{ position number} = 2(n+1)/4$$
$$Q_3 \text{ position number} = 3(n+1)/4$$

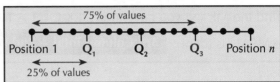

3) The <u>INTERQUARTILE RANGE</u> (IQR) is the <u>difference</u> between the <u>upper quartile</u> and the <u>lower quartile</u> and contains the <u>middle 50%</u> of values.

EXAMPLE:

a) **Here are the ages, in months, of a number of fine cheeses:**
7, 12, 5, 4, 3, 9, 5, 11, 7, 5, 7
Find the median and interquartile range of the ages.

Check you've got the right number of values — 11 ✓

1) Put the data in <u>order of size</u>. → 3, 4, 5, 5, 5, 7, 7, 7, 9, 11, 12

2) Find the median Q_2 — $n = 11$, so Q_2 is in position $2(11 + 1)/4 = 6$ — i.e. $Q_2 = 7$ **months.**

3) Find Q_1 — And since $n = 11$, Q_1 is in position $(11 + 1)/4 = 3$. So $Q_1 = \underline{5}$.

4) Find Q_3 — Q_3 is in position $3(11 + 1)/4 = 9$. So $Q_3 = \underline{9}$.

5) <u>Subtract</u> Q_1 from Q_3 — $IQR = Q_3 - Q_1 = 9 - 5 = 4$ **months**

Careful — the formulas tell you the position of the quartile, not its value.

Compare Data Using Averages and Spread

To <u>compare</u> two sets of data, you should look at:

1 AVERAGES — <u>MEAN</u>, <u>MEDIAN</u> or <u>MODE</u>. Say which data set has the <u>higher</u> or <u>lower</u> value and <u>what that means</u> in the context of the data.

You could also compare other key values like <u>quartiles</u> or <u>min/max values</u>.

2 SPREAD — <u>RANGE</u> or <u>INTERQUARTILE RANGE</u>. Say which data set has the <u>larger</u> or <u>smaller</u> value. A <u>larger spread</u> means the values are <u>less consistent</u> or there is <u>more variation</u> in the data.

If the data contains <u>extreme</u> values, it's better to use the <u>IQR</u> than the range.

EXAMPLE:

b) **A dealer sells fine cheeses whose median age is 9 months and whose interquartile range of ages is 2 months. Compare the ages of the cheeses sold by this dealer with the ones in part a) above.**

1) You need to compare an <u>average</u> → The cheeses sold by this dealer have a greater median age, for the two distributions. so they are generally older than the cheeses in part a).

2) You need to compare a measure → The cheeses sold by this dealer have a smaller of <u>spread</u> for the two distributions. interquartile range, so there appears to be less variation in the ages of these cheeses.

Make sure you know how to find the positions of the quartiles

If you're not told which measures to use when comparing data sets, think about the advantages and disadvantages from the previous page. E.g. if one of the values is miles from the rest, avoid using the mean.

Frequency Tables — Finding Averages

The word <u>frequency</u> means 'how many', so a frequency table is just a 'How many in each category' table. You saw how to find <u>averages and range</u> on p.170 — it's the same ideas here, but with the data in a table.

Find **Averages** from **Frequency Tables**

1) The <u>MODE</u> is just the <u>CATEGORY</u> with the <u>MOST ENTRIES</u>.

2) The <u>RANGE</u> is found from the <u>extremes of the first column</u>.

3) The <u>MEDIAN</u> is the <u>CATEGORY</u> of the <u>middle value in the second column</u>.

4) To find the <u>MEAN</u>, you have to <u>WORK OUT A THIRD COLUMN</u> yourself.

The <u>MEAN</u> is then: **3rd Column Total ÷ 2nd Column Total**

Categories   How many

Number of cats	Frequency	
0	17	
1	22	
2	15	
3	7	

Third column for working out the mean

EXAMPLE: **Some people were asked how many sisters they have. The table opposite shows the results.**

Find the mode, the range, the mean and the median of the data.

Number of sisters	Frequency
0	7
1	15
2	12
3	8
4	4
5	0

1 The <u>mode</u> is the <u>category</u> with the <u>most entries</u> — i.e. the one with the <u>highest frequency</u>:

The highest frequency is 15 for '1 sister', so <u>MODE</u> = 1.

2 The <u>range</u> is the <u>difference</u> between the highest and lowest numbers of sisters — that's 4 sisters (no one has 5 sisters) and no sisters, so:

<u>RANGE</u> = 4 – 0 = 4

3 To find the <u>mean</u>, add a <u>3rd column</u> to the table showing 'number of sisters × frequency'. <u>Add up</u> these values to find the <u>total number of sisters</u> of all the people asked.

You can label the first column x and the frequency column f, then the third column is f × x.

Number of sisters (x)	Frequency (f)	No. of sisters × Frequency ($f \times x$)
0	7	0
1	15	15
2	12	24
3	8	24
4	4	16
5	0	0
Total	46	79

3rd column total

<u>MEAN</u> = $\dfrac{\text{total number of sisters}}{\text{total number of people asked}} = \dfrac{79}{46} = 1.72$ (3 s.f.)

2nd column total

4 The <u>median</u> is the <u>category</u> of the <u>middle</u> value. Work out its <u>position</u>, then <u>count through</u> the 2nd column to find it.

It helps to imagine the data set out in an ordered list:
00000001111111111111112222222222223333333334444

median

There are 46 values, so the middle value is halfway between the 23rd and 24th values. There are a total of (7 + 15) = 22 values in the first two categories, and another 12 in the third category takes you to 34. So the 23rd and 24th values must both be in the category '2 sisters', which means the <u>MEDIAN</u> is 2.

Remember — mode is most, median is middle and mean is average

When you're finding the mean, don't forget to divide by the total of the frequency column, not the category column. Use your calculator to make sure you don't accidentally add the numbers up wrong.

Grouped Frequency Tables

Grouped frequency tables group together the data into classes.
They look like ordinary frequency tables, but they're a slightly trickier kettle of fish...

Non-overlapping classes
- Use inequality symbols to cover all possible values.
- Here, 10 would go in the 1st class, but 10.1 would go in the 2nd class.

Height (h mm)	Frequency
$5 < h \leq 10$	12
$10 < h \leq 15$	15

To find mid-interval values:
- Add together the end values of the class and divide by 2.
- E.g. $\frac{5 + 10}{2} = 7.5$

Find Averages from Grouped Frequency Tables

Unlike with ordinary frequency tables, you don't know the actual data values, only the classes they're in. So you have to estimate the mean, rather than calculate it exactly. Again, you do this by adding columns:

1) Add a 3rd column and enter the mid-interval value for each class.
2) Add a 4th column to show 'frequency × mid-interval value' for each class.

And you'll be asked to find the modal class and the class containing the median, not exact values.

This table shows information about the weights, in kilograms, of 60 school children.

a) Write down the modal class.
b) Write down the class containing the median.
c) Calculate an estimate for the mean weight.

Weight (w kg)	Frequency
$30 < w \leq 40$	8
$40 < w \leq 50$	16
$50 < w \leq 60$	18
$60 < w \leq 70$	12
$70 < w \leq 80$	6

a) The modal class is the one with the highest frequency.

Modal class is $50 < w \leq 60$

b) Work out the position of the median, then count through the 2nd column.

There are 60 values, so the median is halfway between the 30th and 31st values.
Both these values are in the third class, so the class containing the median is $50 < w \leq 60$.

c) Add extra columns for 'mid-interval value' and 'frequency × mid-interval value'.
Add up the values in the 4th column to estimate the total weight of the 60 children.

Weight (w kg)	Frequency (f)	Mid-interval value (x)	fx
$30 < w \leq 40$	8	35	280
$40 < w \leq 50$	16	45	720
$50 < w \leq 60$	18	55	990
$60 < w \leq 70$	12	65	780
$70 < w \leq 80$	6	75	450
Total	60	—	3220

You don't need to add up the mid-interval values.

$$\text{Mean} \approx \frac{\text{total weight}}{\text{number of children}} \quad \begin{array}{l} \leftarrow \text{4th column total} \\ \leftarrow \text{2nd column total} \end{array}$$

$$= \frac{3220}{60}$$

$$= 53.7 \text{ kg (3 s.f.)}$$

This time there are two columns to add

With frequency tables there was just one column to add, but with grouped frequency tables there are two. It's still easy enough though as long as you remember what the columns are and how to find them.

Warm-Up and Worked Exam Questions

Keep it up — this is the last section, then you've got some fun practice papers to do.
Warm up your grey matter with the questions below.

Warm-Up Questions

1) Find the mode, median, mean and range of the following numbers:

    1, 2, −2, 0, 1, 8, 3, −3, 2, 4, −2, 2

2) The data in the table below shows the number of cars owned by 124 households in a survey.
    Find the: a) mean,   b) median,   c) mode,   d) range.

Number of cars	0	1	2	3	4	5	6
Frequency	1	24	36	31	22	9	1

3) The grouped frequency table below represents data from 79 random people.

Height (cm)	$145 \leq x < 155$	$155 \leq x < 165$	$165 \leq x < 175$	$175 \leq x < 185$
Frequency	18	22	24	15

   a) Estimate the mean.   b) Which group contains the median?   c) State the modal group.

Worked Exam Questions

There's no better preparation for exam questions than doing, err... practice exam questions.
Hang on, what's this I see..?

1   During a science experiment 10 seeds were planted and
their growth measured to the nearest cm after 12 days.
The results were recorded in the table on the right.

Growth in cm	Number of plants
$0 \leq x \leq 2$	2
$3 \leq x \leq 5$	4
$6 \leq x \leq 8$	3
$9 \leq x \leq 11$	1

Use the table to find:

a)   the modal class,

> The modal class is the one with
> the highest frequency, so that's $3 \leq x \leq 5$

$3 \leq x \leq 5$

....
[1 mark]

b)   the class which contains the median,

> $(10 + 1) \div 2 = 5.5$, so the median is halfway between
> the 5th and 6th values, so it lies in the group containing
> the 5th and 6th values, which is $3 \leq x \leq 5$

$3 \leq x \leq 5$

....
[1 mark]

c)   an estimate of the mean growth.

> $[(1 \times 2) + (4 \times 4) + (7 \times 3) + (10 \times 1)] \div 10$
> $= 49 \div 10 = 4.9$ cm

This is using the mid-interval values. You could
add a couple of extra columns to the table for
mid-interval values and frequency × mid-interval value.

4.9 cm

....
[4 marks]

Exam Questions

2   15 boys and 13 girls took a Maths test. The mean mark for the boys was b. **(3)**
In the same test the mean mark for the girls was g.
Write down an expression for the mean mark of all 28 pupils.

....
[3 marks]

3   For her homework, Vanessa collected information about the number of text messages that **(4)**
36 pupils in her school sent one day. She recorded her results in the frequency table below.
Use the table to calculate the mean number of text messages sent.

Number of messages	Frequency
0	2
2	4
3	7
5	11
7	6
8	3
10	3
Total	36

....
[3 marks]

4   The data below shows the number of berries collected **(6)**
from each plant during one harvest of two berry patches.

Patch A: 8   13   19   22   8   18   14   16   9   14   12

Patch B: 14   19   11   13   15   11   13

a)   For each patch, work out the interquartile range for the number of berries from each plant.

Patch A: ....   Patch B: ....
[4 marks]

b)   Give one comparison between the plants in Patch A
and the plants in Patch B, based on your results in part a).

....

....
[1 mark]

Cumulative Frequency

Cumulative frequency just means <u>adding it up as you go along</u> — i.e. the <u>total frequency so far</u>. A cumulative frequency <u>graph</u> shows <u>cumulative frequency</u> up the <u>side</u> and the <u>data values</u> along the <u>bottom</u>. You might be asked to draw one in the exam — here's how...

To **Draw** the **Graph...**

1) <u>Add a 'CUMULATIVE FREQUENCY' COLUMN</u> to the grouped frequency table — and fill it in with the <u>RUNNING TOTAL</u> of the <u>frequency column</u>.

2) <u>PLOT</u> points using the <u>HIGHEST VALUE in each class</u> and the <u>CUMULATIVE FREQUENCY</u>.

3) Plot the cumulative frequency as <u>ZERO</u> at the lowest value of the first class.

4) <u>Join</u> the points with a <u>smooth curve</u>.

EXAMPLE: **The table below shows information about the heights of a group of people.**
a) Draw a cumulative frequency graph for the data.

1) Fill in the <u>cumulative frequency column</u>:

For the first class, it's the same as the frequency.

For the other classes, <u>add</u> the frequency for that class to the cumulative frequency of the class above.

Height (h cm)	Frequency	Cumulative Frequency
$140 < h \leq 150$	4	4
$150 < h \leq 160$	9	4 + 9 = <u>13</u>
$160 < h \leq 170$	20	13 + 20 = <u>33</u>
$170 < h \leq 180$	33	33 + 33 = <u>66</u>
$180 < h \leq 190$	36	66 + 36 = <u>102</u>
$190 < h \leq 200$	15	102 + 15 = <u>117</u>
$200 < h \leq 210$	3	117 + 3 = <u>120</u>

2) <u>Plot</u> the points using the <u>highest value</u> in each class, i.e. (150, 4), (160, 13), etc.

3) Plot <u>zero</u> at the lowest value in the first class, i.e. (140, 0).

4) Join up the points with a nice <u>smooth curve</u>.

You might have to use your curve to do some other calculations (see the next page), so make sure you draw it really carefully.

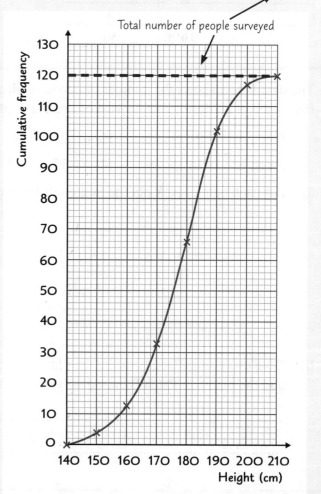

Total number of people surveyed

Cumulative Frequency

I'm afraid it's not enough just to be able to draw a cumulative frequency graph — you also need to be able to make <u>estimates</u> from them, for things like the <u>median</u> and the <u>interquartile range</u>.

EXAMPLE: Continued from the previous page... b) **Use the graph drawn in part a) to estimate the median and interquartile range of the heights.**

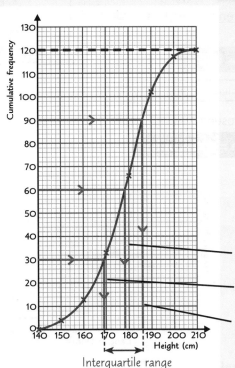

Interquartile range

To **Find** the **Vital Statistics**...

1) <u>MEDIAN</u> — go <u>halfway up</u> the side, <u>across</u> to the <u>curve</u>, then <u>down</u> and read off the bottom scale.

2) <u>LOWER AND UPPER QUARTILES</u> — go ¼ and ¾ up the side, <u>across</u> to the <u>curve</u>, then <u>down</u> and read off the bottom scale.

3) <u>INTERQUARTILE RANGE</u> — the <u>distance</u> <u>between</u> the lower and upper quartiles.

The halfway point is at ½ × 120 = 60.
Reading across and down gives a median of **178 cm**.

¼ of the way up is at ¼ × 120 = 30.
Reading across and down gives a lower quartile of **169 cm**.

¾ of the way up is at ¾ × 120 = 90.
Reading across and down gives an upper quartile of **186 cm**.

The interquartile range = 186 − 169 = **17 cm**.

c) **Use the graph to estimate the number of people who have a height greater than 195 cm.**

More **Estimating**...

To estimate the number of things with a value <u>less than or greater than a given value</u>:

1) Go along the bottom scale to the given value, <u>up</u> to the curve, then <u>across</u> to the cumulative frequency.

2) This gives you the number of things with a value <u>less than</u> the given value.

3) <u>Subtract</u> this from the <u>frequency total</u> to find the number with a value <u>greater than</u> the given value.

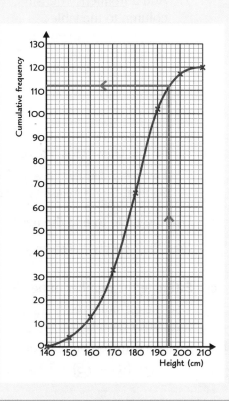

1) Read off the curve (along the green line) to find the number of people with height <u>less than</u> 195 cm:

No. of people with height <u>less than</u> 195 cm = 112

2) <u>Subtract</u> from total frequency:

No. of people with height <u>greater than</u> 195 cm
= 120 − 112 = 8

Plot the points using the highest value in each class

Don't get confused — when working out the mean of grouped data, use the mid-interval value for each class. For cumulative frequency, you always use the upper limit. Remember to add a zero point at the start too.

Histograms and Frequency Density

A <u>histogram</u> is just a bar chart where the bars can be of <u>different widths</u>. This might not sound so bad, but it can change them from nice, easy-to-understand diagrams into quite nasty exam questions.

Histograms Show **Frequency Density**

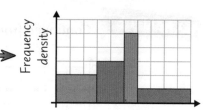

1) The <u>vertical</u> axis on a histogram is always called <u>frequency density</u>. ➡ You work it out using this formula:

Frequency Density = Frequency ÷ Class Width

> Remember, '<u>frequency</u>' is just another way of saying 'how much' or 'how many'.

2) You can rearrange it to work out <u>how much</u> a bar represents.

Frequency = Frequency Density × Class Width = AREA of bar

EXAMPLE: This table and histogram show the lengths of beetles found in a garden.

Length (mm)	Frequency
$0 < x \leq 10$	32
$10 < x \leq 15$	36
$15 < x \leq 18$	
$18 < x \leq 22$	28
$22 < x \leq 30$	16

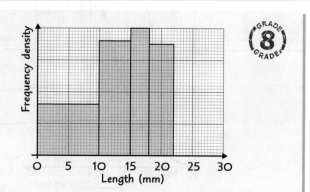

a) **Use the histogram to find the missing entry in the table.**

1) Add a <u>frequency density</u> column to the table and fill in what you can using the formula.

Frequency density
32 ÷ 10 = 3.2
36 ÷ 5 = 7.2
28 ÷ 4 = 7
16 ÷ 8 = 2

2) Use the frequency densities to <u>label</u> the <u>vertical axis</u> of the graph.

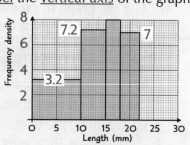

3) Now use the <u>3rd bar</u> to find the frequency for the class '$15 < x \leq 18$'.

Frequency density = 8 and class width = 3.
So frequency = frequency density × class width = 8 × 3 = 24

b) **Use the table to add the bar for the class '$22 < x \leq 30$' to the histogram.**

Frequency density = frequency ÷ class width = $\frac{16}{8}$ = 2

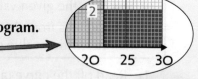

c) **Estimate the number of beetles between 7.5 mm and 12.5 mm in length.**

Use the formula <u>frequency = frequency density × class width</u> — multiply the frequency density of the <u>class</u> by the width of the <u>part of that class</u> you're interested in.

So the estimated number of beetles between 7.5 mm and 12.5 mm is:

3.2 × (10 − 7.5) + 7.2 × (12.5 − 10) = 3.2 × 2.5 + 7.2 × 2.5 = 8 + 18 = 26

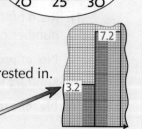

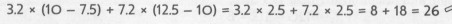

You need to use the height and width of a bar to find its frequency

Although they look very like harmless bar charts, histograms are actually pretty unpleasant. Make sure you get your head around the method above.

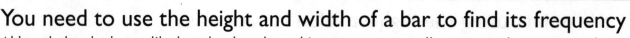

Simple Charts

These charts all show <u>frequencies</u>. (Remember... frequency = '<u>how many</u> of something'.)

Pictograms Show Frequencies Using **Symbols**

Every pictogram has a <u>key</u> telling you what one symbol represents.

> With pictograms, you <u>must</u> use the key.

EXAMPLE: **This pictogram shows how many peaches were sold in a shop on different days.**

a) **How many peaches were sold on Tuesday?**
Each circle represents 4 peaches. There are 2 circles for Tuesday.
4 × 2 = 8 peaches

b) **10 peaches were sold on Friday.**
Use this information to complete the diagram.
You need 2 whole circles (= 8 peaches),
plus another half a circle (= 2 peaches).

| Friday | ●●◖ |

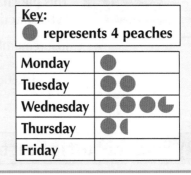

Key:	● represents 4 peaches
Monday	●
Tuesday	●●
Wednesday	●●●◖
Thursday	●◖
Friday	

Bar Charts Show Frequencies Using **Bars**

1) <u>Bar charts</u> are very similar to pictograms. Frequencies are shown by the <u>heights</u> of the different bars.
2) <u>Dual bar charts</u> show two things at once — they're good for <u>comparing</u> different sets of data.

EXAMPLE: **This dual bar chart shows the number of men and women visiting a coffee shop on different days.**

a) **How many men visited the coffee shop altogether?**
Men are shown by the <u>red bars</u>.
Add up the numbers shown by the heights.
4 + 3 + 6 + 2 = 15 men

b) **On which day did the most women visit the coffee shop?**
Find the <u>tallest</u> green bar.   Tuesday

<u>Both</u> axes on a bar chart <u>must</u> be <u>labelled</u>.

Bars representing different categories are separated by gaps.

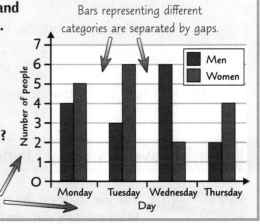

Two-Way Tables Show **How Many** in each **Category**

EXAMPLE: **This two-way table shows the number of cakes and loaves of bread a bakery sells on Friday and Saturday one week.**

	Cakes	Loaves of bread	Total
Friday	12	10	
Saturday	4	14	18
Total	16	24	40

a) **How many loaves of bread were sold on Saturday?**
Read across to 'Loaves of bread'
and down to 'Saturday'.   14 loaves of bread

	Cakes	Loaves of bread	Total
Friday	12	10	
Saturday	4	14	18
Total	16	24	40

b) **How many items were sold in total on Friday?**
Add the number of cakes for Friday
to the number of loaves of bread.   12 + 10 = 22

Or you could subtract the total for Saturday from the overall total: 40 − 18 = 22.

Pie Charts

They might seem pretty simple, but examiners can make <u>pie charts</u> into tricky exam questions. Just remember the <u>Golden Pie Chart Rule</u>...

> **The TOTAL of Everything = 360°**

1) **Fraction** of the Total = **Angle ÷ 360°**

EXAMPLE: This pie chart shows the colour of all the cars sold by a dealer. **What fraction of the cars were red?**

Just remember that 'everything = 360°'.

$$\text{Fraction of red cars} = \frac{\text{angle of red cars}}{\text{angle of everything}} = \frac{72°}{360°} = \frac{1}{5}$$

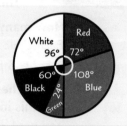

2) Find a **Multiplier** to Calculate Your **Angles**

EXAMPLE: Draw a pie chart to show this information about the types of animal in a petting zoo.

Animal	Geese	Hamsters	Guinea pigs	Rabbits	Ducks
Number	12	20	17	15	26

1) Find the <u>total</u> by <u>adding</u>. 12 + 20 + 17 + 15 + 26 = 90

2) 'Everything = 360°' — so find the <u>multiplier</u> (or <u>divider</u>) that turns your total into 360°.   Multiplier = 360 ÷ 90 = 4

3) Now <u>multiply every number</u> by 4 to get the <u>angle</u> for each sector.

Angle	12 × 4 = 48°	20 × 4 = 80°	17 × 4 = 68°	15 × 4 = 60°	26 × 4 = 104°	Total = 360°

4) Draw your pie chart accurately using a <u>protractor</u>.

3) Find **How Many** by Using the Angle for **1 Thing**

EXAMPLE: The pie chart on the right shows information about the types of animals liked most by different students. There were 9 students altogether.

a) **Work out the number of students who liked dogs most.**

1) 'Everything = 360°', so: → 9 students = 360°

2) <u>Divide by 9</u> to find: → 1 student = 40°

3) The <u>angle</u> for dogs is 160°, and 160° ÷ 40° = 4: → 4 students = 160° — 4 students liked dogs most

b) **The pie chart on the left shows information about the types of animals liked most by a different group of students. Dafydd says, "This means that 4 students in this group like dogs most." Explain why Dafydd is not correct.**

We don't know how many students in total the pie chart represents, so we can't work out how many students liked dogs most.

It's important to know the uses of each graph and chart

Knowing the type of data shown on different graphs and charts will help you to interpret them.

Warm-Up and Worked Exam Questions

There are some lovely warm-up questions here covering stats graphs. Now's the time to go back over any bits you're not sure of — in the exam it'll be too late.

Warm-Up Questions

The table on the right shows data on the lengths of slugs in a garden.

1) Using this data, draw:
   a) a cumulative frequency diagram
   b) a histogram
   c) a pie chart

2) Using one of your diagrams, work out the median of the data.

3) Estimate the number of slugs that were less than 70 mm long.

Length (mm)	Frequency
$0 < x \le 40$	30
$40 < x \le 60$	55
$60 < x \le 75$	75
$75 < x \le 100$	20

Worked Exam Questions

To get you started, I've worked through this question for you. Have your pencil at the ready, though — there'll be plenty of diagrams for you to draw in the questions on the next page...

1   The cumulative frequency table below gives information about the length of time it takes to travel between Udderston and Trundle on the main road each morning.

Journey Time (t mins)	$0 < t \le 20$	$0 < t \le 25$	$0 < t \le 30$	$0 < t \le 35$	$0 < t \le 45$	$0 < t \le 60$
Cumulative Frequency	7	22	36	45	49	50

a)   On the graph paper below, draw a cumulative frequency graph for the table.

The table gives you the cumulative frequency already, so you don't need to work it out yourself.

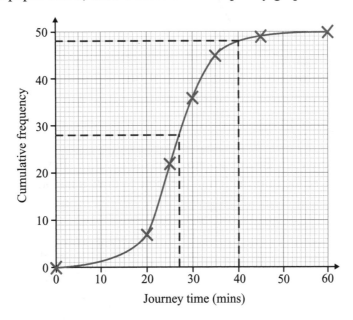

[2 marks]

b)   Use your graph to estimate the number of journeys that took between 27 and 40 minutes.

Draw lines on the graph at 27 mins and 40 mins.

$48 - 28 = 20$

..........20.......... journeys

[2 marks]

Exam Questions

2 One hundred vehicles on a road were recorded as part of a traffic study. The results were collected in a two-way table. Part of this table is shown below.

	Van	Motorbike	Car	Total
Travelling North	15	....	....	48
Travelling South	20	....	23	....
Total	....	21	....	100

a) Fill in the missing numbers in the two-way table.

[3 marks]

b) Of the vehicles travelling north, how many were not cars?

....
[1 mark]

3 30 pet owners were asked what their first pet was. Some of the results are shown in the table below.

a) Accurately complete the pie chart to show this information.

First Pet	Frequency
Cat	
Dog	15
Hamster	
Other	1

[3 marks]

b) How many people had a hamster as their first pet?

....
[2 marks]

4 100 Year 11 pupils were each given a potato. The table below shows how long it took the pupils to peel their potato. Use the information in the table to draw a histogram on the grid below.

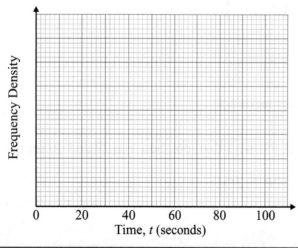

Time, t (s)	Frequency
$0 < t \leq 20$	15
$20 < t \leq 30$	35
$30 < t \leq 40$	30
$40 < t \leq 60$	15
$60 < t \leq 100$	5

[2 marks]

Probability Basics

A lot of people reckon <u>probability</u> is pretty tough. But learn the <u>basics</u> well, and it'll all make sense.

All **Probabilities** are **Between 0 and 1**

Probabilities are <u>always</u> between 0 and 1. The <u>higher</u> the probability of something, the <u>more likely</u> it is.
- A probability of <u>zero</u> means it will <u>never</u> happen.
- A probability of <u>one</u> means it <u>definitely</u> will.

You <u>can't</u> have a probability <u>bigger than 1</u>.

Probabilities can be given as <u>fractions</u>, <u>decimals</u> or <u>percentages</u>.

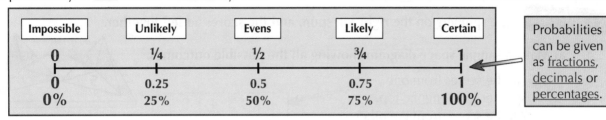

Impossible	Unlikely	Evens	Likely	Certain
0	¼	½	¾	1
0	0.25	0.5	0.75	1
0%	25%	50%	75%	100%

You Can Find **Some** Probabilities Using a **Formula**

A <u>word of warning</u>... the following formula only works if <u>all</u> the possible results are <u>equally likely</u>.

$$\text{Probability} = \frac{\text{Number of ways for something to happen}}{\text{Total number of possible results}}$$

Words like '<u>fair</u>' and '<u>at random</u>' show possible results are all equally likely. '<u>Biased</u>' and '<u>unfair</u>' mean the opposite.

EXAMPLE: **Work out the probability of randomly picking a letter 'P' from the tiles below.**

APPLE PIE

1) There are <u>3 P's</u> — so there are <u>3 different ways</u> to 'pick a letter P'.

2) And there are <u>8 tiles</u> altogether — each of these is a <u>possible result</u>.

$$\text{Probability} = \frac{\text{number of ways to pick a P}}{\text{total number of possible results}}$$

$$= \frac{3}{8} \text{ (or 0.375)}$$

Probabilities **Add Up to 1**

1) If <u>only one</u> possible result can happen at a time, then the probabilities of <u>all</u> the results <u>add up to 1</u>.

Probabilities always ADD UP to 1

2) So since something must either <u>happen</u> or <u>not happen</u> (i.e. <u>only one</u> of these can happen at a time):

P(event happens) + P(event doesn't happen) = 1

So the probability of an event <u>not happening</u> equals <u>1 minus</u> the probability of it happening.

EXAMPLE: **A spinner has different numbers of red, blue, yellow and green sections. What is the probability of spinning green?**

Colour	red	blue	yellow	green
Probability	0.1	0.4	0.3	

<u>Only one</u> of the results can happen at a time, so all the probabilities must <u>add up to 1</u>.

$$P(\text{green}) = 1 - (0.1 + 0.4 + 0.3) = 0.2$$

Probabilities are between 0 and 1

If this page hasn't totally sunk in, go back through it again — you need to get the basics clear in your head.

Listing Outcomes and Expected Frequency

With a lot of probability questions, a good place to start is with a list of all the <u>things that could happen</u> (also known as <u>outcomes</u>). Once you've got a list of outcomes, the rest of the question is easy.

Listing **All Outcomes**: **Two Coins, Dice, Spinners**

A <u>sample space diagram</u> is a good way to show all the possible outcomes if there are <u>two activities</u> going on (e.g. two coins being tossed, or a dice being thrown and a spinner being spun, etc.).

> **EXAMPLE:** **The spinners on the right are spun, and the scores added together.**
>
> **a) Make a sample space diagram showing all the possible outcomes.**
>
> 1) All the scores from one spinner go <u>along the top</u>. All the scores from the other spinner go <u>down the side</u>.
>
> 2) <u>Add</u> the two scores together to get the different possible totals (the <u>outcomes</u>).
>
> | + | 3 | 4 | 5 |
> |---|---|---|---|
> | 1 | 4 | 5 | 6 |
> | 2 | 5 | 6 | 7 |
> | 3 | 6 | 7 | 8 |
>
> There are <u>9 outcomes</u> — even though some of the totals are repeated.
>
> **b) Find the probability of spinning a total of 6.**
>
> There are <u>9 possible outcomes</u> altogether, and <u>3 ways</u> to score 6.
>
> $$P(\text{total} = 6) = \frac{\text{ways to score 6}}{\text{total number of possible outcomes}} = \frac{3}{9} = \frac{1}{3}$$

Use Probability to Find an "**Expected Frequency**"

You can <u>estimate</u> how often you'd <u>expect</u> something to happen if you carry out an experiment <u>n times</u>.

> **Expected times outcome will happen = probability × number of trials**

> **EXAMPLE:** **A game involves throwing a fair six-sided dice. The player wins if they score either a 5 or a 6. If one person plays the game 180 times, estimate the number of times they will win.**
>
> 1) First calculate the probability that they win <u>each game</u>.
>
> $$\text{Probability of winning} = \frac{\text{number of ways to win}}{\text{total number of possible results}}$$
> $$= \frac{2}{6} = \frac{1}{3}$$
>
> 2) Then <u>estimate</u> the number of times they'll win in <u>180</u> separate attempts.
>
> $$\text{Expected number of wins} = \text{probability of winning} \times \text{number of trials}$$
> $$= \frac{1}{3} \times 180$$
> $$= 60$$

Expected frequency is how many times you'd expect it to happen

Make sure you can remember the formula for expected frequency in the box above. Try to get your head around drawing sample space diagrams — they're really useful when you've got two activities happening.

The AND / OR Rules

This page is also about when you have <u>more than one</u> thing happening at a time.

Combined Probability — Two or More Events

> 1) **Always break down a complicated-looking probability question into A SEQUENCE of SEPARATE SINGLE EVENTS.**
> 2) **Find the probability of EACH of these SEPARATE SINGLE EVENTS.**
> 3) **Apply the AND/OR rule.**

And now for the rules. Say you have <u>two events</u> — call them A and B...

The **AND Rule** Gives **P(Both Events Happen)**

$$P(A \text{ and } B) = P(A) \times P(B)$$

This says: The probability of Event A <u>AND</u> Event B <u>BOTH</u> happening is equal to the two separate probabilities <u>MULTIPLIED together</u>.

This only works when the two events are <u>independent</u>, i.e. the result of one event <u>does not affect</u> the other event.

 **Dave picks one ball at random from each of bags X and Y. Find the probability that he picks a yellow ball from both bags.**

1) Write down the <u>probabilities</u> of the different events.

P(Dave picks a yellow ball from bag X) = $\frac{4}{10}$ = 0.4.

P(Dave picks a yellow ball from bag Y) = $\frac{2}{8}$ = 0.25.

2) Use the <u>formula</u>.   So P(Dave picks a yellow ball from both bags) = 0.4 × 0.25 = 0.1

The **OR Rule** Gives **P(At Least One Event Happens)**

$$P(A \text{ or } B) = P(A) + P(B)$$

This says: The probability of <u>EITHER</u> Event A <u>OR</u> Event B happening is equal to the two separate probabilities <u>ADDED together</u>.

This only works when the two events are <u>mutually exclusive</u> — in other words, when they <u>can't</u> <u>both happen</u> at the same time.

 **A spinner with red, blue, yellow and green sections was spun. The probability of it landing on each colour is shown in the table. Find the probability of spinning either red or green.**

Colour	red	blue	yellow	green
Probability	0.25	0.3	0.35	0.1

1) Write down the <u>probabilities</u> of the different events.

P(lands on red) = 0.25 and P(lands on green) = 0.1

2) Use the <u>formula</u>.   So P(Lands on either red or green) = 0.25 + 0.1 = 0.35

Two rules to learn here

You won't go far if you don't learn the AND/OR rules. The way to remember them is that it's the wrong way round — you'd want AND to go with '+' but it doesn't. It's 'AND with ×' and 'OR with +'.

Warm-Up and Worked Exam Questions

A few lovely warm-up questions for you here. If you have any problems with these,
flick back and have another look at the last few pages before looking at the exam questions.

Warm-Up Questions

1) Calculate the probability of the fair spinner on the right landing on 4.

2) If the probability of spinning red on a spinner is 0.8,
   find the probability of spinning any colour except red.

3) Two fair 6-sided dice are thrown, and their scores added together.
   a) Find the probability of throwing a total of 7.
   b) If the pair of dice are thrown 300 times, how many times would you expect a total of 7?

4) A card is randomly chosen from a pack of 52 playing cards.
   Find the probability that the card is an ace or a picture card.

Worked Exam Questions

Look through this worked exam question and make sure you understand it — don't leave it to chance.

1   Here is a 5-sided spinner. The spinner is biased.

    The probability that the spinner will land on each of
    the numbers 1 to 4 is given in the table below.

Number	1	2	3	4	5
Probability	0.3	0.15	0.2	0.25	

The spinner is spun once.

a)   Work out the probability the spinner will not land on 2.

$$P(\text{not } 2) = 1 - P(2) = 1 - 0.15 = 0.85$$

0.85
....
[2 marks]

b)   Work out the probability the spinner will land on an odd number.

$$P(\text{even}) = P(2 \text{ or } 4) = 0.15 + 0.25 = 0.4$$
$$\text{So } P(\text{odd}) = 1 - P(\text{even}) = 1 - 0.4 = 0.6$$

You could also work out P(5) first by doing
1 − (0.3 + 0.15 + 0.2 + 0.25) = 0.1
Then P(odd) = P(1 or 3 or 5) = 0.3 + 0.2 + 0.1

0.6
....
[3 marks]

The spinner is spun twice.

c)   Work out the probability that the spinner will land on 3 both times. (6)

$$P(3 \text{ both times}) = P(3 \text{ first time and 3 second time})$$
$$= P(3) \times P(3) = 0.2 \times 0.2 = 0.04$$

0.04
....
[2 marks]

Exam Questions

2   There are 10 counters in a bag. Four of the counters are blue and the rest are red. **(3)**
One counter is picked out at random.

   a)   Work out the probability that the counter picked is red.
        Give your answer as a fraction in its lowest terms.

        ....
        [2 mark]

   b)   What is the probability that the counter picked is green?

        ....
        [1 mark]

3   The total number of pupils in a school is 834. **(4)**
Work out an estimate for the number of pupils who were born on a Tuesday.

   TIP: the answer has to be
   a whole number of pupils,
    so you'll need to round.

        .... pupils
        [4 marks]

4   Josie has six different cards, shown below.

   a)   Find the probability that a randomly chosen card will have fewer than 3 dots on it. **(5)**

        ....
        [2 marks]

   b)   Josie picks a card, replaces it and picks another card. **(8)**
        What is the probability that the total number of dots on the two cards will be 4?

        ....
        [3 marks]

   c)   Josie picks another two cards at random, but this time she does not replace them. **(8)**
        What is the probability that the total number of dots on the cards will be more than 9?

        ....
        [3 marks]

Tree Diagrams

Learn these basic details (which apply to ALL tree diagrams). Then you'll be ready for the one in the exam.

Remember These **Four** Key **Tree Diagram Facts**

1) On any set of branches which meet at a point, the probabilities must add up to 1.

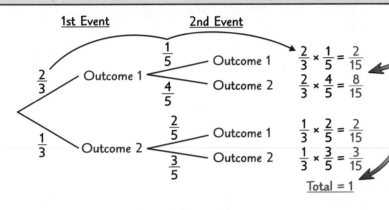

2) Multiply along the branches to get the end probabilities.

3) Check your diagram — the end probabilities must add up to 1.

4) To answer any question, add up the relevant end probabilities (see below).

EXAMPLES:

1. A box contains 5 red discs and 3 green discs. One disc is taken at random and its colour noted before being replaced. A second disc is then taken. Find the probability that both discs are the same colour.

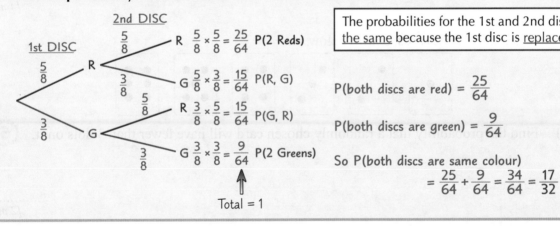

The probabilities for the 1st and 2nd discs are the same because the 1st disc is replaced.

P(both discs are red) = $\frac{25}{64}$

P(both discs are green) = $\frac{9}{64}$

So P(both discs are same colour)
$= \frac{25}{64} + \frac{9}{64} = \frac{34}{64} = \frac{17}{32}$

2. A box contains 5 red discs and 3 green discs. Two discs are taken at random without replacement. Find the probability that both discs are the same colour.

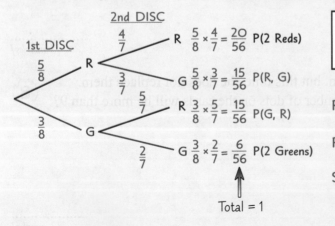

The probabilities for the 2nd pick depend on the colour of the 1st disc picked (i.e. they're conditional probabilities) because the 1st disc is not replaced.

P(both discs are red) = $\frac{20}{56} = \frac{5}{14}$

P(both discs are green) = $\frac{6}{56} = \frac{3}{28}$

So P(both discs are same colour)
$= \frac{5}{14} + \frac{3}{28} = \frac{13}{28}$

Tree Diagrams

Four Extra Details for the Tree Diagram Method:

1) Always break up the question into a sequence of separate events.

You need a sequence of events to be able to draw any sort of tree diagram.
For example... '3 coins are tossed at the same time' — just split it into 3 separate events.

2) Don't feel you have to draw complete tree diagrams.

For example... 'What is the probability of throwing a fair six-sided
dice 3 times and getting 2 sixes followed by an even number?'

The diagram on the right is all you need to get the answer: $\frac{1}{6} \times \frac{1}{6} \times \frac{1}{2} = \frac{1}{72}$

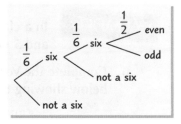

3) Watch out for conditional probabilities.

This is where the probabilities on a set of branches change, depending on the
result of the previous event. For example... if you're picking things at random
(e.g. cards from a pack, or balls out of a bag) without replacing your earlier picks.

See the last example on p.188.

4) With 'AT LEAST' questions, it's always (1 – probability of 'LESS THAN that many'):

For example... 'I throw 3 fair six-sided dice. Find the probability of throwing AT LEAST one six.'

There are in fact quite a few different ways of 'throwing AT LEAST one six',
and you could spend a long time working out all the different probabilities.

The clever trick you should know is this:
The probability of 'AT LEAST something or other' is just: 1 – probability of 'less than that many'.
So: P(at least one six) = 1 – P(less than one six) = 1 – P(no sixes).

EXAMPLE: Tiles showing the following letters are placed in a hat.

BARBARA

Two tiles are picked out at random and their letters noted, without replacement.

a) Complete the tree diagram below to show whether or not each of the letters picked is a 'B'.

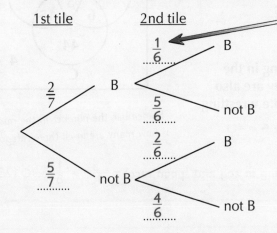

The probabilities for the 2nd tile depend on what you pick for the 1st tile — so these are conditional probabilities.

b) Calculate the probability that at least one of the selected tiles is a 'B'.

P(at least 1 tile is B) = 1 – P(less than 1 tile is B)

= 1 – P(neither tile is B)

$= 1 - \frac{5}{7} \times \frac{4}{6}$

$= 1 - \frac{20}{42} = \frac{22}{42} = \frac{11}{21}$

See how useful tree diagrams are

With probability questions that seem hard, drawing a tree diagram can be a good place to start.
It takes some thinking to decide how to draw it and which bits you need, but after that it's plain sailing.

Probability from Venn Diagrams

If you can't remember everything about <u>Venn diagrams</u> and need a refresher, head back to pages 40-41. Once you've done that, <u>read on</u> to find out how they can be used to <u>calculate probabilities</u>.

Finding Probabilities from **Venn Diagrams**

<u>Venn diagrams</u> can be used to show the number of things in <u>different groups</u>, or with certain characteristics. You can easily work out probabilities by <u>counting up</u> the things you're interested in.

EXAMPLE: In a class of 30 pupils, 8 of them like mustard, 24 of them like ketchup and 5 of them like both mustard and ketchup.

a) **Complete the Venn diagram below showing this information.**

Start by filling in the <u>overlap</u>.

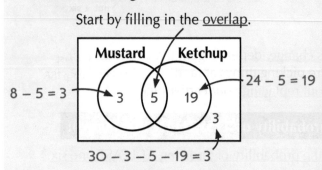

$8 - 5 = 3$

$24 - 5 = 19$

$30 - 3 - 5 - 19 = 3$

b) **How many pupils like mustard or ketchup?**

This is the number of pupils in the <u>union</u> of the two sets.

$3 + 5 + 19 = 27$

c) **What is the probability that a randomly selected pupil will like mustard and ketchup?**

<u>5 out of 30</u> pupils are in the <u>intersection</u>. $\frac{5}{30} = \frac{1}{6}$

You could get a question in your exam about finding probabilities from a Venn diagram with <u>three</u> circles. Don't panic — it works <u>the same</u> as one with two circles, but the calculations are a bit <u>trickier</u>.

EXAMPLE: The Venn diagram below shows the number of children competing in the egg and spoon race (E), sack race (S) and crocodile wrestling (C) at a school sports day.

a) **Find the probability that a randomly selected child is not competing in the crocodile wrestling.**

n(children) = 4 + 44 + 15 + 5 + 6 + 17 + 12 + 32 = 135

n(not competing in crocodile wrestling) = 17 + 12 + 32 + 4 = 65

P(not competing in crocodile wrestling) = $\frac{65}{135} = \frac{13}{27}$

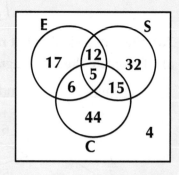

b) **Given that a randomly selected child is competing in the egg and spoon race, find the probability that they are also competing in both the sack race and the crocodile wrestling.**

n(competing in egg and spoon race) = 17 + 12 + 5 + 6 = 40

n(competing in all three events) = 5

Remember, the number in the middle is how many are in all three categories.

P(competing in all three events given they're competing in egg and spoon race) = $\frac{5}{40} = \frac{1}{8}$ or 0.125

Make sure you can remember all the set notation from Section One

All the stuff that you did on intersections and unions before relates to the AND/OR rules in probability. To find P(A and B), you want to find A ∩ B on your Venn diagram, and P(A or B) corresponds to A ∪ B. If you're asked to find a probability given an event, only consider the bits inside the circle for that event.

Relative Frequency

You need to know how to use probability <u>experiments</u> to find <u>relative frequencies</u>.

Fair or Biased?

The probability of rolling a three on a normal dice is $\frac{1}{6}$ — you know that each of the 6 numbers on the dice is <u>equally likely</u> to be rolled, and there's <u>only 1 three</u>.

BUT this only works if it's a <u>fair dice</u>. If the dice is a bit <u>wonky</u> (the technical term is 'biased') then each number <u>won't</u> have an equal chance of being rolled. This is where <u>relative frequency</u> comes in — you can use it to <u>estimate</u> probabilities when things might be wonky.

Do the Experiment **Again** and **Again** and **Again...**

You need to do an experiment <u>over and over again</u> and count how often an outcome happens (its <u>frequency</u>). Then you can do a quick calculation to find the <u>relative frequency</u> of something.

$$\text{Relative frequency} = \frac{\text{Frequency}}{\text{Number of times you tried the experiment}}$$

An experiment could just mean rolling a dice.

You can use the <u>relative frequency</u> of an outcome to <u>estimate</u> its <u>probability</u>.

 **The spinner on the right was spun 100 times. Use the results in the table below to estimate the probability of getting each of the scores.**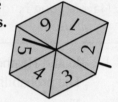

Score	1	2	3	4	5	6
Frequency	10	14	36	20	11	9

<u>Divide</u> each of the frequencies by 100 to find the <u>relative frequencies</u>.

Score	1	2	3	4	5	6
Frequency	10	14	36	20	11	9
Relative Frequency	$\frac{10}{100} = 0.1$	$\frac{14}{100} = 0.14$	$\frac{36}{100} = 0.36$	$\frac{20}{100} = 0.2$	$\frac{11}{100} = 0.11$	$\frac{9}{100} = 0.09$

The <u>MORE TIMES</u> you do the experiment, the <u>MORE ACCURATE</u> your estimate of the probability should be.

E.g. If you spun the above spinner <u>1000 times</u>, you'd get a <u>better</u> estimate of the probability of each score.

If your answers are <u>far away</u> from what you'd expect, then you can say that the dice/spinner/etc. is <u>biased</u>.

EXAMPLE: **Do the above results suggest that the spinner is biased?**

Yes, because the relative frequency of 3 is much higher than you'd expect, while the relative frequencies of 1, 5 and 6 are much lower.

For a <u>fair</u> 6-sided spinner, you'd expect all the relative frequencies to be about 1 ÷ 6 = 0.17(ish).

More experiments mean a more accurate probability estimate

Learn the formula for calculating relative frequency. If something is biased, this just means it isn't fair. Remember that even with a fair dice you're unlikely to get exactly the expected result, but the more experiments you do, the closer to the true probability you'll get.

Warm-Up and Worked Exam Questions

Probability is really not that difficult once you get the hang of it, but it's important to get loads of practice, so try these warm-up questions. Take a look back at anything you're unsure about.

Warm-Up Questions

1) A bag contains 6 red balls and 4 black ones. Two balls are picked at random (with replacement). Use a tree diagram to find the probability that they're different colours.

2) There are 21 numbers, 1-21, in a lottery draw. A machine selects the numbers randomly (without replacement). Using a tree diagram, find the probability that out of the first two numbers selected:
   a) at least one is even,   b) one is odd and one is even.

3) Out of 80 customers at an ice cream van, 48 had syrup, 28 had sprinkles and 16 had both toppings on their ice cream. Use a Venn diagram to find the probability that a randomly selected customer doesn't have either topping, given that they don't have sprinkles.

4) Sandro rolled a dice 1000 times and got the results shown in the table below.

Score	1	2	3	4	5	6
Frequency	140	137	138	259	161	165

Find the relative frequencies for each of the scores 1-6. Do you think the dice is biased?

Worked Exam Questions

Have a good hard look at this worked exam question. Make sure you understand each bit — you'll usually get at least one probability question in the exam.

1   Jo and Heather are meeting for coffee.
     The probability that Jo will wear burgundy trousers is $\frac{2}{5}$.

     There is a one in four chance that Heather will wear burgundy trousers.
     The two events are independent.

     a)   Complete the tree diagram below.

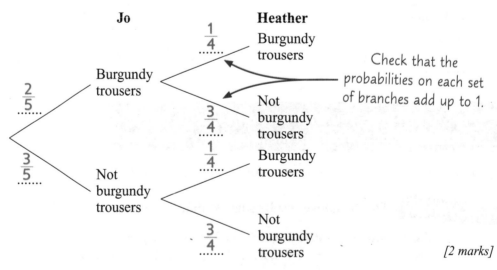

Check that the probabilities on each set of branches add up to 1.

[2 marks]

     b)   What is the probability that neither of them wear burgundy trousers?

$$\text{P(neither wear burgundy trousers)} = \frac{3}{5} \times \frac{3}{4} = \frac{3 \times 3}{5 \times 4} = \frac{9}{20}$$

$\frac{9}{20}$

[2 marks]

Exam Questions

2 The Venn diagram on the right shows the number
   of female contestants (*F*) and singers (*S*)
   in a talent competition.

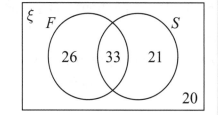

a) Find the probability that a randomly selected
    contestant isn't a singer.

....
[1 mark]

b) Find the probability that a randomly selected contestant
    isn't female, given that they're a singer.

....
[1 mark]

3 A box of chocolates contains 12 chocolates.
   5 of the chocolates are milk chocolate, 4 are plain chocolate and 3 are white chocolate. **⑧**
   Two chocolates are chosen at random without replacement.

a) Complete the tree diagram below.

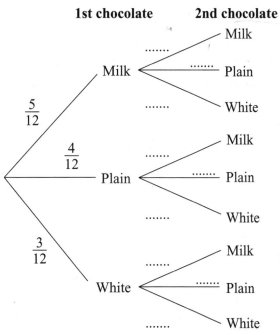

[2 marks]

b) Calculate the probability that one milk chocolate and one white chocolate are chosen.

....
[3 marks]

c) Work out the probability that at least one plain chocolate is chosen.

....
[3 marks]

Revision Questions for Section Six

Here's the inevitable list of straight-down-the-middle questions to test how much you know.
- Try these questions and <u>tick off each one</u> when you <u>get it right</u>.
- When you've done <u>all the questions</u> for a topic and are <u>completely happy</u> with it, tick off the topic.

Averages and Spread (p.170-171) ☑

1) Write down the definitions for the mode, median, mean and range. ☑

2) a) Find the mode, median, mean and range of this data: 2, 8, 11, 15, 22, 24, 27, 30, 31, 31, 41 ☑
   b) For the above data, find the lower and upper quartiles and the interquartile range. ☑

3) Name two things you should look at when you compare two data sets. ☑

Frequency Tables and Cumulative Frequency (p.172-177) ☑

4) For this grouped frequency table showing the lengths of some pet alligators:
   a) find the modal class,
   b) find the class containing the median,
   c) estimate the mean. ☑

Length (y m)	Frequency
$1.4 \leq y < 1.5$	4
$1.5 \leq y < 1.6$	8
$1.6 \leq y < 1.7$	5
$1.7 \leq y < 1.8$	2

5) Draw a cumulative frequency graph for the data in the above grouped frequency table. ☑

More Graphs and Charts (p.178-180) ☑

6) How do you work out what frequency a bar on a histogram represents? ☑

7) As well as counting the number of symbols on a pictogram, you need to check
   one other thing before you can find a frequency. What's the other thing? ☑

8) The numbers of students in different years at a village school
   are shown in this table. Draw a bar chart to show this data. ☑

School Year	7	8	9	10	11
No. of students	40	30	40	45	25

9) Draw a pie chart to represent the data in question 8. Label each sector with its angle. ☑

Easy Probability (p.183-184) ☑

10) What does a probability of 0 mean? What about a probability of $\frac{1}{2}$? ☑

11) I pick a random number between 1 and 50. Find the probability that my number is a multiple of 6. ☑

12) What do the probabilities of all possible outcomes of an experiment add up to
    (if none of them can happen together)? ☑

13) I flip a fair coin twice.   HT means Heads on the first flip and Tails on the second.
    a) Complete this sample space diagram showing all the possible results.
    b) Use your diagram to find the probability of getting 2 Heads. ☑

	Second flip	
	Heads	Tails
First flip Heads		HT
Tails		

14) Write down the formula for estimating how many times you'd expect something to happen in n trials. ☑

Harder Probability (p.185-191) ☑

15) I throw a fair six-sided dice twice. Find P(I throw a 6 and then an even number). ☑

16) I throw a fair six-sided dice. Find P(I throw either a 5 or a multiple of 3). ☑

17) I pick a card at random from a normal pack of cards. I make a note of it, but don't replace it
    before I then pick a second card. Use a tree diagram to find the probability of me getting two kings. ☑

18) 100 people were asked whether they like tea or coffee. Half the people said they like coffee,
    34 people said they like tea, 20 people said they like both.
    a) Show this information on a Venn diagram.
    b) If one of the 100 people is randomly chosen, find the probability of them liking tea or coffee. ☑

19) When might you need to use relative frequency to find a probability? ☑

Practice Paper 1
As final preparation for the exams, we've included two full practice papers to really put your Maths skills to the test. There's a whole page of formulas you can use on p.252. Good luck...

Candidate Surname

Candidate Forename(s)

Centre Number

Candidate Number

Candidate Signature

Edexcel International GCSE

Mathematics

Practice Paper 1

Time allowed: 2 hours

You must have:
Pen, pencil, eraser, ruler, protractor, pair of compasses.
You may use tracing paper.

You **may use** a calculator.

Instructions to candidates
*   Use **black** ink to write your answers.
*   Write your name and other details in the spaces provided above.
*   Answer **all** questions in the spaces provided.
*   Correct answers without sufficient working might not be awarded any marks.
*   Do all rough work on the paper.
*   Anything you write on the formula sheet will **not** gain any credit.

Information for candidates
*   The marks available are given in brackets at the end of each question.
*   There are 24 questions in this paper. There are no blank pages.
*   There are 100 marks available for this paper.

196

Answer ALL the questions.

Write your answers in the spaces provided.

You must show all of your working.

1   Katie averages a speed of 90 km/h driving home from work. The trip takes 40 minutes.
    How far is Katie's journey home?

.... km

[Total 3 marks]

2   Last year a bookshop sold 9000 books.
    Three-quarters of all the books sold were fiction.
    The rest were autobiographies and revision guides in the ratio 7 : 3.

    How many revision guides were sold?

....

[Total 3 marks]

3   The diagram below shows a regular hexagon inside a regular octagon.
    Vertices *A* and *B* coincide with vertices *I* and *J* respectively.

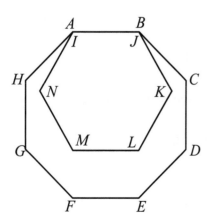

Find the size of angle *CBK*.

Not to scale

.... °

[Total 2 marks]

1

4 Ben has four number cards.

| 7 | | 12 | | ? | | ? |

His four numbers have a median value of 12 and a mean of 13.
Work out the range of Ben's four numbers. Show how you worked out your answer.

....

[Total 3 marks]

5 Adam is a car salesman with an annual salary of £21 000.
He also gets paid commission of 2% on any sales that he makes.
Last year his salary made up 60% of his total earnings.

What was the total value of the cars he sold last year?

£ ....

[Total 4 marks]

6 Factorise the following expressions fully.

(a) $9x + 6$

....

[1]

(b) $8y^3 + 4y$

....

[2]

(c) $25a^2 - b^2$

....

[2]

[Total 5 marks]

---

7 The shape below is a kite made up of three triangles.

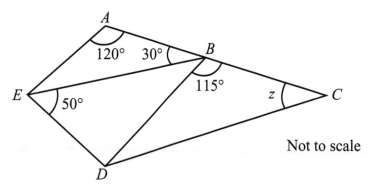

Not to scale

Work out the size of angle z.

$\circ$

....

[Total 3 marks]

8 $X = 2^8$, $Y = 2^5 \times 5^3$ and $Z = 2^6 \times 5^2 \times 7$.

Write as the product of prime factors:

(a) the LCM of X, Y and Z,

....

[2]

(b) the HCF of X, Y and Z.

....

[2]

[Total 4 marks]

9 Rearrange the equations below to make b the subject in each case.

(a) $a = \frac{1}{2}bc^2$

....

[2]

(b) $12 = \dfrac{bx + 8}{by - 4}$

....

[3]

[Total 5 marks]

4

10 (a) Find the equation of the line that passes through points $(-2, -2)$ and $(4, 7)$.
Give your answer in the form $ax + by + c = 0$, where a, b and c are integers.

....

[4]

(b) Find the equation of the line that is perpendicular to the line $y = 4x - 2$
and passes through the point $(8, 1)$.

....

[3]

[Total 7 marks]

5

11 Solve the following pair of simultaneous equations.

$$3x + 5y = 5$$
$$3y - 2x = -16$$

$x = $ .... $y = $ ....

[Total 4 marks]

12 The distance from London to New York is 5600 km to the nearest 100 km.

(a) Write down the shortest possible distance between the two cities.

.... km

[1]

(b) Calculate the longest possible distance for a trip from London to New York and back again.

.... km

[2]

[Total 3 marks]

6

13 (a) Simplify $(8n^6)^{\frac{1}{3}}$

....

[2]

(b) Expand and simplify $(p + 1)(p - 3)(p + 5)$

....

[3]

(c) Solve $q(2q - 4) + 4(q^2 + q + 11) = 68$

....

[3]

[Total 8 marks]

---

14 A biased 5-sided spinner is numbered 1-5.

The probability that the spinner will land on each of the numbers 1 to 5 is given in this table.

Number	1	2	3	4	5
Probability	0.3	0.15	0.2	0.25	0.1

(a) The spinner is spun twice. What is the probability that it lands on a 2 and then a 3?

....

[2]

(b) What is the probability of the spinner landing on a prime number or a multiple of 2?

....

[2]

[Total 4 marks]

---

15 Megan is the manager of a health club. She wants to know if the BMIs (Body Mass Indexes) of the female members have improved since she last surveyed them. She intends to publish her findings in an information leaflet. The cumulative frequency table below shows the new data she's collected from the 40 female members.

BMI (b)	Cumulative Frequency
$15 < b \leq 20$	4
$20 < b \leq 25$	18
$25 < b \leq 30$	30
$30 < b \leq 35$	35
$35 < b \leq 40$	38
$40 < b \leq 45$	40

(a) Use this information to draw a cumulative frequency graph on the axes below.

[2]

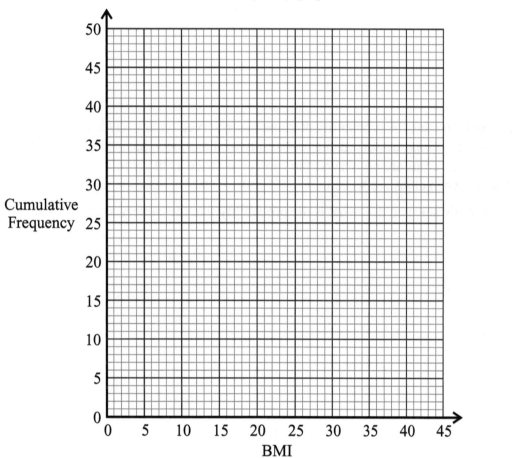

(b) Estimate the median BMI.

....

[1]

(c) Estimate the interquartile range (IQR).

....

[2]

[Total 5 marks]

8

16 Write 0.1̇5̇ as a fraction. Simplify your answer as far as possible.

....

[Total 2 marks]

17 At a school canteen, the probability of chips being served on any day is 0.2.
On a day when chips are served, the probability of the canteen having ketchup is 0.4.
On a day when chips are not served, the canteen is twice as likely to have ketchup
as on a day when chips are served.

On a randomly selected day, what is the probability that the canteen will have ketchup?

....

[Total 4 marks]

9

18 The expression $\dfrac{\sqrt{72}+6}{\sqrt{2}}$ can be simplified to $a+b\sqrt{2}$, where a and b are integers.

Find the values of a and b.

$a =$ .... $b =$ ....

[Total 3 marks]

19 The 3rd term of an arithmetic sequence is 26 and the 10th term is 75.
Find an expression for the nth term of the sequence.

....

[Total 4 marks]

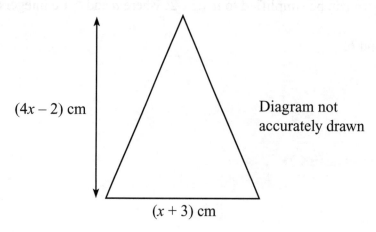

(4x − 2) cm

Diagram not
accurately drawn

(x + 3) cm

The diagram shows a triangle.
The height of the triangle is (4x − 2) cm.
The base length of the triangle is (x + 3) cm.
The area of the triangle is 43 cm².

(a) Show that $2x^2 + 5x - 46 = 0$.

[3]

(b) Find the value of x correct to 3 significant figures.
Show all your working clearly.

....

[3]

[Total 6 marks]

11

21 In the triangle below, $AB = 12$ cm, $BC = 19$ cm and $AC = 14$ cm.
Calculate the area of the triangle. Give your answer to two decimal places.

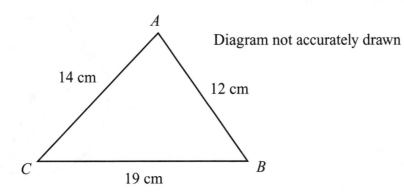

Diagram not accurately drawn

.... cm^2

[Total 5 marks]

Practice Paper 1

22   The diagram shows a circle with centre O.
      DE is a tangent to the circle at A and FG is a tangent to the circle at C.

Prove that $a = x + y - 90°$.
State any circle theorems that you use.

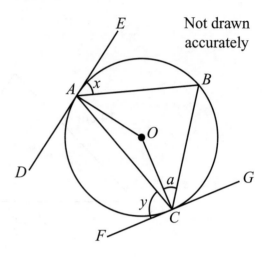

Not drawn
accurately

[Total 4 marks]

13

23 (a) Write the expression $5x^2 + 20x + 12$ in the form $u(x + v)^2 + w$.

....

[3]

(b) Hence find the coordinates of the minimum point of the graph $y = 5x^2 + 20x + 12$.

....

[1]

[Total 4 marks]

24 *ABCDEF* is a triangular prism.

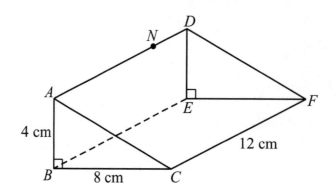

A is vertically above B with AB = 4 cm. BC = 8 cm and CF = 12 cm.
N is the point on AD such that AN : ND = 3 : 1.

Calculate the angle *CNF*. Give your answer to 1 decimal place.

.............................°

[Total 5 marks]

[TOTAL FOR PAPER = 100 MARKS]

Practice Paper 2

Right, here's Practice Paper 2. Don't forget about the formula sheet (p.252) — it's got all of the formulas that you'll be given in your exam, so be sure to make the most of it.

Candidate Surname		Candidate Forename(s)	

Centre Number	Candidate Number	Candidate Signature

Edexcel International GCSE

Mathematics

Practice Paper 2

Time allowed: 2 hours

You must have:
Pen, pencil, eraser, ruler, protractor, pair of compasses.
You may use tracing paper.

You **may use** a calculator.

Instructions to candidates

- Use **black** ink to write your answers.
- Write your name and other details in the spaces provided above.
- Answer **all** questions in the spaces provided.
- Correct answers without sufficient working might not be awarded any marks.
- Do all rough work on the paper.
- Anything you write on the formula sheet will **not** gain any credit.

Information for candidates

- The marks available are given in brackets at the end of each question.
- There are 21 questions in this paper. There are no blank pages.
- There are 100 marks available for this paper.

Answer ALL the questions.

Write your answers in the spaces provided.

You must show all of your working.

1   In a class of 25 children, the ratio of boys to girls is $2:3$.
     (a) Work out how many girls are in the class.

.... girls
[2]

Another class has children with brown hair, blonde hair and black hair in the ratio $7:6:1$.
     (b) There are ten more children with blonde hair than black hair.
          How many children have brown hair?

.... children
[3]

[Total 5 marks]

2   Tim's annual salary in 2014 was £42 000. His salary increased by 2.5% in 2015.
     Calculate how much Tim earned in the first five months of 2015.

£...

[Total 4 marks]

1

3 The table below gives information about the heights of the children in Class A.

Height in cm (h)	Frequency
$130 \leq h < 140$	5
$140 \leq h < 150$	10
$150 \leq h < 160$	14
$160 \leq h < 170$	8
$170 \leq h < 180$	3

(a) State the modal class.

....
[1]

(b) Calculate an estimate for the mean height of the children in Class A.

.... cm
[4]

[Total 5 marks]

4 On the number line below, plot the range of numbers which satisfy the inequality $2a - 1 < 7a - 16$.

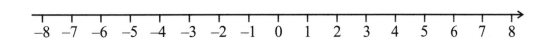

[Total 3 marks]

2

5 On the grid below, shade the region that satisfies all three of these inequalities:

$$x \leq 3 \qquad y > -4 \qquad y \leq x + 2$$

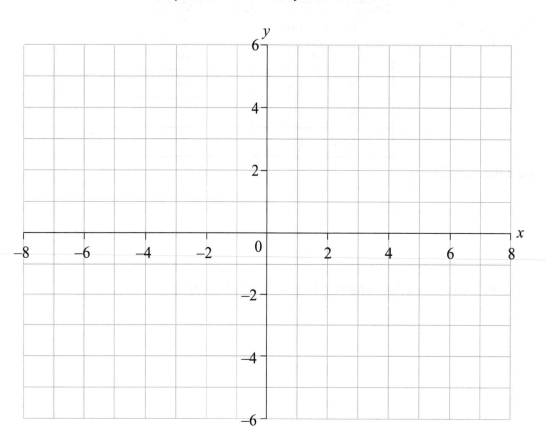

[Total 4 marks]

---

6 In February 2010, the UK population was estimated to be 62 000 000 people.

The UK national debt is the money that the UK government owes to people who have bought government bonds. In February 2010, the debt was calculated to be £8.494 × 10¹¹.

Use this information to estimate the national debt per person in the UK in February 2010.
Give your answer in standard form.

£ ....

[Total 2 marks]

3

7   The diagram below shows a trapezium. *FG* is parallel to *EH*.
     EH is 15.5 cm, *EF* is 4.8 cm and *FG* is 10 cm.

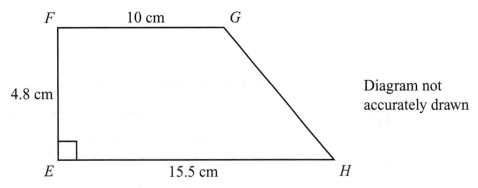

Diagram not accurately drawn

(a) Calculate the length of *GH*.

.... cm

[3]

(b) Calculate the size of angle *EHG*.
     Give your answer correct to 1 decimal place.

....

[3]

[Total 6 marks]

4

8 There are 128 students in Year 11. A teacher asks them all if they like football (F) and if they like badminton (B). He records the following results:

$n(B) = 102$

$F \cap B' = \emptyset$

$n(F \cap B) = 56$

(a) Complete the Venn diagram below to show the number of elements.

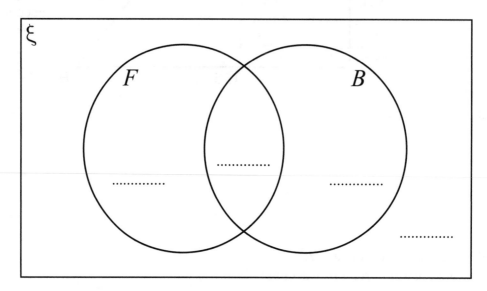

[2]

(b) Use the information in the Venn diagram to write a statement about students who like football in Year 11.

....

....

[1]

(c) Find $n(F \cup B')$

....

[1]

(d) A year 11 student who likes badminton is chosen at random.
What is the probability that this student also likes football?

....

[1]

[Total 5 marks]

5

9

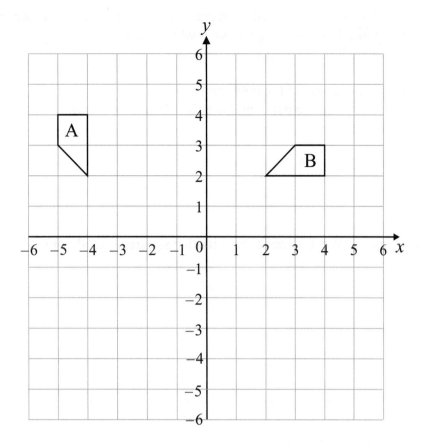

(a) Translate shape A by column vector $\begin{pmatrix} -1 \\ -7 \end{pmatrix}$. Label this shape C.

[1]

(b) Reflect shape B in the mirror line $y = -x$ and then enlarge the reflected shape with centre $(-5, -4)$ and scale factor 2. Label this shape D.

[3]

(c) Describe the single transformation that maps shape A onto shape B.

[3]

[Total 7 marks]

6

10 Kristina is doing a blind taste-test for a jelly company. There are 3 pots of strawberry jelly, 2 pots of blackcurrant jelly, 1 pot of orange jelly and 2 pots of raspberry jelly.
After a pot has been tasted, it is removed from the plate.

(a) Kristina randomly selects one of the pots and tastes it.
What is the probability that the pot contains either orange or strawberry jelly?

....

[2]

(b) Kristina tests 2 jellies. What is the probability that she tries exactly **one** raspberry jelly?

....

[3]

[Total 5 marks]

---

11 Simplify the following algebraic fractions.

(a) $\dfrac{x^2 - 25}{x^2 + 6x + 5}$

....

[3]

(b) $\dfrac{2x^2 + 7x + 6}{x^2 - 2x - 8}$

....

[3]

[Total 6 marks]

7

12 The quadrilaterals *ABCD* and *DEFG* are similar.

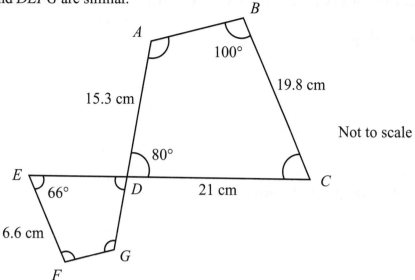

Not to scale

(a) Find angle *DGF*.

.... °

[1]

(b) Find the length of *ED*.

.... cm

[2]

The area of quadrilateral *ABCD* is 264.3 cm².

(c) What is the area of quadrilateral *DEFG*? Give your answer to 3 significant figures.

.... cm²

[2]

[Total 5 marks]

8

13 The curve with equation $y = \frac{1}{3}x^3 - 3x^2 - 16x + 7$ has two turning points.

(a) Find $\frac{dy}{dx}$.

....

[2]

(b) Find the gradient when $x = 4$.

....

[1]

(c) Find the x-coordinates at the turning points of the curve.

....

[2]

[Total 5 marks]

14 A spherical ball has volume 478 cm³.

Find the surface area of the ball, giving your answer correct to 1 d.p.

.... cm²

[Total 4 marks]

15 A company is testing an air pressure gauge that is based on a gas-filled ball.

The air pressure is inversely proportional to the cube of the diameter of the ball.
When the air pressure, p, is 60 bars, the diameter of the ball, d, is 2 cm.

(a) Write down a formula connecting p and d.

....

[3]

(b) What diameter will the ball be when the pressure is 100 bars?
Give your answer correct to 2 decimal places.

.... cm

[2]

[Total 5 marks]

16 Let $f(x) = 3x^2$ and $g(x) = \dfrac{3}{x-2}$

(a) Express the inverse function of $g(x)$ in the form $g^{-1}(x)$.

....

[2]

(b) Find the composite function $gf(x)$.

....

[2]

(c) Work out which values of x cannot be included in the domain of $gf(x)$.

....

[2]

[Total 6 marks]

10

17 The histogram below shows information about the length of time
100 cars were parked in a supermarket car park.

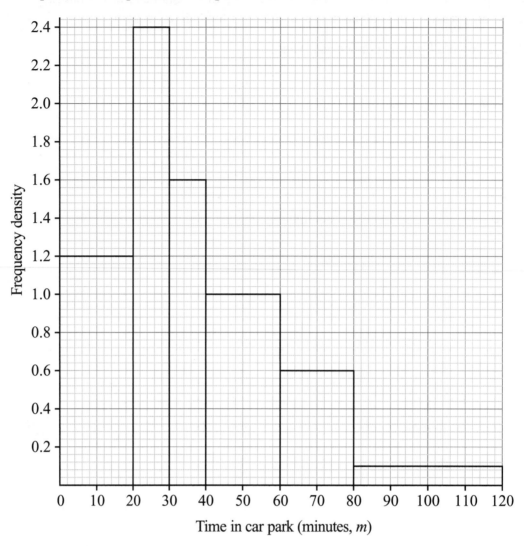

(a) Estimate how many cars were parked for more than 70 minutes.

....
[2]

(b) Calculate an estimate of the mean length of time the cars were parked for.

.... minutes
[3]
[Total 5 marks]

18 *ABCD* is a parallelogram.

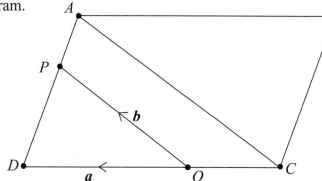

Diagram not
accurately drawn

$\overrightarrow{QP} = b$ and $\overrightarrow{QD} = a$.

Triangles *PQD* and *ACD* are similar.

$AD:PD = 5:3$

(a) Find $\overrightarrow{CA}$ in terms of *a* and *b*.

....
[1]

R is a point on *AC* so that $5\overrightarrow{AR} = 2\overrightarrow{AC}$.

(b) Given that $\overrightarrow{PR} = k\overrightarrow{DQ}$, find the value of *k*.

$k = $ ....
[3]

[Total 4 marks]

12

224

19 The curve shown by a dotted line on each grid is $y = \cos x$.

(a) For each part, work out a possible equation of the curve shown by the solid line.

(i)

$y = $ ....

[1]

(ii)

$y = $ ....

[1]

(iii)

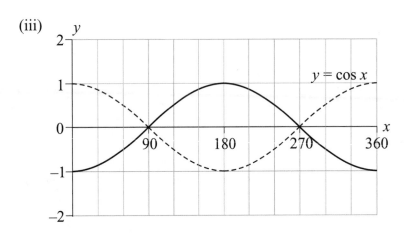

$y = $ ....

[1]

(b) Sketch $y = \cos(3x)$ on the graph below.

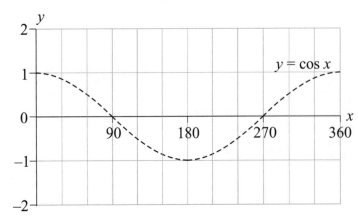

[1]

[Total 4 marks]

13

20 Show that the expression $\dfrac{\sqrt{27} + 7}{1 + \sqrt{3}}$ can be written as $1 + 2\sqrt{3}$.

[Total 4 marks]

21 Solve the simultaneous equations

$$y^2 + x^2 = 5$$
$$y = 2x + 4$$

....

[Total 6 marks]

[TOTAL FOR PAPER = 100 MARKS]

Section One — Numbers

Page 5 (Warm-Up Questions)

1 a) 11   b) 37   c) 3

2 0.0253040584425048
Your answer might have more or fewer digits, depending on the number of figures displayed on your calculator.

3 a) 1, 10, –4, 7   b) $\sqrt{2}$, 6π

4 $n = 12$
The only square numbers between 10 and 50 are 16, 25, 36 and 49. Then only 36 is a multiple of 3.

5 $(-3)^3 = (-3) \times (-3) \times (-3) = 9 \times (-3) = -27$
So $(-3)^3$ is not 27, meaning that –3 is not a cube root of 27.

Page 6 (Exam Questions)

3 a) The third odd number is 5 (1, 3, 5, ...)
The third square number is 9 (1, 4, 9, ...)
The third cube number is 27 (1, 8, 27, ...)
So the largest is 27, the third cube number. *[1 mark]*

  b) The sixth odd number is 11 (1, 3, 5, 7, 9, 11, ...)
The fourth square number is 16 (1, 4, 9, 16, ...)
The second cube number is 8 (1, 8, ...)
So the largest is 16, the fourth square number.
[2 marks available — 1 mark for a correct method, 1 mark for the correct answer]

4 Try each number until you find the answer:
$1^3 = 1$, $(2 \times 1)^2 = 2^2 = 4$
$2^3 = 8$, $(2 \times 2)^2 = 4^2 = 16$
$3^3 = 27$, $(2 \times 3)^2 = 6^2 = 36$
$4^3 = 64$, $(2 \times 4)^2 = 8^2 = 64$
So Juliette's number is 4.
[2 marks available — 1 mark for a correct method, 1 mark for the correct answer]

5 –10.6419373361169
[1 mark for the correct answer to a suitable number of figures]

6 E.g. $6 = \sqrt{3x + 2y}$, so $36 = 3x + 2y$
Try different values of x and see what y-value each one gives:
$x = 2$: $3x = 6 \Rightarrow 2y = 36 - 6 = 30 \Rightarrow y = 15$
$x = 4$: $3x = 12 \Rightarrow 2y = 36 - 12 = 24 \Rightarrow y = 12$
[2 marks available — 1 mark for each correct pair of x and y values]
The only other possible solution is x = 6, y = 9.

Page 10 (Warm-Up Questions)

1 1, 2, 4, 5, 8, 10, 20, 40

2 34, 51, 68

3 $231 \div 3 = 77$ or $231 \div 7 = 33$ or $231 \div 11 = 21$.
So 231 has more than 2 factors.

4 $2 \times 2 \times 2 \times 5$ (or $2^3 \times 5$)

5 a) 36   b) 6

Page 11 (Exam Questions)

3 a) $30 = 1 \times 30$, 2×15, 3×10, $4 \times ...$, 5×6, 6×5, etc...
So the factors of 30 are: 1, 2, 3, 5, 6, 10, 15, 30
[2 marks available — 2 marks for all eight factors, otherwise 1 mark for at least five correct factors]

  b) $48 = 1 \times 48$, 2×24, 3×18, 4×12, $5 \times ...$,
      6×8, $7 \times ...$, 8×6, etc...
So the factors of 48 are: 1, 2, 3, 4, 6, 8, 12, 16, 24, 48
[2 marks available — 2 marks for all ten factors, otherwise 1 mark for at least seven correct factors]

  c) The HCF is the highest number in both lists, which is 6. *[1 mark]*

4 The first car takes 30 seconds to complete a circuit, the second car takes 70 seconds to complete a circuit.
Multiples of 30 are: 30, 60, 90, 120, 150, 180, ⟨210⟩ 240, ...
Multiples of 70 are: 70, 140, ⟨210⟩ 280, ...
So it will be 210 seconds or 3.5 minutes until they are side by side on the start line.
[2 marks available — 1 mark for a correct method, 1 mark for the correct answer]

5 $25 \times 10^2 - 1 = 2499$, so $x = 10$ *[1 mark]*
Substituting 10 into the factorised expression gives
$2499 = (5 \times 10 - 1)(5 \times 10 + 1) = 49 \times 51$ *[1 mark]*
$49 = 7^2$ and $51 = 17 \times 3$,
so 2499 as a product of its prime factors is $3 \times 7^2 \times 17$ *[1 mark]*
[3 marks available in total — as above]

Page 18 (Warm-Up Questions)

1 a) $\dfrac{4}{15}$ b) $\dfrac{3}{5}$ c) $\dfrac{16}{15}$ or $1\dfrac{1}{15}$
  d) $\dfrac{4}{15}$ e) 48   f) 80

2 a) $\dfrac{22}{5}$ b) $7\dfrac{1}{3}$

3 a) 40%   b) 66.6...% or $66\dfrac{2}{3}$%

4 a) $\dfrac{4}{10}$ or $\dfrac{2}{5}$ b) $\dfrac{4}{9}$ c) $\dfrac{45}{99}$ or $\dfrac{5}{11}$

5 a) 0.7   b) $0.777... = 0.\dot{7}$

Page 19 (Exam Questions)

3 Number of chocolate muffins $= \dfrac{2}{5} \times 550$
$= (550 \div 5) \times 2 = 110 \times 2 = 220$ *[1 mark]*
Number of lemon muffins $= \dfrac{3}{11} \times 550$
$= (550 \div 11) \times 3 = 50 \times 3 = 150$ *[1 mark]*
So number of beetroot muffins
$= 550 - 220 - 150$ *[1 mark]* $= 180$ *[1 mark]*
[4 marks available in total — as above]
You could also have worked out the fraction of muffins that are beetroot, then multiplied that by 550.

4 $a = \dfrac{3}{4}$, $b = \dfrac{5}{2}$, so $\dfrac{1}{a} + \dfrac{1}{b} = \dfrac{4}{3} + \dfrac{2}{5} = \dfrac{20}{15} + \dfrac{6}{15} = \dfrac{26}{15}$ or $1\dfrac{11}{15}$
[3 marks available — 1 mark for reciprocal fractions, 1 mark for rewriting over a common denominator, 1 mark for the correct answer]

5 From calculator, $7 \div 33 = 0.212121... = 0.\dot{2}\dot{1}$ *[1 mark]*

6 Let $10r = 5.9\dot{0}$, so $1000r = 590.9\dot{0}$
$990r = 585$ *[1 mark]* $\Rightarrow r = \dfrac{585}{990} = \dfrac{13}{22}$ *[1 mark]*
[2 marks available in total — as above]

Page 23 (Warm-Up Questions)

1 £13.50

2 £129.60

3 45%

4 £208

5 £3376.53

Page 24 (Exam Questions)

3 Number of male pigs $= 40 - 24 = 16$ *[1 mark]*
Fraction male $= \dfrac{16}{40} = \dfrac{2}{5}$ *[1 mark]*
So percentage male $= 40\%$ *[1 mark]*
[3 marks available in total — as above]

4 a) 18 500 – 12 600 = £5900 *[1 mark]*
    $\frac{5900}{18\,500} \times 100$ *[1 mark]* = 31.891... = 31.9% *[1 mark]*
    [3 marks available in total — as above]

   b) $\frac{11\,549}{70}$ *[1 mark]* = 164.9857...
    164.9857... × 100 *[1 mark]*
    = £16 498.57... = £16 499 *[1 mark]*
    [3 marks available in total — as above]

5 $3995 \div \left(1 - \frac{11}{100}\right)^6 = 8038.53... = 8000$ ml (to nearest 100 ml)
   [3 marks available — 1 mark for a correct formula, 1 mark for substituting numbers correctly, 1 mark for the correct answer]

6 Let r be the interest rate.
   $£2704 = £2500 \times \left(1 + \frac{r}{100}\right)^2$ *[1 mark]*
   $\left(1 + \frac{r}{100}\right)^2 = \frac{2704}{2500} = 1.0816$
   $1 + \frac{r}{100} = \sqrt{1.0816} = 1.04$ *[1 mark]*
   So the interest rate = 4% *[1 mark]*
   [3 marks available in total — as above]

Page 28 (Warm-Up Questions)

1 a) 1 : 2   b) 4 : 9   c) 2 : 9
   d) 16 : 7   e) 5 : 4

2 1 : 4.4

3 450 g

4 45, 60, 75
   3 + 4 + 5 = 12 parts, so 180 ÷ 12 = 15 per part.

5 35 years old

6 £67.50

Page 29 (Exam Questions)

3 286 ÷ 13 = 22 *[1 mark]*
   22 × (5 + 1) *[1 mark]* = 132 in total *[1 mark]*
   [3 marks available in total — as above]

4 a) 150 g ÷ 12 = 12.5 g of butter for 1 flapjack
      12.5 × 18 = 225 g of butter for 18 flapjacks
      [2 marks available — 1 mark for a correct method, 1 mark for the correct answer]

   b) 300 ÷ 75 = 4, so she can make the recipe 4 times.
      4 × 12 flapjacks = 48 flapjacks
      [2 marks available — 1 mark for a correct method, 1 mark for the correct answer]

5 Longest – shortest = 7 – 5 = 2 parts = 9 cm *[1 mark]*
   1 part = 9 ÷ 2 = 4.5 cm
   Original piece of wood is 5 + 6 + 6 + 7 = 24 parts *[1 mark]*
   So, the original piece of wood is 24 × 4.5 = 108 cm *[1 mark]*
   [3 marks available in total — as above]

Page 35 (Warm-Up Questions)

1 a) 40.22   b) 39.9   c) 28

2 $\frac{94 \times 1.9}{0.328 + 0.201} \approx \frac{90 \times 2}{0.3 + 0.2} = \frac{180}{0.5} = 360$

3 Upper bound = 14.5 km. Lower bound = 13.5 km

4 a) Maximum = 9.3, minimum = 9.1
   b) Maximum = 3.5, minimum = 3.3
   c) Maximum = 18.7325, minimum = 17.8125
   d) Maximum = 2.23 (2 d.p.), minimum = 2.12 (2 d.p.)

5 2.7×10^{-6} seconds

6 a) 2.4×10^{11} b) 2×10^4 c) 7.797×10^6

Page 36 (Exam Questions)

3 a) $\frac{215.7 \times 44.8}{460} \approx \frac{200 \times 40}{500} = \frac{8000}{500} = 16$
      [3 marks available — 1 mark for correctly rounding one number to 1 significant figure, 1 mark for correctly rounding the other two numbers to 1 significant figure, 1 mark for correct answer]

   b) The answer to a) will be smaller than the exact answer, because in the rounded fraction the numerator is smaller and denominator is larger compared to the exact calculation.
      [2 marks available — 1 mark for 'smaller than the exact answer', 1 mark for correct reasoning]

4 a) $2.1 \times 10^5 = 0.021 \times 10^7$ *[1 mark]*
      $7.59 \times 10^7 + 0.021 \times 10^7 = 7.611 \times 10^7$ kg *[1 mark]*
      [2 marks available in total — as above]

   b) $(2.1 \times 10^5) \div (7.611 \times 10^7) = 0.002759...$ *[1 mark]*
      $0.002759 \times 100 = 0.28\%$ (2 d.p.) *[1 mark]*
      [2 marks available in total — as above]

5 Upper bound for x = 57.5 mm *[1 mark]*
   Upper bound for y = 32.5 mm *[1 mark]*
   Upper bound for area = 57.5 mm × 32.5 mm = 1868.75 mm^2
                        = 1870 mm^2 to 3 s.f. *[1 mark]*
   [3 marks available in total — as above]

Page 42 (Warm-Up Questions)

1 Peter does not play badminton.

2 Trees that are 3 m or under in height.

3 a) $K \cap L = \{2, 3\}$
   b) 2
   c) Yes, the statement is true.
      $J \cup K = \{2, 3, 4, 5, 6, 7, 8, 9, 11, 12\}$, and $L = \{2, 3, 5, 7, 11\}$
   d)

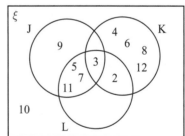

   You might have drawn your circles differently to how they're shown here — as long as all of the numbers are inside the right circles, you'll get the marks.

Page 43 (Exam Questions)

3 a) There are no students who are in both the basketball and football clubs. *[1 mark]*
   b) There are 5 students who are in both the cycling and football clubs. *[1 mark]*

4 a), b)

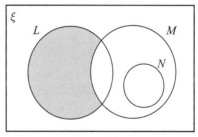

   [2 marks available — 1 mark for the correct shaded area, 1 mark for correct N]

5 3, 9, 15
   [2 marks available — 2 marks for the correct answer, otherwise 1 mark for one or more members correct]

Page 44 (Revision Questions)

1 a) Whole numbers — either positive or negative, or zero
   b) Numbers that can be written as fractions
   c) Numbers which will only divide by themselves or 1

2 a) 169   b) 7   c) 3   d) 125

3 a) $1050 = 2 \times 3 \times 5^2 \times 7$
   b) $360 = 2^3 \times 3^2 \times 5$

4 a) $320 = 2 \times 2 \times 2 \times 2 \times 2 \times 2 \times 5$
         $= 2^6 \times 5$
      $880 = 2 \times 2 \times 2 \times 2 \times 5 \times 11$
         $= 2^4 \times 5 \times 11$
   b) $\text{LCM} = 2^6 \times 5 \times 11 = 3520$
      $\text{HCF} = 2^4 \times 5 = 80$

5 a) $8\frac{2}{9}$ b) $\frac{33}{7}$

6 Multiplying: Multiply top and bottom numbers separately.
   Dividing: Turn the second fraction upside down, then multiply.
   Adding/subtracting: Put fractions over a common denominator, then add/subtract the numerators.

7 a) $\frac{14}{99}$ b) $\frac{22}{7} = 3\frac{1}{7}$
   c) $\frac{11}{24}$ d) $\frac{151}{20} = 7\frac{11}{20}$

8 a) Divide the top by the bottom.
   b) Put the digits after the decimal point on the top, and a power of 10 with the same number of zeros as there were decimal places on the bottom.

9 a) (i) $\frac{4}{100} = \frac{1}{25}$ (ii) 4%
   b) (i) $\frac{65}{100} = \frac{13}{20}$ (ii) 0.65

10 Let $r = 0.5\dot{1}$.
   Then $100r - r = 51.5\dot{1} - 0.5\dot{1}$
   $\Rightarrow 99r = 51 \Rightarrow r = \frac{51}{99} = \frac{17}{33}$

11 To find x as a percentage of y, make sure both amounts are in the same units, then divide x by y and multiply by 100.

12 17.6 m

13 6% simple interest pays £59.62 more (to the nearest penny)

14 240

15 1. Add up the parts.
   2. Divide to find one part.
   3. Multiply to find the amounts.

16 600, 960, 1440

17 £1.41

18 a) 427.96   b) 428.0
   c) 430   d) 428.0

19 Estimates should be in the range 20-24

20 132.2425 m^2

21 1. The front number must always be between 1 and 10.
   2. The power of 10, n, is how far the decimal point moves.
   3. n is positive for big numbers, and negative for small numbers.

22 a) 9.7×10^5 b) 3.56×10^9 c) 2.75×10^{-6}

23 a) 1.5875×10^3 b) 2.739×10^{12}

24 a) 5 and 10
   b)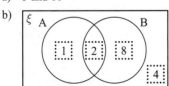
   c) 11

Section Two — Algebra

Page 52 (Warm-Up Questions)

1 a) $4^3 = 64$ b) $1\frac{32}{49}$ c) 9   d) $\frac{9}{4}$

2 a) $2a - 5c$ b) $7r^2 - 5r - 1$

3 $C = 12d + 18$

4 a) $8p + 28$ b) $8x^2 - 2$ c) $5a^2 - 3a$

5 a) $2(3p - 6q + 2)$ b) $2cd(2d - 1 + 5cd^2)$

6 $(x + 2y)(x - 2y)$

7 $\sqrt{30}$

Page 53 (Exam Questions)

3 $T = (73 + 27)p + 15l = 100p + 15l$
   [2 marks available — 2 marks for the correct formula, otherwise 1 mark for 100p or 15l]

4 $2v^3w + 8v^2w^2 = 2(v^3w + 4v^2w^2)$ *[1 mark]*
          $= 2v^2w(v + 4w)$ *[1 mark]*
   [2 marks available in total — as above]

5 Area $= \frac{1}{2} \times$ base $\times$ height
   $= \frac{1}{2} \times (3x + 5) \times (2x - 4) = \frac{1}{2}(3x + 5)(2x - 4)$ *[1 mark]*
   $= \frac{1}{2} \times ((3x \times 2x) + (3x \times -4) + (5 \times 2x) + (5 \times -4))$
   $= \frac{1}{2} \times (6x^2 - 12x + 10x - 20)$
   $= \frac{1}{2} \times (6x^2 - 2x - 20)$ *[1 mark]*
   $= 3x^2 - x - 10$ *[1 mark]*
   [3 marks available in total — as above]
   You could also have multiplied (2x − 4) by ½ first of all. The area would then just be (3x + 5)(x − 2), which is a bit simpler to multiply out.

6 $(9a^4)^{\frac{1}{2}} = \sqrt{9a^4} = 3a^2$ *[1 mark]*
   $\frac{2ab^2}{6a^3b} = \frac{2}{6} \times \frac{a}{a^3} \times \frac{b^2}{b} = \frac{1}{3} \times \frac{1}{a^2} \times b = \frac{b}{3a^2}$ *[1 mark]*
   so $(9a^4)^{\frac{1}{2}} \times \frac{2ab^2}{6a^3b} = 3a^2 \times \frac{b}{3a^2} = b$ *[1 mark]*
   [3 marks available in total — as above]

7 $\frac{1 + \sqrt{7}}{3 - \sqrt{7}} = \frac{(1 + \sqrt{7})(3 + \sqrt{7})}{(3 - \sqrt{7})(3 + \sqrt{7})}$ *[1 mark]*
   $= \frac{3 + \sqrt{7} + 3\sqrt{7} + 7}{9 - 7}$ *[1 mark]*
   $= \frac{10 + 4\sqrt{7}}{2}$ *[1 mark]*
   $= 5 + 2\sqrt{7}$ *[1 mark]*
   [4 marks available in total — as above]

Page 58 (Warm-Up Questions)

1 a) $x = 3$ b) $x = -3$ c) $x = 5$

2 a) p b) t

3 $q = 7(p - 2r)$ or $q = 7p - 14r$

4 $z = \frac{3x - y}{2}$

Page 59 (Exam Questions)

3 a) $2(5x - 8) + 2(2x + 3) = 2(3x + 6) + 2y$ *[1 mark]*
      $14x - 10 = 6x + 12 + 2y$ *[1 mark]*
      $8x - 22 = 2y \Rightarrow y = 4x - 11$ *[1 mark]*
      So u = 4 and v = −11.
      [3 marks available in total — as above]
   b) $14x - 10 = 32$ *[1 mark]*
      $14x = 42$
         $x = 3$ *[1 mark]*
      $y = 4x - 11$ so if $x = 3$, $y = 4 \times 3 - 11 = 12 - 11 = 1$ *[1 mark]*
      [3 marks available in total — as above]

4 a) $a + y = \dfrac{b-y}{a}$, so:

$a(a+y) = b - y$ *[1 mark]* $\Rightarrow a^2 + ay = b - y$

$\Rightarrow ay + y = b - a^2$ *[1 mark]* $\Rightarrow y(a+1) = b - a^2$ *[1 mark]*

$\Rightarrow y = \dfrac{b - a^2}{a+1}$ *[1 mark]*

[4 marks available in total — as above]

b) When $a = 3$ and $b = 6$, $y = \dfrac{6 - 3^2}{3+1} = -\dfrac{3}{4}$ or -0.75

[2 marks available — 1 mark for correct substitution, 1 mark for the correct answer]

5 $x = \sqrt{\dfrac{(1+n)}{(1-n)}}$, so $x^2 = \dfrac{(1+n)}{(1-n)}$ *[1 mark]* $\Rightarrow x^2(1-n) = 1 + n$

$\Rightarrow x^2 - x^2 n = 1 + n$ *[1 mark]* $\Rightarrow x^2 - 1 = n + x^2 n$ *[1 mark]*

$\Rightarrow x^2 - 1 = n(1+x^2)$ *[1 mark]*

$\Rightarrow n = \dfrac{x^2 - 1}{1 + x^2}$ *[1 mark]*

[5 marks available in total — as above]

Page 66 (Warm-Up Questions)

1 a) $(x+4)(x+7)$ b) $(x+14)(x+2)$

c) $(x+14)(x-2)$.

2 a) $x = -3$ or $x = -5$ *(it factorises to $(x+3)(x+5) = 0$)*

b) $x = 2$ or $x = -7$ *(it factorises to $(x-2)(x+7) = 0$)*

c) $x = 3$ or $x = 4$
Rearrange to give $x^2 - 7x + 12 = 0$, then factorise to give $(x-3)(x-4) = 0$, so $x = 3$ or $x = 4$.

3 $(3x+2)(x+10)$

4 $x = -\dfrac{2}{5}$ or $x = 3$ *(it factorises to $(5x+2)(x-3) = 0$)*

5 $x = 1.46$ or $x = -0.46$
Use the quadratic formula, with $a = 3$, $b = -3$ and $c = -2$.

6 $(x-5)^2 - 16$, so $x = 9$ or $x = 1$
$(x-5)^2$ gives $x^2 - 10x + 25$
so complete the square by subtracting 16:
$(x-5)^2 - 16 = 0$
$(x-5)^2 = 16$
$(x-5) = \pm\sqrt{16}$
$(x-5) = 4$ or $(x-5) = -4$
$x = 9$ or $x = 1$

7 $2(x+4)^2 + 7$
$2(x+4)^2 = 2x^2 + 16x + 32$, so add $+7$ to complete the square.

Page 67 (Exam Questions)

3 $3x^2 + 18x + 24 = 0 \Rightarrow x^2 + 6x + 8 = 0$ *[1 mark]*
$(x+4)(x+2) = 0$ *[1 mark]*
$x + 4 = 0$ or $x + 2 = 0$
$x = -4$ or $x = -2$
[1 mark for both solutions]
[3 marks available in total — as above]

4 The area of the square is $(x+3)(x+3) = x^2 + 6x + 9$. *[1 mark]*
The area of the triangle is $\dfrac{1}{2}(2x+2)(x+3)$

$= \dfrac{1}{2}(2x^2 + 6x + 2x + 6) = \dfrac{1}{2}(2x^2 + 8x + 6)$

$= x^2 + 4x + 3$ *[1 mark]*
So the area of the whole shape is $x^2 + 6x + 9 + x^2 + 4x + 3$
$= 2x^2 + 10x + 12$ *[1 mark]*
$2x^2 + 10x + 12 = 60$, so $2x^2 + 10x - 48 = 0$ *[1 mark]*
Dividing by 2 here will make $a = 1$ and the quadratic easier to solve.
So $x^2 + 5x - 24 = 0$
$(x-3)(x+8) = 0$ *[1 mark]*
$x - 3 = 0$ or $x + 8 = 0$
$x = 3$ or $x = -8$
[1 mark for both solutions]
A length can't have a negative value
so the answer must be $x = 3$. *[1 mark]*
[7 marks available in total — as above]
If $x = -8$ then the square would have sides of length $-8 + 3 = -5$ cm and the triangle would have a height of $2 \times -8 + 2 = -14$ cm, neither of which are possible.

5 a) $2(x^2 - 4x) + 19$ *[1 mark]*
$4 \div 2 = 2$, so the first bit is $2[(x-2)^2]$
Expanding the brackets: $2(x^2 - 4x + 4) = 2x^2 - 8x + 8$
To complete the square: $19 - 8 = 11$ *[1 mark]*
So $2x^2 - 8x + 19 = 2(x-2)^2 + 11$ *[1 mark]*
[3 marks available in total — as above]

b) Minimum value $= 11$, which occurs at $x = 2$, so the coordinates of the minimum point are $(2, 11)$ *[1 mark]*

c) This quadratic is u-shaped and its minimum value is 11, so it's always greater than 0. This means it never crosses the x-axis. *[1 mark]*

Page 72 (Warm-Up Questions)

1 a) $\dfrac{4ab}{c^2}$ b) $\dfrac{x^2 + 2y}{x}$

2 a) $n = 13, 14, 15, 16$

b) $n = -3, -2, -1, 0, 1, 2, 3$

c) $n = 3, 4$
Dividing by 4 gives $2 < n < 5$, but n must be an integer.

3 a) $q \le 5$ b) $p > 4.5$

4 a) and b)

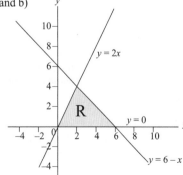

Page 73 (Exam Questions)

4 $\frac{2x}{5} \leq 3$, so $2x \leq 15$ *[1 mark]* $\Rightarrow x \leq 7.5$ *[1 mark]*

[2 marks available in total — as above]

5

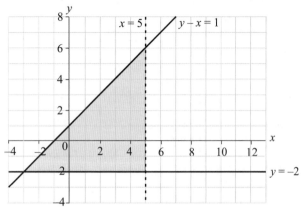

[4 marks available — 1 mark for drawing each line correctly, 1 mark for shading the correct area]

6 $\frac{1}{x-5} + \frac{2}{x-2} = \frac{x-2}{(x-5)(x-2)} + \frac{2(x-5)}{(x-5)(x-2)}$

$= \frac{(x-2)+2(x-5)}{(x-5)(x-2)} = \frac{x-2+2x-10}{(x-5)(x-2)} = \frac{3x-12}{(x-5)(x-2)}$

[3 marks available — 1 mark for finding the common denominator, 1 mark for a correct method for addition, 1 mark for the correct final answer]

7 $(x+3) \div \frac{x^2+4x+3}{x+4} + 2 = (x+3) \times \frac{x+4}{x^2+4x+3} + 2$ *[1 mark]*

$= (x+3) \times \frac{x+4}{(x+1)(x+3)} + 2 = \frac{x+4}{(x+1)} + 2$ *[1 mark]*

$= \frac{x+4+2(x+1)}{(x+1)}$ *[1 mark]*

$= \frac{3x+6}{x+1} = \frac{3(x+2)}{x+1}$ as required *[1 mark]*

[4 marks available in total — as above]

8 a) $x^2 + 1 > 37$
$x^2 > 36$ so $x < -6$ *[1 mark]* or $x > 6$ *[1 mark]*
[2 marks available in total — as above]

b) $x^2 + 1 = x + 7$ rearranges to give $x^2 - x - 6 = 0$.
$x^2 - x - 6 = 0$ factorises to give $(x+2)(x-3) = 0$.
The graph of $y = x^2 - x - 6$ is a u-shaped quadratic that crosses the x-axis at $x = -2$ and $x = 3$:

The graph is below 0 when x is greater than –2 and less than 3. So $-2 < x < 3$.
[3 marks available — 1 mark for rearranging and factorising the quadratic to find the solutions, 1 mark for $-2 < x$, 1 mark for $x < 3$]

Page 77 (Warm-Up Questions)

1 a) $x = 3, y = 3$ b) $x = 1, y = 2$ c) $x = 3, y = 2$
2 $x = 2, y = 4$
3 $x = 2, y = 5$
4 $x = 1, y = -1$ and $x = -4, y = 14$
5 $x = 3, y = -1$

Page 78 (Exam Questions)

3 $2x + 3y = 12$ (1) $\xrightarrow{\times 5}$ $10x + 15y = 60$ (3) *[1 mark]*
$5x + 4y = 9$ (2) $\xrightarrow{\times 2}$ $10x + 8y = 18$ (4) *[1 mark]*

(3) − (4): $10x + 15y = 60$ $2x + 3y = 12$
$\underline{-10x + 8y = 18}$ $2x = 12 - (3 \times 6)$
        $7y = 42$ $2x = -6$
         $y = 6$ *[1 mark]* $x = -3$ *[1 mark]*

[4 marks available in total — as above]
Simultaneous equations usually have a few different ways to solve them. E.g. you could substitute y into equation (2) instead of (1) to find x. So long as you get the right solution, you'll get the marks.

4

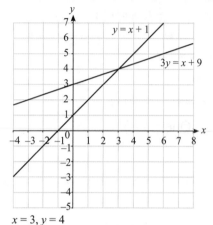

$x = 3, y = 4$
[3 marks available — 1 mark for correctly drawing the line $y = x + 1$, 1 mark for correctly drawing the line $3y = x + 9$, 1 mark for the correct solution]

5

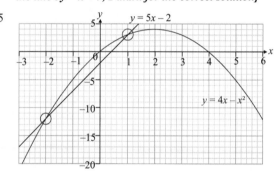

$x = 1, y = 3$ and $x = -2, y = -12$
[3 marks available — 1 mark for correctly drawing the line $y = 5x - 2$, 1 mark for each correct solution]

6 $y = x + 6$, so $2x^2 + (x+6)^2 = 51$ *[1 mark]*
$2x^2 + x^2 + 12x + 36 = 51$
$3x^2 + 12x - 15 = 0$ *[1 mark]*
Dividing by 3: $x^2 + 4x - 5 = 0$
$(x-1)(x+5) = 0$ *[1 mark]*
$x = 1$ or $x = -5$ *[1 mark]*
When $x = 1$, $y = 1 + 6 = 7$
When $x = -5$, $y = -5 + 6 = 1$
So the solutions are $x = 1, y = 7$ *[1 mark]*
and $x = -5, y = 1$ *[1 mark]*
[6 marks available in total — as above]

Page 84 (Warm-Up Questions)

1 a) 8, 13, 18, 23, 28, 33
b) 8, 11, 14, 17, 20, 23

2 a) $5n$ b) $3n + 4$

3 There is always one cross in the centre, and the number of other crosses is 4 times the pattern number (because there are 4 "arms" coming from the centre). So in the nth pattern there will be a total of $4n + 1$ crosses.

4 Take two consecutive even numbers, $2n$ and $2n + 2$, where n is an integer. Then $2n + (2n + 2) = 4n + 2 = 2(2n + 1)$, which is even, as $(2n + 1)$ is an integer.

5 $4x + 2 = 3(3a + x)$, so $x = 9a - 2$. If a is odd, then $9a$ is also odd (as odd × odd = odd). $9a - 2$ is always odd (as odd − even = odd), so x cannot be a multiple of 8 as all multiples of 8 are even.

6 a) $A = kr^2$ b) $D = \dfrac{k}{R}$ c) $H = \dfrac{k}{D^3}$ d) $V = kS^3$

Page 85 (Exam Questions)

3 a) Common difference = 5, so $5n$ is in the formula.
To get from $5n$ to each term, you have to subtract 2, so the expression for the nth term is $5n - 2$.
[2 marks available — 2 marks for correct expression, otherwise 1 mark for finding 5n]

b) If 107 is a term in the sequence then $107 = 5n - 2$ for some integer value of n. If this is true then $n = 21.8$, but this is not an integer. So 107 can't be a term in the sequence.
[2 marks available — 1 mark for 5n – 2 = 107, 1 mark for the correct conclusion and explanation]

4 a) $S \propto \dfrac{1}{d}$, so $S = \dfrac{k}{d}$ *[1 mark]*
When $S = 60$ and $d = 15$, $60 = \dfrac{k}{15}$, so $k = 900$ *[1 mark]*
So $S = \dfrac{900}{d}$ *[1 mark]*
[3 marks available in total — as above]

b)
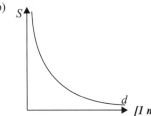
[1 mark]

5 $a + (3 - 1)d \Rightarrow a + 2d = 11$ (1)
$a + (8 - 1)d \Rightarrow a + 7d = 31$ (2)
Subtract (1) from (2) to get:
$7d - 2d = 31 - 11$
$5d = 20$, so $d = 4$
Substituting this back into (1) gives:
$a + 2 \times 4 = 11$
$a + 8 = 11$, so $a = 3$
Substitute $a = 3$, $d = 4$ and $n = 65$ into the formula for S_n to get:
$S_{65} = \dfrac{65}{2}(2 \times 3 + (65 - 1) \times 4)$
$= \dfrac{65}{2}(6 + 64 \times 4)$
$= \dfrac{65}{2}(262) = 65 \times 131 = 8515$
[5 marks available — 1 mark for both equations involving a and d, 1 mark for correctly finding a, 1 mark for correctly finding d, 1 mark for using the correct formula for S_n, 1 mark for the correct answer]

6 If $2^{64} - 1$ is prime then its only factors are 1 and itself.
$2^{64} - 1 = (2^{32})^2 - 1^2 = (2^{32} + 1)(2^{32} - 1)$ *[1 mark]*
So $(2^{32} + 1)$ and $(2^{32} - 1)$ are factors of $2^{64} - 1$. *[1 mark]*
But neither $(2^{32} + 1)$ or $(2^{32} - 1)$ are equal to 1 or $2^{64} - 1$ so $2^{64} - 1$ cannot be prime. *[1 mark]*
[3 marks available in total — as above]

Page 86 (Revision Questions)

1 a) x^9 b) y^2 c) z^{12}

2 $5x - 4y - 5$

3 $P = 7d + 5c$

4 a) $6x + 3$ b) $x^2 - x - 6$ c) $x^3 + 7x^2 + 7x - 15$

5 a) $7x(xy + 3z^2)$ b) $(7 + 9pq)(7 - 9pq)$
c) $12(x + 2y)(x - 2y)$

6 a) $3\sqrt{3}$ b) 5

7 a) $x = 2$ b) $x = \pm 3$

8 a) $p = \dfrac{qr}{q + r}$ b) $p = -\dfrac{4y}{3}$

9 a) $x = -3$ or $x = -6$ b) $x = 4$ or $x = -\dfrac{3}{5}$

10 a) $x = 1.56$ or $x = -2.56$
b) $x = 0.27$ or $x = -1.47$
c) $x = 0.44$ or $x = -3.44$

11 a) $x = -6 \pm \sqrt{21}$ b) $x = 3$ or $x = -\dfrac{1}{2}$

12 $\dfrac{3x + 1}{(x + 3)(x - 1)}$

13 a) $x \geq -2$ b) $-1 < x \leq 6$

14 $x < -5$ or $x > 5$

15
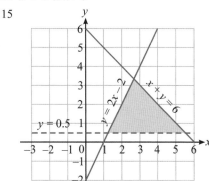

16 $x = 2$, $y = 3$

17 $x = -2$, $y = -2$ or $x = -4$, $y = -8$

18 a) 31, rule is add 7
b) 256, rule is multiply by 4
c) 19, rule is add two previous terms.

19 a) $4n + 1$ b) $-3n + 14$

20 a) 1080 b) 5145

21 Take an even number, $2p$, and an odd number, $2q + 1$.
Their product is $2p \times (2q + 1) = 4pq + 2p = 2(2pq + p)$, which is even as $(2pq + p)$ is an integer.

22 $y = kx^2$

23 $p = 72$

Section Three — Graphs, Functions and Calculus

Page 93 (Warm-Up Questions)

1   a) $y = x$
    b) Horizontal line ($y = 4$)
    c) Vertical line ($x = -1$)
    d) $y = -x$

2   a)

x	0	2	3
y	–4	2	5

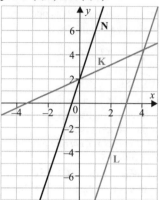

The graph shows a straight line labelled $y = 3x - 4$ passing through the points.

   b) $y = 3x + 2$ has the same gradient as $y = 3x - 4$ (the lines are parallel) and the y-intercept is 6 units higher (it's at $y = 2$).

3   a) $y = -5x + 4$ b) $\frac{1}{5}$

Page 94 (Exam Questions)

2   a) $\left(\dfrac{(6 + (-4))}{2}, \dfrac{(2 + 1)}{2} \right)$ *[1 mark]*

   $= (1, 1.5)$ *[1 mark]*
   [2 marks available in total — as above]

   b) $\dfrac{(6 + a)}{2} = 3 \Rightarrow a = 6 - 6 \Rightarrow a = 0$

   $\dfrac{2 + b}{2} = 5 \Rightarrow b = 10 - 2 \Rightarrow b = 8$
   *[3 marks available — 1 mark for a correct method,
   1 mark for each correct a and b value]*

3   a) Pick two points on the line, e.g. (0, 2) and (5, 5).
   Gradient $= m = \dfrac{\text{change in } y}{\text{change in } x} = \dfrac{5 - 2}{5 - 0} = \dfrac{3}{5}$ *[1 mark]*
   y-intercept $= c = 2$ *[1 mark]*
   So the equation of the line is $y = \dfrac{3}{5}x + 2$ *[1 mark]*
   [3 marks available in total — as above]

   b) Get **N** in the form $y = mx + c$ by dividing by 2: $y = 4x + 2$.
   So **N** goes through (0, 2). It has a gradient of 4, so every time you go across 1, you go up 4. So draw a line through points (0, 2) and (1, 6).

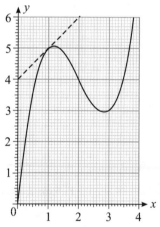

   *[2 marks available — 2 marks for the correct line,
   otherwise 1 mark for a line with gradient 4
   or a line with y-intercept 2]*

   c) **L** has a gradient of 4 (you can either work this out or see that it's parallel to **N**). So it's equation is of the form $y = 4x + c$. The point (3, 0) is on the line, so $0 = 4 \times 3 + c \Rightarrow c = -12$. So the y-intercept is (0, –12).
   *[2 marks available — 1 mark for a correct method,
   1 mark for the correct answer]*
   Alternatively, you can see that (1, −8) is on the line. Then, since the gradient is 4, you can go left 1 and down 4 to reach (O, −12).

4

The graph shows a curve with a tangent drawn as a dashed line.

Gradient $= \dfrac{6 - 4}{2 - 0} = \dfrac{2}{2} = 1$

*[3 marks available — 1 mark for drawing a tangent,
1 mark for the correct method to find the gradient
of the tangent, 1 mark for the correct final answer]*
Allow answers between O.5 and 1.5.

Page 98 (Warm-Up Questions)

1 a)

x	−2	−1	0	1	2	3	4	5
y	7	2	−1	−2	−1	2	7	14

b)

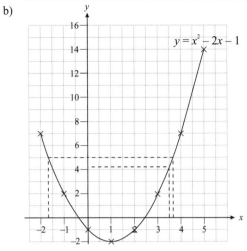

c) 4.25 *Allow answers between 4 and 4.5.*

d) $x = -1.65$ and 3.65
*Allow answers between −1.6 and −1.7,
and between 3.6 and 3.7.*

2 a) and b)

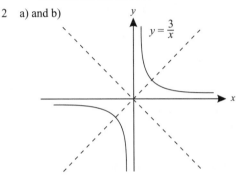

3 $x = 310°$ *Allow answers between 308° and 312°.*

Pages 99-100 (Exam Questions)

2 a)

x	1	2	3
y	2	0	2

[1 mark]

b)

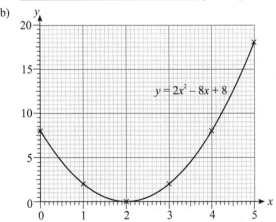

*[2 marks available — 1 mark for plotting correct points,
1 mark for joining them with a smooth curve]*

c) Draw the line $y = 4$ on the graph.

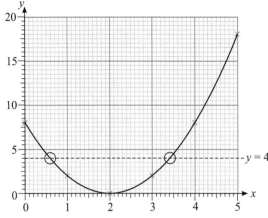

The solutions to $4 = 2x^2 - 8x + 8$ occur where the line
and the curve intersect: $x = 0.6$ and $x = 3.4$ (both 1 d.p.)
*[2 marks available — 1 mark for using y = 4,
1 mark for both correct solutions]*
Allow solutions between 0.5 and 0.7, and between 3.3 and 3.5.

3 a)

x	0.2	5
y	17.2	2.8

[1 mark]

b)

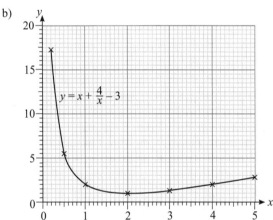

*[2 marks available — 1 mark for plotting correct points,
1 mark for joining them with a smooth curve]*

c) Draw the line of $y = 5x + 5$ on the graph.

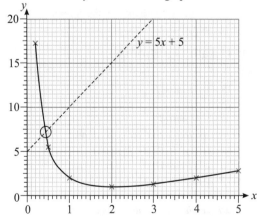

The solutions to the equation occur where the line
and the curve intersect: $x = 0.4$ (1 d.p.)
*[3 marks available — 2 marks for drawing the line
y = 5x + 5 correctly on the graph, otherwise 1 mark for
drawing a straight line with gradient 5 or y-intercept 5;
1 mark for the correct solution]*
Allow solutions between 0.2 and 0.6.

4 a)

x	−90°	−30°	30°	90°
y	−1	−0.5	0.5	1

[2 marks available — 2 marks for all answers correct, otherwise 1 mark for two correct answers]

b)

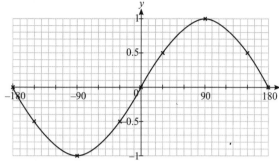

[2 marks available — 1 mark for plotting correct points, 1 mark for joining them with a smooth curve]

c) Draw the line of $y = 0.3$ on the graph:

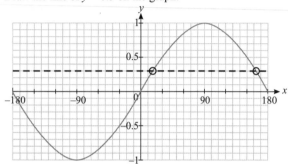

Find the solutions where this line intersects the curve:
$x = 17°$ or $x = 163°$.

[2 marks available — 1 mark for drawing the line $y = 0.3$ on the graph, 1 mark for the correct solutions]
You'll still get the mark if your answers are within 5° of the correct answer.

Page 105 (Warm-Up Questions)

1 a) 19   b) 7   c) $10 - 10x$
   d) $5x^2 + 14$ e) −16   f) $\dfrac{x+1}{5}$

2 a) $x > 4$ b) $x \leq 0$ c) $x = 0$
   d) $x \leq -3.5$ e) $x = -0.75$

3 The graphs have the same shape, but the second is shifted up the y-axis by 2 units.

Page 106 (Exam Questions)

2 a) $f(13) = \sqrt{13^2 - 25} = \sqrt{169 - 25} = \sqrt{144} = 12$ *[1 mark]*
   b) $x^2 - 25 < 0$ *[1 mark]*
       $x^2 < 25$
       $-5 < x < 5$ *[1 mark]*
       [2 marks available in total — as above]
   c) If $f(x) = 1$, $\sqrt{x^2 - 25} = 1$ *[1 mark]*
       $x^2 - 25 = 1^2$ *[1 mark]*
       $x^2 = 1 + 25$
       $x = \pm\sqrt{26}$ *[1 mark]*
       [3 marks available in total — as above]
   d) Reading from the graph $g(1) = -10$ *[1 mark]*
       $fg(1) = f(g(1)) = f(-10) = \sqrt{(-10)^2 - 25} = \sqrt{75}$ *[1 mark]*
       [2 marks available in total — as above]

3 a) and b)

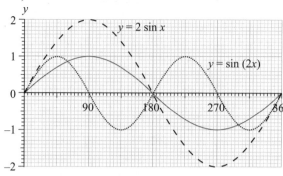

[2 marks available — 1 mark for each correct graph]

Page 110 (Warm-Up Questions)

1 a) $7a^6$ b) $50t^4$ c) 1   d) $-4w^5$
2 $36x^3 + 3x^2 + 8x + 6$
3 a) −2   b) 24   c) −6   d) −0.5
4 a) $(0, 0)$ minimum
       It's a quadratic with a > O so it's u-shaped.
   b) $(2, -4)$ maximum
       It's a quadratic with a < O so it's n-shaped.
   c) $(-4, 33)$ maximum, $(0, 1)$ minimum
       It's a cubic with a > O. So it rises from the bottom left to a peak (the maximum), then descends into a trough (the minimum), then rises again to the top right.

Page 111 (Exam Questions)

3 a) $A = (5x + 1)(5 - 2x)$ *[1 mark]*
       $= -10x^2 + 25x - 2x + 5$
       $= -10x^2 + 23x + 5$ *[1 mark]*
       [2 marks available in total — as above]
   b) $\dfrac{dA}{dx} = -20x + 23$
       [2 marks available — 1 mark for each correct term]
   c) Maximum is at $\dfrac{dA}{dx} = 0$, so
       $-20x + 23 = 0$ *[1 mark]*
       $-20x = -23$
       $x = 1.15$ *[1 mark]*
       $A = -10 \times 1.15^2 + (23 \times 1.15) + 5 = 18.225$ km^2 *[1 mark]*
       [3 marks available in total — as above]

4 $\dfrac{dy}{dx} = 3x^2 + 12x + 9$
   Set this equal to zero to find the stationary points:
   $3x^2 + 12x + 9 = 0 \Rightarrow x^2 + 4x + 3 = 0 \Rightarrow (x + 3)(x + 1) = 0$
   The stationary points are at $x = -3$ and $x = -1$ (i.e. both negative x-values) and so the correct graph must be A.
   [4 marks available in total — 2 marks for a fully correct differentiation (otherwise 1 mark for two terms correct), 1 mark for setting the derivative equal to 0, 1 mark for using the position of the stationary points to correctly identify the graph]

5 a) $s = 2t^3 - 3t^2 + 8$
       $v = \dfrac{ds}{dt} = 6t^2 - 6t$ *[2 marks — 1 mark for each correct term]*
       When $t = 4$, $v = (6 \times 4^2) - (6 \times 4) = 72$ m/s *[1 mark]*
       [3 marks available in total — as above]
   b) $a = \dfrac{dv}{dt} = 12t - 6$ *[1 mark]*
       When $a = 0$,
       $0 = 12t - 6$ *[1 mark]*
       $6 = 12t$
       $t = 0.5$ seconds *[1 mark]*
       [3 marks available in total — as above]

Page 112 (Revision Questions)

1   A(5, –3),   B(4, 0),   C(0, 3),   D(–4, 5),   E(–2, –3)

2   (2, 1.5)

3   (6, 9)

4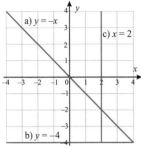

5   Straight-line equations just contain something x, something y and a number. They don't contain any powers of x or y, xy, $\frac{1}{x}$ or $\frac{1}{y}$.

6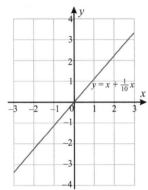

7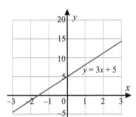

8   2

9   'm' is the gradient and 'c' is the y-intercept.

10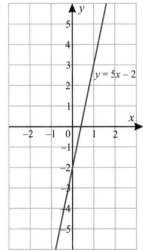

11 $y = 2x + 10$

12 a)   5   b) $-\frac{1}{5}$

13 They are both symmetrical 'bucket shaped' graphs.
    $y = x^2 + 2x – 8$ is like a 'u' whereas $y = –x^2 + 2x – 8$ is like an 'n' (or an upturned bucket).

14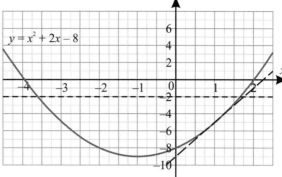

a) $x = –3.6$ (allow –3.8 to –3.5) or $x = 1.6$ (allow 1.5 to 1.8)

b)   4 (allow gradients between 3 and 5)

15 a)   A graph with a "wiggle" in the middle. E.g.

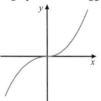

b)   A graph made up of two curves in diagonally opposite quadrants. The graph is symmetrical about the lines $y = x$ and $y = –x$. E.g.

c)   A graph made up of two curves in adjacent quadrants, either both above or both below the x-axis. The graph is symmetrical about the y-axis. E.g.

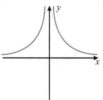

16 5

17 a)   +1 and –1   b) $x < –2$

18 0.04 or $\frac{1}{25}$

19 Write out the equation $x = f(y)$, then rearrange the equation to make y the subject.

20 a) $y = (–x)^3 + 1$ is the original graph reflected in the y-axis.

b) $y = (x + 2)^3 + 1$ is the original graph translated by 2 units in the negative x-direction.

c) $y = (3x)^2 + 1$ is the original graph stretched in the x-direction by a scale factor of $\frac{1}{3}$.

d) $y = x^3 – 1$ is the original graph translated downwards by 2 units.

21 $15x^4 + 2$
    Gradient = 1217

22 $v = 6 \text{ ms}^{-1}$, $a = 2 \text{ ms}^{-2}$

23 a) (1, –1) minimum   b) (–1, 1) maximum

Section Four — Geometry and Measures

Page 119 (Warm-Up Questions)

1 40 cm

2 $a = 115°$, angles on a straight line add to 180°, so $a = 180° – 65°$
   $b = 115°$, a and b are corresponding angles, so $a = b$
   $c = 65°$, c and 65° are also corresponding angles
   $d = 115°$, angles on a line add to 180°, so $d = 180° – c$
   There are often different ways of going about angle questions.
   Just keep scribbling down angles as you find them. It can make
   it easier to get the angle you want.

3 6 sides

4 Pentagon

5 24°

6 Kite

Page 120 (Exam Questions)

2 Angle $ABJ = 180° – 140° = 40°$ *[1 mark]*
   Angle $JAB = 180° – 150° = 30°$ *[1 mark]*
   Angle $AJB = 180° – 40° – 30° = 110°$ *[1 mark]*
   Angle $x = 180° – 110° = 70°$ *[1 mark]*
   [4 marks available in total — as above]
   Instead of working out angle AJB, you could use Rule 5 from p.114 —
   angle x is the exterior angle of the triangle ABJ, and angles ABJ and
   JAB are the opposite interior angles. You'll still pick up all the marks.

3 Exterior angle = 180° – 150° = 30° *[1 mark]*
   Number of sides = 360° ÷ 30° *[1 mark]* = 12 *[1 mark]*
   [3 marks available in total — as above]

4 Angles on a straight line add up to 180°,
   so angle $ADO = 180° – 142° = 38°$ *[1 mark]*
   Angles in a triangle add up to 180°,
   so angle $AOD = 180° – 38° – 90° = 52°$ *[1 mark]*
   OCB is an isosceles triangle so angle OBC = angle $OCB = 27°$,
   so angle $COB = 180° – 27° – 27° = 126°$ *[1 mark]*
   angle AOC = angle AOD + angle $COB = 52° + 126° = 178°$ *[1 mark]*
   [4 marks available in total — as above]

Page 124 (Warm-Up Questions)

1 $y = z = 64°$
   (Angles y and z are equal to the 64° angle given
   using the alternate segment theorem.)
   $x = 52°$ *(Angles in a triangle add to 180°, so 180° – 64° – 64° = 52°.)*

2 7.5 cm

Pages 125-126 (Exam Questions)

2 a) 5 cm *[1 mark]* *(The tangents AB and AC are equal.)*
   b) $ACO = 90°$ since a tangent and radius meet at 90° *[1 mark]*
       $AOC = 180° – 90 ° – 20° = 70°$ *[1 mark]*
       The triangles AOC and AOB are congruent so
       $AOB = AOC = 70°$. So $BOC = 70° + 70° = 140°$ *[1 mark]*
       [3 marks available in total — as above]
   c) The triangle OBC is isosceles since OB and OC are radii.
       So $OBC = OCB$ and then $(2 × OBC) + BOC = 180°$ *[1 mark]*
       $\Rightarrow 2OBC = 180° – 140° = 40°$
       $\Rightarrow OBC = 40° ÷ 2 = 20°$ *[1 mark]*
       [2 marks available in total — as above]

3 a) Angle $BCD = 150° ÷ 2 = 75°$ *[1 mark]*
       Angle at the centre is 2 × angle at circumference. *[1 mark]*
       [2 marks available in total — as above]
   b) Opposite angles in a cyclic quadrilateral sum to 180°. *[1 mark]*

4 Angle $DBC = 62°$ *[1 mark]*
   Angle $ABC = 90°$ *[1 mark]*
   Angle $x = 90° – 62° = 28°$ *[1 mark]*
   [3 marks available in total — as above]

5 Using the external intersection of two chords property:
   $AC × AB = AD × AE$
   $(10 + 6) × 6 = (8 + x) × 8$ *[1 mark]*
   $96 = 64 + 8x$
   So $x = 4$ cm *[1 mark]*
   [2 marks available in total — as above]

6 BO is the perpendicular bisector of the chord AD,
   so $FD = AF = 6$ cm *[1 mark]*
   Using the internal intersection of two chords property:
   $AF × FD = CF × FE$ *[1 mark]*
   $6 × 6 = CF × 9$
   $CF = 4$ cm *[1 mark]*
   [3 marks available in total — as above]

7 By the alternate segment theorem, $DBA = DAE = 32°$ *[1 mark]*
   The angle at the centre is twice the angle at the circumference,
   so $BOD = 2 × 53° = 106°$ *[1 mark]*
   The triangle BOD is isosceles since OB and OD are radii,
   so $OBD = ODB$ and then $(2 × OBD) + BOD = 180°$
   $\Rightarrow 2 × OBD = 180° – 106° = 74°$
   $\Rightarrow OBD = 74° ÷ 2 = 37°$ *[1 mark]*
   Then $OBA = OBD + DBA = 37° + 32° = 69°$ *[1 mark]*
   [4 marks available in total — as above]

Page 131 (Warm-Up Questions)

1 $\begin{pmatrix} -3 \\ 3 \end{pmatrix}$

2 (–3, 5)

3 a) $\frac{2}{9}$ or 0.222...
       Note that the enlargement scale factor is less than one —
       so the 'enlargement' actually makes the shape smaller.
   b) 2.6 cm

4 a) A and E   b) B and F

Page 132 (Exam Questions)

3 a) Scale factor from DEF to $ABC = 30 ÷ 12 = 2.5$ *[1 mark]*
       $AB = 7 × 2.5 = 17.5$ cm *[1 mark]*
       [2 marks available in total — as above]
   b) $DF = 35 ÷ 2.5 = 14$ cm *[1 mark]*

4 a) and b)

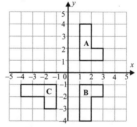

[2 marks available for part a) — 2 marks if shape correctly
reflected and in the right place on the grid, otherwise
1 mark if shape correctly reflected but in wrong location]
[2 marks available for part b) — 1 mark for a rotation of
90° clockwise around any point, 1 mark for the correct
centre of rotation]
   c) Reflection in the line $y = –x$
       [2 marks available — 1 mark for reflection,
       1 mark for correct line of reflection]

5 a) Scale factor from **A** to **C**:
$n^2 = 108\pi \div 12\pi = 9$ *[1 mark]*
$n = 3$ *[1 mark]*
Volume of **A** = 135π cm³ ÷ 3³ *[1 mark]*
= 5π cm³ *[1 mark]*
[4 marks available in total — as above]

b) Scale factor from **A** to **B**:
$m^2 = 48\pi \div 12\pi = 4$ *[1 mark]*
$m = 2$ *[1 mark]*
Perpendicular height of **B** = 4 cm × 2 *[1 mark]*
= 8 cm *[1 mark]*
[4 marks available in total — as above]

Page 138 (Warm-Up Questions)

1 a) 625π mm²

b) $(45\,000 - 2500\pi)$ mm²

c) $(180\,000 - 10\,000\pi)$ mm³

2 a) Net B

b) $2bh$ $(4 \times$ area of triangle $= 4 \times \frac{1}{2} \times b \times h)$

3 672 cm³

4 1440 m³

Page 139 (Exam Questions)

2 Area of triangle $= \frac{1}{2} \times 16 \times 5 = 40$ cm² *[1 mark]*
Area of rectangle $= 4x$ cm² *[1 mark]*
So $40 = 4x$ *[1 mark]* $\Rightarrow$ $x = 40 \div 4 = 10$ *[1 mark]*
[4 marks available in total — as above]

3 Volume of pool $= \pi \times (2 \div 2)^2 \times 0.4 = 0.4\pi$ m³ *[1 mark]*
Volume of water Amy should use $= 0.4\pi \times \frac{3}{4}$ *[1 mark]*
= 0.94 m³ (to 2 d.p.) *[1 mark]*
[3 marks available in total — as above]

4 Area of full circle $= \pi \times 12^2 = 144\pi$ cm²
Area of sector $= (50° \div 360°) \times$ area of circle
$= (50° \div 360°) \times 144\pi$ cm² $= 62.831...$ cm² $= 62.8$ cm² (3 s.f.)
[3 marks available — 1 mark for a correct method for finding the area of the full circle, 1 mark for a correct method for calculating the area of the sector, 1 mark for the correct answer]

5 Slanting length of cone = 16 cm
Length of arc $= (90° \div 360°) \times (2 \times \pi \times 16) = 8\pi$ *[1 mark]*
The circumference of the base is 8π, so the diameter of the base is $8\pi \div \pi = 8$. The radius is therefore $8 \div 2 = 4$ cm *[1 mark]*
Curved surface area of cone $= (\pi \times 4 \times 16) = 64\pi$ *[1 mark]*
Area of base of cone $= (\pi \times 4^2) = 16\pi$ *[1 mark]*
Total surface area of cone $= 64\pi + 16\pi = 80\pi$ cm² *[1 mark]*
[5 marks available in total — as above]

Page 146 (Warm-Up Questions)

1 99 minutes

2 11.3 g/cm³ (3 s.f.)

3 96 g

4 90 km/h

5 9 km

6 a) 12.7 × 1000 = 12 700 g   b) 1430 ÷ 100 = 14.3 m

7 3 000 000 000 mm³

Page 147 (Exam Questions)

3 a) Gradient $= \dfrac{\text{change in } y}{\text{change in } x} = \dfrac{15 - 0}{1 - 0}$ *[1 mark]*
$= 15 \div 1 = 15$ *[1 mark]*
[2 marks available in total — as above]

b) The speed (in km/h) at which Selby is travelling. *[1 mark]*

c)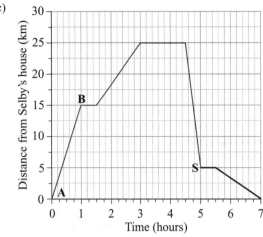

[2 marks available — 1 mark for a flat line from point S to (5.5, 5), 1 mark for a straight line from the end of the flat line to (7, 0)]

4 a) Volume = 360 ÷ 1800 *[1 mark]*
= 0.2 m³ *[1 mark]*
[2 marks available in total — as above]

b) 80 000 cm³ = 80 000 ÷ (100 × 100 × 100) = 0.08 m³ *[1 mark]*
Density = 360 ÷ 0.8 *[1 mark]*
= 4500 kg/m³ *[1 mark]*
[3 marks available in total — as above]

5 a) Area of circular base $= \pi \times (10x)^2 = 100\pi x^2$ cm² *[1 mark]*
$100\pi x^2$ cm² $= 100\pi x^2 \div (100 \times 100) = 0.01\pi x^2$ m² *[1 mark]*
Weight $= 650 \times 0.01\pi x^2$ *[1 mark]* $= 6.5\pi x^2$ N *[1 mark]*
[4 marks available in total — as above]

b) If the diameter is halved then so is the radius.
Call the original radius r and the new one s, so $s = \frac{r}{2}$.
Then the new pressure is:
$$\frac{\text{weight}}{\text{area}} = \frac{\text{weight}}{\pi s^2} = \frac{\text{weight}}{\pi\left(\frac{r}{2}\right)^2} = \frac{\text{weight}}{\pi\left(\frac{r^2}{4}\right)} = 4 \times \frac{\text{weight}}{\pi r^2}$$
So if the diameter of the circle is halved then the pressure increases and is 4 times greater.
[2 marks available — 1 mark for saying that the pressure increases, 1 mark for saying it's 4 times greater]

Page 151 (Warm-Up Questions)

1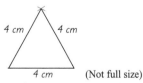

All the angles should measure 60°.

2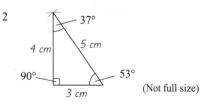

238

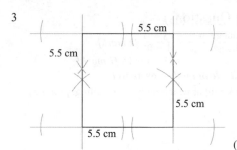

3

5.5 cm

5.5 cm

5.5 cm

5.5 cm

5.5 cm

(Not full size)

4   300°

Page 152 (Exam Questions)

3   a)   Measure 40° from the northline. Using a suitable scale
         (e.g. 1 cm : 100 m), draw along this line the equivalent of
         350 m (so 3.5 cm using the scale suggested) to find the
         location of the boat.
         [1 mark for the boat marked on a correct bearing of 040°,
         1 mark for a labelled distance with a sensible scale]
         Measure another 40° as shown below and draw down (south)
         to get a line parallel to the northline. *[1 mark]*
         Measure 90° from the northline and draw right (east) — the tree
         is located where this line intersects the south line. *[1 mark]*

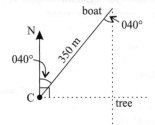

boat

N

040°

040°

350 m

C

tree

         [4 mark available in total — as above]

    b)   (i)   Accept 250-280 m *[1 mark]*
         (ii) Accept 210-240 m *[1 mark]*
         You'll measure in cm (or mm) but you need to make sure you
         convert your answer back into metres using the scale you chose
         for your diagram.

4   Construct a 90° angle, put your compass point on the right angle
    and mark a point on each line equidistant from the right angle,
    then join these points.

    Alternatively construct a 90° angle and bisect it to get a 45°
    angle. Then construct a second 90° angle.

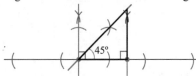

45°

    [3 marks available — 1 mark for constructing a 90° angle,
    1 mark for either marking equidistant points or bisecting
    the angle, 1 mark for a fully correct triangle with all
    construction marks visible]

5

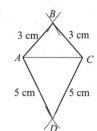

B

3 cm   3 cm

A   C

5 cm   5 cm

D

[3 marks available — 1 mark for correct 3 cm construction
arcs, 1 mark for correct 5 cm construction arcs, 1 mark for a
fully correct kite including labels]

Pages 153-154 (Revision Questions)

1   Multiply by the map scale to go from map distance to real life.
    Divide by the map scale to go from real life to map distance.
    The scale needs to be in the form 1 cm = ...

2   Plan should be a rectangle that's 20 cm long and 12 cm wide.

3   360°

4   a) $x = 154°$ b) $y = 112°$ c) $z = 58°$

5   60°

6   a)   3   b)   3

7   90°

8   a) $x = 53°$ b) $y = 69°$ c) $z = 33°$

9   5 cm

10 a)   Translation by the vector $\begin{pmatrix} -2 \\ -4 \end{pmatrix}$

    b)   Reflection in the y-axis

11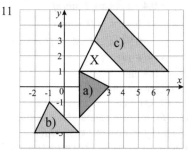

12 80 cm²

13 Congruent shapes are exactly the same size and same shape.
    Similar shapes are the same shape but different sizes.

14 $x = 2.5$ cm

15 $A = \frac{1}{2}(a + b) \times h_v$

16 220 cm²

17 Circumference = 16π cm, area = 64π cm²

18 39.27 cm² (2 d.p.)

19 Surface area = $4\pi r^2$

20 75π cm²

21 396 cm³

22 129.85 cm³ (2 d.p.)

23 a)   16:20   b)   7.52 am

24 151 minutes

25 a)   12:18   b)   11:58

26 42 km/h

27 12 500 cm³

28 11 m²

29 a) On a distance-time graph, it means the object has stopped.

    b) On a speed-time graph, it means the object is travelling at a steady speed.

30 36 km/h

31 a) 5600 cm³   b) 0.083 kg

    c) 10.8 km/h   d) 5 690 000 cm²

32

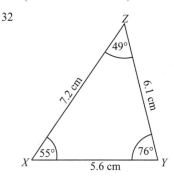

33

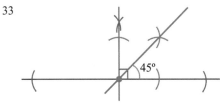

34

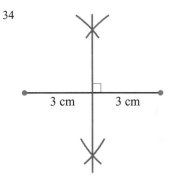

35 Put your pencil on the diagram at the point you're going FROM — point A. Draw a northline at this point. Measure the angle to the line AB clockwise from the northline — this is the bearing you want.

36

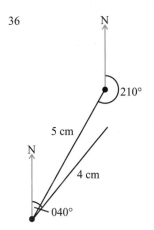

Section Five — Pythagoras and Trigonometry

Page 158 (Warm-Up Questions)

1 314 m (to the nearest metre)
The diagonal of the field is the hypotenuse of a right-angled triangle with shorter sides of length 250 m and 190 m.

2 a) 0.292   0.956   0.306

    b) 0.993   0.122   8.14

    c) 0.0872   0.996   0.0875

    d) 0.469   0.883   0.532

    e) 0.707   0.707   1.00

3 a) 13.1 cm (3 s.f.)   b) 40° (nearest degree)

4 3 cm

Page 159 (Exam Questions)

3 $3.5^2 = x^2 + 2.1^2$ *[1 mark]*
$x = \sqrt{12.25 - 4.41} = \sqrt{7.84}$ *[1 mark]*
$x = 2.8$ m *[1 mark]*
[3 marks available in total — as above]

4 Length of *EA*:
$28.3^2 = 20^2 + EA^2$ *[1 mark]*
$EA = \sqrt{800.89 - 400} = 20.02...$ *[1 mark]*
Length of *CE*:
$54.3^2 = 20^2 + CE^2$ *[1 mark]*
$CE = \sqrt{2948.49 - 400} = 50.48...$ *[1 mark]*
Perimeter = $28.3 + 54.3 + EA + CE = 153.1$ cm (1 d.p) *[1 mark]*
[5 marks available in total — as above]

5 a) $\sin 34° = \dfrac{h}{10}$ *[1 mark]*
    $h = 10 \times \sin 34°$ *[1 mark]*
    $h = 5.59$ m (2 d.p) *[1 mark]*
    [3 marks available in total — as above]

    b) *Split ABC into two right-angled triangles, and find half of AC (call it x).*
    $\cos 34° = \dfrac{x}{10}$ *[1 mark]*
    $x = 10 \times \cos 34°$ *[1 mark]*
    $x = 8.29...$
    $AC = 8.29... \times 2 = 16.58$ m (2 d.p) *[1 mark]*
    [3 marks available in total — as above]
    Alternatively, you could find x by using Pythagoras' theorem and the length h you found in part a).

6 Call the distance from the centre of the circle to the centre of an edge, *x*. The radius bisects the internal angle forming angle *a*.

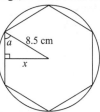

Sum of the internal angles of a hexagon
$= (2 \times 6 - 4) \times 90° = 720°$
Each internal angle of a hexagon = $720° \div 6 = 120°$ *[1 mark]*
$a = 120 \div 2 = 60°$ *[1 mark]*
$\sin 60° = \dfrac{x}{8.5}$ *[1 mark]*
$x = 8.5 \times \sin 60°$ *[1 mark]*
$x = 7.36$ cm (2 d.p) *[1 mark]*
[5 marks available in total — as above]
You could also use the calculation cos 30° × 8.5 to find the value of x. As long as you make sure you show your working, you'll get full marks if your answer is correct.

Page 167 (Warm-Up Questions)

1 $AC = 9.6$ cm (1 d.p.)

2 104.5° (1 d.p.)

3 $FDG = 31°$ (nearest degree)

4 a) 122.9°   b) 170.0°   c) 135.0°   d) 94.0°

5 $\sqrt{29}$ or 5.39 (3 s.f.)

6 a) $\overrightarrow{CD} = -2\mathbf{a}$ *(since ABCD is a parallelogram, AB = DC)*

   b) $\overrightarrow{AC} = 2\mathbf{d} + 2\mathbf{a}$

   c) $\overrightarrow{BL} = \mathbf{d} - \mathbf{a}$ *(you could find this in a few different ways —*
     for example $\overrightarrow{BL} = \overrightarrow{BC} + \frac{1}{2}\overrightarrow{CA} = 2\mathbf{d} - (\mathbf{d} + \mathbf{a}) = \mathbf{d} - \mathbf{a}$)

Page 168 (Exam Questions)

2 Angle $ABD = 180° - 90° - 31° - 12° = 47°$

  Angle $ACB = 180° - 12° - 47° = 121°$ *[1 mark]*

  Use the sine rule: $\dfrac{3.3}{\sin 12°} = \dfrac{AB}{\sin 121°}$ *[1 mark]*

  $AB = \dfrac{3.3}{\sin 12°} \times \sin 121°$ *[1 mark]*

  $AB = 13.6050...$ m *[1 mark]*

  Find length BD: $\cos 47° = \dfrac{BD}{13.6050...}$ *[1 mark]*

  $BD = \cos 47° \times 13.6050...$
  $BD = 9.2786... = 9.28$ m (3 s.f.) *[1 mark]*
  [6 marks available in total — as above]

  There's more than one way of doing this question. As long as you've
  used a correct method to get the right answer you'll still get the marks.

3 Find length DC: $5^2 - (7 - 4)^2 = DC^2$ *[1 mark]*
  $DC^2 = 16 \Rightarrow DC = 4$ cm
  Find length DG: $4^2 + 11^2 = DG^2$ *[1 mark]*
  $DG^2 = 137 \Rightarrow DG = 11.704...$ cm *[1 mark]*

  Find angle AGD: $\tan AGD = \dfrac{7}{11.704...}$ *[1 mark]*

  $AGD = \tan^{-1}\left(\dfrac{7}{11.704...}\right) = 30.9°$ (3 s.f.) *[1 mark]*

  [5 marks available in total — as above]

4 a) $\overrightarrow{BX} = \overrightarrow{BC} + \overrightarrow{CX} = \overrightarrow{BC} - \overrightarrow{XC}$ *[1 mark]*
   $\overrightarrow{BC} = 6\overrightarrow{BW} = 6\mathbf{b}$

   As $AX = 2XC$, CX must be one third of AC, so:

   $\overrightarrow{CX} = -\overrightarrow{XC} = -\frac{1}{3}\overrightarrow{AC}$ (or $\overrightarrow{CX} = \frac{1}{3}\overrightarrow{CA}$) *[1 mark]*

   $\overrightarrow{AC} = \overrightarrow{AB} + \overrightarrow{BC} = 3\mathbf{a} + 6\mathbf{b}$ (or $\overrightarrow{CA} = -3\mathbf{a} - 6\mathbf{b}$)

   $\overrightarrow{CX} = -\frac{1}{3}(3\mathbf{a} + 6\mathbf{b}) = -\mathbf{a} - 2\mathbf{b}$

   $\overrightarrow{BX} = 6\mathbf{b} - \mathbf{a} - 2\mathbf{b} = 4\mathbf{b} - \mathbf{a}$ *[1 mark]*
   [3 marks available in total — as above]
   You could have solved this a little differently,
   for instance starting by writing $\overrightarrow{BX} = \overrightarrow{BA} + \overrightarrow{AX}$

  b) From part a), $\overrightarrow{BX} = 4\mathbf{b} - \mathbf{a}$:
   $ABCD$ is a parallelogram, so:
   $\overrightarrow{CD} = \overrightarrow{BA} = -\overrightarrow{AB} = -3\mathbf{a}$
   $\overrightarrow{CM} = \frac{1}{2}\overrightarrow{CD} = -\frac{3}{2}\mathbf{a}$
   $\overrightarrow{BM} = \overrightarrow{BC} + \overrightarrow{CM}$ *[1 mark]*
      $= 6\mathbf{b} - \frac{3}{2}\mathbf{a} = \frac{3}{2}(4\mathbf{b} - \mathbf{a})$ *[1 mark]*

   B, X and M must be three points on a straight line because the
   lines BM and BX are both scalar multiples of the vector $4\mathbf{b} - \mathbf{a}$.
   [2 marks available in total — as above]

Page 169 (Revision Questions)

1 $a^2 + b^2 = c^2$
  You use Pythagoras' theorem to find the
  missing side of a right-angled triangle.

2 4.72 m (3 s.f.)

3 7.8 (1 d.p.)

4

5 33.4° (1 d.p.)

6 5.77 cm (3 s.f.)

7 21.5° (1 d.p.)

8 Sine rule: $\dfrac{a}{\sin A} = \dfrac{b}{\sin B} = \dfrac{c}{\sin C}$
  Cosine rule: $a^2 = b^2 + c^2 - 2bc \cos A$
  Area $= \frac{1}{2}ab \sin C$

9 Two angles given plus any side — sine rule.
  Two sides given plus an angle not enclosed by them — sine rule.
  Two sides given plus the angle enclosed by them — cosine rule.
  All three sides given but no angles — cosine rule.

10 6.84 cm (3 s.f.)

11 48.1 cm² (3 s.f.)

12 $a^2 + b^2 + c^2 = d^2$

13 11.9 m (3 s.f.)

14 15.2° (3 s.f.)

15 54° (nearest degree)

16 120.6° (1 d.p.)

17 Multiplying by a scalar changes the size
  of a vector but not its direction.

18 5.4 (1 d.p.)

19 a) $\overrightarrow{AX} = \frac{1}{3}\mathbf{a}$

  b) $\overrightarrow{DX} = \frac{4}{3}\mathbf{a} - \mathbf{b}$ $\overrightarrow{XB} = \frac{8}{3}\mathbf{a} - 2\mathbf{b}$

  c) $\overrightarrow{XB} = 2\overrightarrow{DX}$, so DXB is a straight line.

Section Six — Statistics and Probability

Page 174 (Warm-Up Questions)

1   Mode = 2, median = 1.5, mean = 1.333..., range = 11

2

Number of cars	0	1	2	3	4	5	6	Total
Frequency	1	24	36	31	22	9	1	124
No. of cars × F	0	24	72	93	88	45	6	328

a)   Mean = 328 ÷ 124 = 2.645 (3 d.p.)

b)   Median is half-way between the 62nd and 63rd values,
so median = 3

c)   Mode = 2   d)   Range = 6 – 0 = 6

3

Height (cm)	$145 \leq x$ < 155	$155 \leq x$ < 165	$165 \leq x$ < 175	$175 \leq x$ < 185	Total
Frequency	18	22	24	15	79
Midpoint	150	160	170	180	—
Midpoint × F	2700	3520	4080	2700	13 000

a)   Mean = 13000 ÷ 79 = 164.56 cm (2 d.p.)

b)   Median is in the group containing the 40th value,
so the median group is $155 \leq x$ < 165.

c)   Modal Group = $165 \leq x$ < 175

Page 175 (Exam Questions)

2   Total mark for boys = 15b, total mark for girls = 13g
Total number of pupils = 15 + 13 = 28
So mean mark for all pupils = $\dfrac{15b + 13g}{28}$

*[3 marks available — 1 mark for correct total marks for boys
and girls, 1 mark for the total number of pupils,
1 mark for correct answer]*

3   (0 × 2) + (2 × 4) + (3 × 7) + (5 × 11)
      + (7 × 6) + (8 × 3) + (10 × 3) = 180
180 ÷ 36 = 5

*[3 marks available — 1 mark for finding the total
number of messages, 1 mark for the correct calculation
to find the mean, 1 mark for the correct answer]*
*You could have done this question by adding an extra column
to the table for 'number of messages × frequency'.*

4   a)   Patch A: 8, 8, 9, 12, 13, 14, 14, 16, 18, 19, 22
              lower quartile = 9 (3rd value)
              upper quartile = 18 (9th value)
              IQR = 18 – 9 = 9
      Patch B: 11, 11, 13, 13, 14, 15, 19
              lower quartile = 11 (2nd value)
              upper quartile = 15 (6th value)
              IQR = 15 – 11 = 4

*[4 marks available — 2 marks for each correct interquartile
range, otherwise 1 mark for each correct lower or upper
quartile up to a maximum of 2 marks]*

   b)   E.g. the interquartile range is smaller in Patch B,
so the number of strawberries per plant in Patch B
is more consistent. *[1 mark]*

Page 181 (Warm-Up Questions)

1   a)
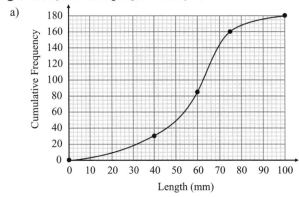

   b)
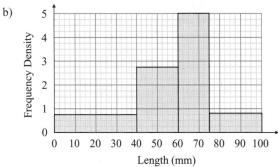

   c)
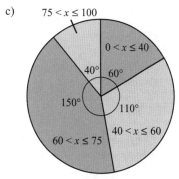

2   Median = 61 mm (accept answers of 60-65 mm)

3   Around 145 (accept answers of 130-160)

*The easiest way to get the estimates in Q2 and Q3 is by using the
cumulative frequency diagram from part Q1a).*

Page 182 (Exam Questions)

2   a)

	Van	Motorbike	Car	Total
Travelling North	15	12	21	48
Travelling South	20	9	23	52
Total	35	21	44	100

*[3 marks available — award 3 marks for all numbers
correct, otherwise award 2 marks for at least four numbers
correct or 1 mark for at least two numbers correct]*

   b)   15 + 12 = 27 *[1 mark]*

3 a) Total = 30, so multiplier = 360° ÷ 30 = 12°
       So Dog = 15 × 12° = 180° and Other = 1 × 12° = 12°:

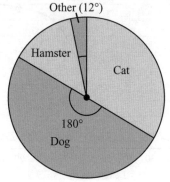

[3 marks available — 1 mark for a correct method for calculating the angles, 1 mark for all angles correct, 1 mark for an accurately drawn pie chart]

   b) 30 people = 360°, so 1 person = 12°
       Measuring the angle from the pie chart,
       Hamsters = 48°, so 48° ÷ 12° = 4 people
       [2 marks available — 1 mark for a correct method, 1 mark for the correct answer]
       You could also have measured the angle in the Cat part of the diagram, then used this to complete the frequency table.

4

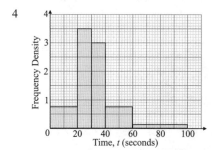

[3 marks available — 1 mark for finding frequency densities, 2 marks for all bars drawn correctly, otherwise 1 mark for one bar drawn correctly]

Page 186 (Warm-Up Questions)

1 $\frac{3}{10}$ or 0.3

2 0.2

3 a) $\frac{1}{6}$ b) Approximately 50 times

4 $\frac{16}{52}$ or $\frac{4}{13}$

Page 187 (Exam Questions)

2 a) Number of red counters = 10 − 4 = 6 *[1 mark]*
       Probability of getting a red counter = $\frac{6}{10} = \frac{3}{5}$ *[1 mark]*
       [2 marks available in total — as above]

   b) No green counters so probability of getting a green = 0
       [1 mark]

3 P(being born on a Tuesday) = $\frac{1}{7}$ *[1 mark]*
   $\frac{1}{7}$ × 834 *[1 mark]* = 119.1428... *[1 mark]*
                      ≈ 119 pupils *[1 mark]*
   [4 marks available in total — as above]

4 a) P(fewer than 3 dots) = P(1 dot) + P(2 dots)
                            = $\frac{1}{6} + \frac{1}{6} = \frac{2}{6} = \frac{1}{3}$
       [2 marks available — 1 mark finding the probabilities of choosing cards with one dot and two dots on, 1 mark for the correct answer]

   b) P(sum of dots = 4) = P(1 dot then 3 dots)
                           + P(2 dots then 2 dots)
                           + P(3 dots then 1 dot)
       $= \left(\frac{1}{6} \times \frac{1}{6}\right) + \left(\frac{1}{6} \times \frac{1}{6}\right) + \left(\frac{1}{6} \times \frac{1}{6}\right) = 3 \times \frac{1}{6 \times 6} = \frac{1}{12}$
       [3 marks available — 1 mark for multiplying the correct probabilities in one case, 1 mark for adding the correct probabilities of all three cases together, 1 mark for the correct answer]

   c) P(sum of dots > 9)
       = P(4 dots then 6 dots)
           + P(6 dots then 4 dots)
           + P(5 dots then 6 dots)
           + P(6 dots then 5 dots)
       $= \left(\frac{1}{6} \times \frac{1}{5}\right) + \left(\frac{1}{6} \times \frac{1}{5}\right) + \left(\frac{1}{6} \times \frac{1}{5}\right) + \left(\frac{1}{6} \times \frac{1}{5}\right)$
       $= 4 \times \frac{1}{6 \times 5} = \frac{2}{15}$
       [3 marks available — 1 mark for multiplying the correct probabilities in one case, 1 mark for adding the correct probabilities of all four cases together, 1 mark for the correct answer]

Page 192 (Warm-Up Questions)

1
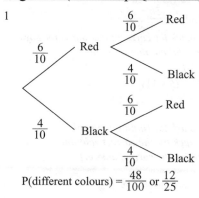

P(different colours) = $\frac{48}{100}$ or $\frac{12}{25}$

2
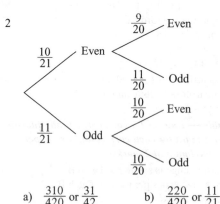

   a) $\frac{310}{420}$ or $\frac{31}{42}$ b) $\frac{220}{420}$ or $\frac{11}{21}$

3
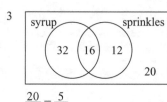

$\frac{20}{52} = \frac{5}{13}$

4

Score	Relative frequency
1	0.14
2	0.137
3	0.138
4	0.259
5	0.161
6	0.165

E.g. Expected probability of each is $\frac{1}{6} = 0.1666...$

P(4) is much higher than expected, so the dice is probably biased.

Page 193 (Exam Questions)

2 a) Total = 26 + 33 + 21 + 20 = 100
n(not a singer) = 26 + 20 = 46
So P(not a singer) = $\frac{46}{100}$ or $\frac{23}{50}$ *[1 mark]*

   b) n(singers) = 33 + 21 = 54
n(singer and not female) = 21
So P(not female, given singer) = $\frac{21}{54}$ or $\frac{7}{18}$ *[1 mark]*

3 a)
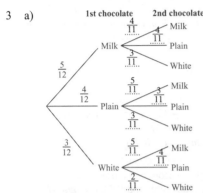

[2 marks available — 2 marks for all probabilities correct, 1 mark for four or more probabilities correct]

   b) Outcomes that are one milk and one white: MW and WM
P(one milk and one white) = P(MW) + P(WM)
$$= \left(\frac{5}{12} \times \frac{3}{11}\right) + \left(\frac{3}{12} \times \frac{5}{11}\right) = \frac{5}{22}$$

[3 marks available — 1 mark for multiplying the probabilities of the two chocolates together, 1 mark for adding the probabilities for each possible case together, 1 mark for the correct answer]

   c) P(at least 1 plain) = 1 – P(no plain)
= 1 – (P(MM) + P(WW) + P(one milk and one white))
$$= 1 - \left(\left(\frac{5}{12} \times \frac{4}{11}\right) + \left(\frac{3}{12} \times \frac{2}{11}\right) + \frac{5}{22}\right)$$
$$= 1 - \left(\frac{10}{66} + \frac{3}{66} + \frac{15}{66}\right) = 1 - \frac{28}{66} = \frac{38}{66} = \frac{19}{33}$$

[3 marks available — 1 mark for working out at least one of P(MM) and P(WW) correctly, 1 mark for a correct calculation to find the answer, 1 mark for the correct answer]

You could also answer this by working out P(first one plain) + P(MP) + P(WP), but it's a bit more work to get to the answer.

Page 194 (Revision Questions)

1 The mode is the most common value.
The median is the middle value when the data has been arranged in order of size.
The mean is the total of the data values divided by the number of data values.
The range is the difference between the highest and lowest data values.

2 a) Mode = 31, Median = 24
Mean = 22, Range = 39

   b) Lower quartile = 11
Upper quartile = 31
Interquartile range = 20

3 Averages (mean, median or mode) and spread (range or interquartile range)

4 a) Modal class is: $1.5 \le y < 1.6$.

   b) Class containing median is: $1.5 \le y < 1.6$

   c) Estimated mean = 1.58 m (2 d.p.)

5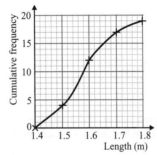

6 Calculate the bar's area or use the formula:
Frequency = Frequency Density × Class Width.

7 You need to look at the key to see what each symbol represents.

8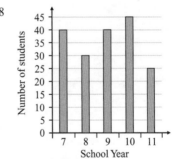

9

10 A probability of 0 means something will never happen.
    A probability of $\frac{1}{2}$ means something is as likely to happen as not.

11 $\frac{8}{50}$ or $\frac{4}{25}$

12 1

13 a)

Second flip

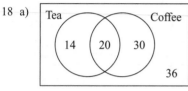

		Heads	Tails
First flip	Heads	HH	HT
	Tails	TH	TT

b) $\frac{1}{4}$

14 Expected times outcome will happen = probability × n

15 $\frac{1}{12}$

16 $\frac{1}{2}$

17 $\frac{1}{221}$

18 a)

Tea   Coffee

14   20   30

36

b) $\frac{64}{100} = \frac{16}{25}$

19 When you can't tell what the probabilities of different outcomes
    are 'just by looking', e.g. when you have a biased dice/spinner etc.

Practice Paper 1

1 40 minutes = $\frac{2}{3}$ hours

   Distance = speed × time = $90 \times \frac{2}{3}$ = 60 km

   *[3 marks available — 1 mark for using the correct formula,
   1 mark for a correct calculation and 1 mark for the correct
   final answer]*

2 Revision guides and autobiographies make up a quarter of the
   total books. $\frac{1}{4}$ of 9000 = 2250 *[1 mark]*

   Total number of parts = 7 + 3 = 10

   so one part is: $\frac{2250}{10}$ = 225 *[1 mark]*

   Revision guides are 3 parts, so 225 × 3 = 675 *[1 mark]*

   [3 marks available in total — as above]

3 Interior angle of regular n-sided polygon = 180° – exterior angle
                                              = 180° – (360° ÷ n)

   Interior angle of regular octagon = 180° – (360° ÷ 8) = 135°
   Interior angle of regular hexagon = 180° – (360° ÷ 6) = 120°
   Angle CBK = angle ABC – angle IJK = 135° – 120° = 15°

   *[2 marks available in total — 1 mark for using correct method
   to find interior angle of octagon or hexagon, 1 mark for
   correct answer]*

4 The median is 12, so one of the unknown cards must be
   another 12. *[1 mark]*

   The mean is 13 so the sum of the cards is 13 × 4 = 52.
   The last card must be 52 – 7 – 12 – 12 = 21 *[1 mark]*
   The range is 21 – 7 = 14 *[1 mark]*
   [3 marks available in total — as above]

5 60% of his total earnings = £21 000, so
   40% of his total earnings was from commission.
   1% of his total earnings = £21 000 ÷ 60 = £350 *[1 mark]*
   40% of his total earnings = £350 × 40 = £14 000 *[1 mark]*
   So he earned £14 000 in commission, which is
   2% of the value of the cars he sold last year.
   1% of the value of the cars = £14 000 ÷ 2 = £7000 *[1 mark]*
   So 100% of the value of the cars he sold last year is
   £7000 × 100 = £700 000 *[1 mark]*
   [4 marks available in total — as above]

6 a) $9x + 6 = 3(3x + 2)$ *[1 mark]*

   b) $8y^3 + 4y = 4(2y^3 + y)$
                  $= 4y(2y^2 + 1)$

       *[2 marks available — 2 marks for correct answer,
       otherwise 1 mark for a correct partial factorisation]*

   c) Use the difference of two squares.
       $25a^2 - b^2 = (5a)^2 - b^2$
                    $= (5a + b)(5a - b)$
       *[2 marks available — 2 marks for correct answer,
       otherwise 1 mark for a correct partial factorisation]*

7 Angle EBD = 180° – 115° – 30° = 35°
   Angle BDE = 180° – 50° – 35° = 95°
   $EDC = EAC$ so angle CDB = 120° – 95° = 25°
   z = 180° – 115° – 25° = 40°
   *[3 marks available — 1 mark for correct values of angles
   EBD and BDE, 1 mark for the correct value of angle CDB,
   1 mark for the correct answer]*

8 a) $\text{LCM} = 2^8 \times 5^3 \times 7$
*[2 marks available — 2 marks for the correct answer,
otherwise 1 mark for a common multiple of all
three numbers]*

   b) $\text{HCF} = 2^5$
*[2 marks available — 2 marks for the correct answer,
otherwise 1 mark for a common factor of all
three numbers]*

9 a) $a = \frac{1}{2}bc^2$
$2a = bc^2$
$b = \frac{2a}{c^2}$
*[2 marks available — 1 mark for multiplying both sides by 2,
1 mark for the correct answer]*

   b) $12 = \frac{bx+8}{by-4}$
$12(by-4) = bx+8$ *[1 mark]*
$12by - 48 = bx + 8$
$12by - bx = 56$
$b(12y - x) = 56$ *[1 mark]*
$b = \frac{56}{12y - x}$ *[1 mark]*
[3 marks available in total — as above]

10 a) $\text{Gradient} = \frac{\text{change in } y}{\text{change in } x} = \frac{-2-7}{-2-4} = \frac{-9}{-6} = \frac{3}{2}$ *[1 mark]*
So, $y = \frac{3}{2}x + c$, plug in point $(-2, -2)$ to find c: *[1 mark]*
$-2 = \frac{3}{2}(-2) + c$, so $c = -2 + 3 = 1$, so $y = \frac{3}{2}x + 1$ *[1 mark]*
$2y = 3x + 2$
$3x - 2y + 2 = 0$ *[1 mark]*
[4 marks available in total — as above]
This could also be given as $-3x + 2y - 2 = 0$.

   b) Gradient of the perpendicular line is $m = -\frac{1}{4}$ *[1 mark]*
$y = -\frac{1}{4}x + c$
When $x = 8$, $y = 1$, so $1 = -\frac{1}{4} \times 8 + c$ *[1 mark]*
$1 = -2 + c$, so $c = 3$
$y = -\frac{1}{4}x + 3$ *[1 mark]*
[3 marks available in total — as above]

11 $3x + 5y = 5$ $\xrightarrow{\times 2}$ $6x + 10y = 10$ *[1 mark]*
$3y - 2x = -16$ $\xrightarrow{\times 3}$ $9y - 6x = -48$ *[1 mark]*

$\begin{array}{r} 6x + 10y = 10 \\ +\ -6x + 9y = -48 \\ \hline 19y = -38 \\ y = -2 \end{array}$ *[1 mark]*

To find x, substitute this value of y into
one of the original equations.
$3x + 5y = 5$
$3x + 5(-2) = 5$
$3x - 10 = 5$
$3x = 15$
$x = 5$ *[1 mark]*
[4 marks available in total — as above]

12 a) 5550 km *[1 mark]*

   b) 5650 km × 2 = 11300 km
*[2 marks available — 1 mark for showing a suitable
method, 1 mark for the correct answer]*

13 a) $(8n^6)^{\frac{1}{3}} = 8^{\frac{1}{3}} \times n^{\frac{6}{3}} = \sqrt[3]{8} \times n^2 = 2n^2$
*[2 marks available — 1 mark for correct working,
1 mark for the correct answer]*

   b) $(p+1)(p-3)(p+5) = (p+1)(p^2 + 5p - 3p - 15)$
$= (p+1)(p^2 + 2p - 15)$
$= p(p^2 + 2p - 15) + 1(p^2 + 2p - 15)$
$= p^3 + 2p^2 + -15p + p^2 + 2p - 15$
$= p^3 + 3p^2 - 13p - 15$
*[3 marks available — 3 marks for the correct answer,
otherwise 1 mark for correctly multiplying two sets of
brackets together, 1 mark for attempting to multiply this
product by the third set of brackets]*

   c) $q(2q - 4) + 4(q^2 + q + 11) = 68$
$2q^2 - 4q + 4q^2 + 4q + 44 = 68$
$6q^2 + 44 = 68$, so $6q^2 = 24$
$q^2 = 4$ so $q = \pm 2$
*[3 marks available — 1 mark for correctly expanding out
the brackets, 1 mark for collecting like terms to simplify
and 1 mark for the correct answer]*

14 a) P(lands on a 2 and then a 3) = 0.15 × 0.2 *[1 mark]*
$= 0.03$ *[1 mark]*
[2 marks available in total — as above]

   b) 2, 3 and 5 are prime, and 2 and 4 are multiples of 2. So find
the probability of the spinner landing on a 2, 3, 4 or 5:
P(2, 3, 4 or 5) = 0.15 + 0.2 + 0.25 + 0.1 = 0.7.
*[2 marks available — 1 mark for a correct method,
1 mark for the correct answer]*

15 a)
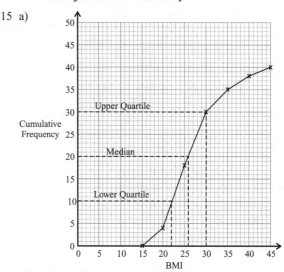
*[2 marks available — 1 mark for plotting the points correctly,
1 mark for joining them with straight lines or a smooth curve]*
*You're asked to draw a cumulative frequency graph, so you can
choose whether to join the points with a curve or straight lines.*

   b) Median BMI = 26 (see graph)
[1 mark, accept answers ±1]

   c) Lower quartile: BMI = 22 (see graph)
Upper quartile: BMI = 30 (see graph)
Interquartile range = 30 − 22 = 8
*[2 marks available — 1 mark for correct method,
1 mark for correct answer, accept answers ±2]*

16 Let $r = 0.1\dot{5}$, so $100r = 15.1\dot{5}$
$100r - r = 15.1\dot{5} - 0.1\dot{5}$
$99r = 15$ *[1 mark]*
$r = \frac{15}{99} = \frac{5}{33}$ *[1 mark]*
[2 marks available in total — as above]

17 P(Chips not served) $= 1 - 0.2 = 0.8$
On a day when chips aren't served,
P(ketchup) $= 0.4 \times 2 = 0.8$ *[1 mark]*

Use a tree diagram:

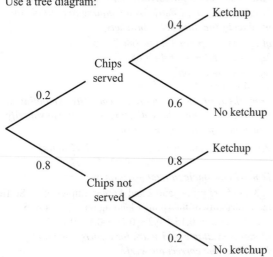

P(Ketchup) = P(Chips served and ketchup)
            + P(Chips not served and ketchup) *[1 mark]*
$= (0.2 \times 0.4) + (0.8 \times 0.8)$ *[1 mark]*
$= 0.08 + 0.64 = 0.72$ *[1 mark]*
[4 marks available in total — as above]

18 Multiply numerator and denominator by the root in the
denominator. $\dfrac{\sqrt{2}(\sqrt{72} + 6)}{\sqrt{2}\sqrt{2}} = \dfrac{\sqrt{2}\sqrt{72} + 6\sqrt{2}}{2}$ *[1 mark]*

$= \dfrac{\sqrt{144} + 6\sqrt{2}}{2} = \dfrac{12 + 6\sqrt{2}}{2}$ *[1 mark]*

$= 6 + 3\sqrt{2}$ and so $a = 6$, $b = 3$ *[1 mark]*
[3 marks available in total — as above]

19 $a + (3 - 1)d = 26 \Rightarrow a + 2d = 26$ (1)
$a + (10 - 1)d = 75 \Rightarrow a + 9d = 75$ (2)
Subtract (1) from (2) to get:
$9d - 2d = 75 - 26$
$\quad\quad 7d = 49$
$\quad\quad\quad d = 7$
Substituting this back into (1) gives
$a + 2 \times 7 = 26$
$\quad a + 14 = 26$
$\quad\quad\quad a = 12$

So, the nth term is given by $12 + 7(n - 1) = 7n + 5$
*[4 marks available in total — 1 mark for both equations
involving a and d, 1 mark for correctly finding a, 1 mark for
correctly finding d, and 1 mark for the correct answer]*

20 a) $\frac{1}{2}(x + 3)(4x - 2) = 43$ *[1 mark]*
$(x + 3)(2x - 1) = 43$
$2x^2 - x + 6x - 3 = 43$ *[1 mark]*
$2x^2 + 5x - 46 = 0$ *[1 mark]*
[3 marks available in total — as above]
*You could also multiply the brackets together first and
then multiply by $\frac{1}{2}$.*

   b) $x = \dfrac{-5 \pm \sqrt{5^2 - 4 \times 2 \times -46}}{2 \times 2}$ *[1 mark]*

      $= \dfrac{-5 \pm \sqrt{393}}{4}$ *[1 mark]*

      $= 3.71$ (to 3 s.f.) *[1 mark]*
[3 marks available in total — as above]
*The other solution ($x = -6.21$) can't be true in this context,
because it gives negative dimensions for the triangle.*

21 *First you need to find one angle using the cosine rule.*
E.g. use angle CAB.
$\cos A = \dfrac{14^2 + 12^2 - 19^2}{2 \times 14 \times 12}$ *[1 mark]*
$A = \cos^{-1}\left(\dfrac{-21}{336}\right)$ *[1 mark]*
$A = 93.58...°$ *[1 mark]*
Area $= \dfrac{1}{2} \times 14 \times 12 \times \sin 93.58...°$ *[1 mark]*
Area $= 83.84$ cm^2 (2 d.p) *[1 mark]*
[5 marks available in total — as above]

22 E.g. Angle $ACB = x$ (by the alternate segment theorem) *[1 mark]*
Angle $OCF = 90°$ (tangent meets a radius at 90°) *[1 mark]*
So angle $OCA = 90 - y$ *[1 mark]*
$a =$ angle ACB − angle $OCA = x - (90° - y) = x + y - 90°$ *[1 mark]*
[4 marks available in total — as above]

23 a) Dividing the first two terms by 5: $5(x^2 + 4x) + 12$ *[1 mark]*
      $4 \div 2 = 2$, so the first bit is $5(x + 2)^2$
      Expanding brackets gives: $5(x + 2)^2 = 5(x^2 + 4x + 4)$
                             $= 5x^2 + 20x + 20$
      To complete the square: $12 - 20 = -8$ *[1 mark]*
      So $5x^2 + 20x + 12 = 5(x + 2)^2 - 8$ *[1 mark]*
      [3 marks available — as above]
   b) $(-2, -8)$ *[1 mark]*

24 $AN = 12 \times \dfrac{3}{4} = 9$ cm and $ND = 12 - 9 = 3$ cm *[1 mark for both]*
In triangle CNF: $CF = 12$ cm
$CN^2 = 8^2 + 9^2 + 4^2 = 161$ so $CN = \sqrt{161}$ cm *[1 mark]*
$NF^2 = 3^2 + 8^2 + 4^2 = 89$ so $NF = \sqrt{89}$ cm *[1 mark]*
Now use the cosine rule to find angle CNF:
$\cos CNF = \dfrac{\sqrt{161}^2 + \sqrt{89}^2 - 12^2}{2 \times \sqrt{161} \times \sqrt{89}}$ *[1 mark]* $= 0.442...$
Angle $CNF = \cos^{-1}(0.442...) = 63.719...° = 63.7°$ (1 d.p.)
[1 mark]
[5 marks available in total — as above]

Practice Paper 2

1 a) $25 \div (2 + 3) = 5$ *[1 mark]*
Number of girls is $5 \times 3 = 15$ *[1 mark]*
[2 marks available in total — as above]

b) 10 children = 6 parts − 1 part = 5 parts *[1 mark]*
So, 1 part = $10 \div 5 = 2$ children *[1 mark]*.
So there are $7 \times 2 = 14$ children with brown hair *[1 mark]*.
[3 marks available in total — as above]

2 $0.025 \times £42\,000 = £1050$
So Tim's salary in 2015 was $£42\,000 + £1050 = £43\,050$
One month's salary in 2015 = $£43\,050 \div 12 = £3587.50$
Five months' salary in 2015 = $£3587.50 \times 5 = £17\,937.50$
[4 marks available — 1 mark for calculating the amount Tim's salary increased by, 1 mark for calculating Tim's annual salary in 2015, 1 mark for attempting to calculate five months' salary, 1 mark for the correct answer]

3 a) $150 \le h < 160$ *[1 mark]*

b)

Height in cm (h)	Frequency	Mid-interval value	Frequency × mid-interval value
$130 \le h < 140$	5	$(130 + 140) / 2 = 135$	$5 \times 135 = 675$
$140 \le h < 150$	10	$(140 + 150) / 2 = 145$	$10 \times 145 = 1450$
$150 \le h < 160$	14	$(150 + 160) / 2 = 155$	$14 \times 155 = 2170$
$160 \le h < 170$	8	$(160 + 170) / 2 = 165$	$8 \times 165 = 1320$
$170 \le h < 180$	3	$(170 + 180) / 2 = 175$	$3 \times 175 = 525$

Total number of children = $5 + 10 + 14 + 8 + 3 = 40$
Mean = $(675 + 1450 + 2170 + 1320 + 525) \div 40 = 6140 \div 40$
$= 153.5$ cm
[4 marks available — 1 mark for all mid-interval values, 1 mark for calculation of frequency × mid-interval value, 1 mark for adding these up and dividing by 40, 1 mark for the correct answer]

4       $2a - 1 < 7a - 16$
$-2a$: $-1 < 5a - 16$
$+16$: $15 < 5a$ *[1 mark]*
$\div 5$: $3 < a$ *[1 mark]*

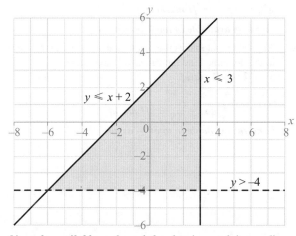

[1 mark]
[3 marks available in total — as above]

5

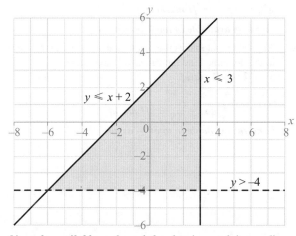

[4 marks available — 1 mark for showing each inequality correctly, 1 mark for shading the correct region]

6 $62\,000\,000 = 6.2 \times 10^7$
Debt per person = debt ÷ population
$= (8.494 \times 10^{11}) \div (6.2 \times 10^7)$
$= (8.494 \div 6.2) \times (10^{11} \div 10^7) = £1.37 \times 10^4$
[2 marks available — 1 mark for calculation, 1 mark for correct answer in standard form]

7 a) Let I be the point directly below G on the line EH.
$IH = 15.5 - 10 = 5.5$ cm
$GH^2 = GI^2 + IH^2$ *[1 mark]* $= 4.8^2 + 5.5^2 = 53.29$ *[1 mark]*
$GH = \sqrt{53.29} = 7.3$ cm *[1 mark]*
[3 marks available in total — as above]

b) Call the missing angle x. Then $\tan x = \dfrac{4.8}{5.5} = 0.8727...$
[1 mark]
$x = \tan^{-1} 0.8727... $ *[1 mark]* $= 41.112... = 41.1°$ (1 d.p.)
[1 mark]

[3 marks available in total — as above]
You know all three sides of the triangle, so you could have used sin or cos instead of tan and got the same answer — just make sure you put the right numbers in.

8 a) People who like football and badminton:
$n(F \cap B) = 56$
People who like badminton but not football:
$n(B) - n(F \cap B) = 102 - 56 = 46$
People who like football and not badminton:
$n(F \cap B') = 0$ (as $F \cap B' = \emptyset$)
People who don't like football and don't like badminton:
$128 - 0 - 56 - 46 = 26$

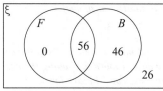

[2 marks for all correct values, otherwise 1 mark for two correct values]

b) E.g. All students in Year 11 who like football also like badminton. *[1 mark]*

c) $F =$

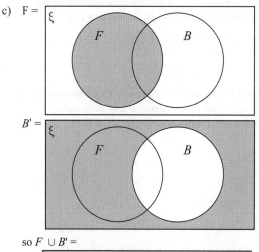

$B' =$

so $F \cup B' =$

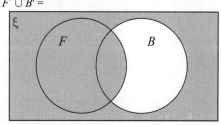

$n(F \cup B') = 0 + 56 + 26 = 82$ *[1 mark]*

d) The number of Year 11 students who like badminton is $56 + 46 = 102$.
So, the probability of choosing a student who also likes football is $\dfrac{56}{102} = \dfrac{28}{51}$. *[1 mark]*

9 a) and b)

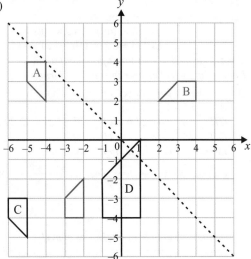

[1 mark available for part a) for correct translation]
[3 marks available for part b) — 1 mark for a correct reflection, 1 mark for a correct enlargement, 1 mark for performing both correctly]

c) Rotation 90° *[1 mark]* anti-clockwise *[1 mark]*
Centre of rotation = $(-1, -1)$ *[1 mark]*
[3 marks available in total — as above]

10 a) $3 + 2 + 1 + 2 = 8$ pots in total. *[1 mark]*
$\frac{1}{8} + \frac{3}{8} = \frac{4}{8} = \frac{1}{2}$ *[1 mark]*
[2 marks available in total — as above]

b) $\left(\frac{2}{8} \times \frac{6}{7}\right) + \left(\frac{6}{8} \times \frac{2}{7}\right) = \frac{24}{56} = \left(\frac{3}{7}\right)$
[3 marks available — 1 mark for multiplying the correct probabilities in one case, 1 mark for adding the correct probabilities of both cases and 1 mark for the correct final answer]

11 a) $\frac{x^2 - 25}{x^2 + 6x + 5} = \frac{(x - 5)(x + 5)}{(x + 5)(x + 1)} = \frac{x - 5}{x + 1}$
[3 marks available – 1 for correctly factorising the denominator, 1 mark for correctly factorising the numerator, 1 mark for the correct answer]

b) $\frac{2x^2 + 7x + 6}{x^2 - 2x - 8} = \frac{(2x + 3)(x + 2)}{(x - 4)(x + 2)}$
$= \frac{2x + 3}{x - 4}$

[3 marks available – 1 for correctly factorising the denominator, 1 mark for correctly factorising the numerator, 1 mark for the correct answer]

12 a) $360° - 100° - 66° - 80° = 114°$ *[1 mark]*

b) Find the scale factor: $19.8 \div 6.6 = 3$ *[1 mark]*
$21 \div 3 = 7$ cm *[1 mark]*
[2 marks available in total — as above]

c) Area $= 264.3 \div 3^2$ *[1 mark]*
Area $= 29.3666...$ cm² $= 29.4$ cm² (3 s.f.) *[1 mark]*
[2 marks available in total — as above]

13 a) $\frac{dy}{dx} = 3\left(\frac{1}{3}x^2\right) - 2(3x) - 16 = x^2 - 6x - 16$

[2 marks available — 2 marks for correct answer, otherwise 1 mark for two correctly differentiated terms]

b) When $x = 4$, $\frac{dy}{dx} = 4^2 - (6 \times 4) - 16 = -24$ *[1 mark]*

c) Gradient at a turning point is 0,
so factorise and solve $x^2 - 6x - 16 = 0$ *[1 mark]*
$(x - 8)(x + 2) = 0$, so $x = 8$ and $x = -2$ *[1 mark]*
[2 marks available in total — as above]

14 Volume $= \frac{4}{3}\pi r^3 = 478$ cm³ *[1 mark]*

$r = \sqrt[3]{\frac{3 \times 478}{4\pi}} = 4.8504...$ cm *[1 mark]*
Surface area $= 4\pi r^2 = 4\pi \times (4.8504...)^2$ *[1 mark]*
$= 295.6$ cm² (1 d.p.) *[1 mark]*
[4 marks available in total — as above]

15 a) $p \propto \frac{1}{d^3}$ so $p = \frac{k}{d^3}$ *[1 mark]*. When $p = 60$, $d = 2$, so $60 = \frac{k}{2^3}$
$k = 60 \times 2^3 = 480$ *[1 mark]*, so $p = \frac{480}{d^3}$ *[1 mark]*
[3 marks available in total — as above]

b) $p = 100$, so $100 = \frac{480}{d^3}$. $d^3 = \frac{480}{100} = 4.8$ *[1 mark]*,
so $d = \sqrt[3]{4.8} = 1.6868... = 1.69$ cm (2 d.p.) *[1 mark]*
[2 marks available in total — as above]

16 a) Replace g(x) with y: $y = \frac{3}{x - 2}$
Now make x the subject:
$y(x - 2) = 3$
$x - 2 = \frac{3}{y}$
$x = \frac{3}{y} + 2$
Replace x with g⁻¹(x) and y with x: g⁻¹(x) $= \frac{3}{x} + 2$
[2 marks available — 1 mark for using a suitable method, 1 mark for the correct answer]

b) gf(x) $=$ g($3x^2$) *[1 mark]*
gf(x) $= \frac{3}{3x^2 - 2}$ *[1 mark]*
[2 marks available in total — as above]

c) Any value that makes the denominator equal to 0 cannot be in the domain. Find the values of x that make:
$3x^2 - 2 = 0$ *[1 mark]*
$3x^2 = 2$
$x^2 = \frac{2}{3}$ so $x = \pm\sqrt{\frac{2}{3}}$ *[1 mark]*
[2 marks available in total — as above]

17 a) $(10 \times 0.6) + (40 \times 0.1)$ *[1 mark]* $= 6 + 4 = 10$ cars *[1 mark]*
[2 marks available in total — as above]
The (10×0.6) comes from splitting the 60–80 interval in half
— you're looking for cars parked for longer than 70 minutes,
so you need the bit of the bar which covers 70–80 mins,
and then the whole of the bar for 80–120 mins.

b) Frequencies: $0–20 = 20 \times 1.2 = 24$,
$20–30 = 10 \times 2.4 = 24$,
$30–40 = 10 \times 1.6 = 16$,
$40–60 = 20 \times 1.0 = 20$,
$60–80 = 20 \times 0.6 = 12$,
$80–120 = 40 \times 0.1 = 4$
Mean = sum of (frequency × mid-interval value)
$\div$ number of cars

$$= \frac{\left[\begin{array}{l}(24 \times 10) + (24 \times 25) + (16 \times 35) + \\ (20 \times 50) + (12 \times 70) + (4 \times 100)\end{array}\right]}{100}$$

$$= \frac{3640}{100} = 36.4 \text{ minutes}$$

[3 marks available — 1 mark for finding frequencies,
1 mark for the working to find the mean,
1 mark for correct answer]

18 a) PQD and ACD are similar, and $AD:PD = 5:3$,
so $\overrightarrow{CA} = \frac{5}{3} \times \overrightarrow{QP} = \frac{5}{3}\boldsymbol{b}$ *[1 mark]*

b) $\overrightarrow{PR} = \overrightarrow{PA} + \overrightarrow{AR}$
$AD:PD = 5:3$ so $AP:PD = 2:3$ and $3\overrightarrow{PA} = 2\overrightarrow{DP}$
$\overrightarrow{PA} = \frac{2}{3}\overrightarrow{DP} = \frac{2}{3}(-\boldsymbol{a}+\boldsymbol{b}) = -\frac{2}{3}\boldsymbol{a} + \frac{2}{3}\boldsymbol{b}$ *[1 mark]*
$\overrightarrow{AR} = \frac{2}{5}\overrightarrow{AC} = -\frac{2}{5}\overrightarrow{CA} = -\frac{2}{5} \times \frac{5}{3}\boldsymbol{b} = -\frac{2}{3}\boldsymbol{b}$ *[1 mark]*
$\overrightarrow{PR} = -\frac{2}{3}\boldsymbol{a} + \frac{2}{3}\boldsymbol{b} - \frac{2}{3}\boldsymbol{b} = -\frac{2}{3}\boldsymbol{a}$
So $k = \frac{2}{3}$ (because $\overrightarrow{DQ} = -\boldsymbol{a}$) *[1 mark]*

[3 marks available in total — as above]

19 a) (i) $y = \cos x$ has been translated 1 unit down.
The curve is $y = \cos x - 1$ *[1 mark]*

(ii) $y = \cos x$ has been translated 30° to the right.
The curve is $y = \cos(x - 30)$ *[1 mark]*

(iii) $y = \cos x$ has been reflected in the x-axis.
The curve is $y = -\cos x$ *[1 mark]*
The curve could also have equation $y = \cos(x + 180°)$.

b)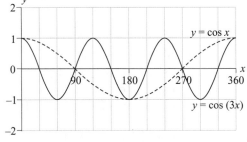

[1 mark]

20 $\dfrac{\sqrt{27}+7}{1+\sqrt{3}} = \dfrac{3\sqrt{3}+7}{1+\sqrt{3}} = \dfrac{(3\sqrt{3}+7)(1-\sqrt{3})}{(1+\sqrt{3})(1-\sqrt{3})}$

$$= \frac{3\sqrt{3}+7-3(\sqrt{3})^2-7\sqrt{3}}{1-(\sqrt{3})^2}$$

$$= \frac{7-3 \times 3-4\sqrt{3}}{1-3}$$

$$= \frac{-2-4\sqrt{3}}{-2} = 1+2\sqrt{3}$$

[4 marks available — 1 mark for correctly simplifying $\sqrt{27}$,
1 mark for rationalising the denominator, 1 mark for correctly
simplifying the numerator and denominator, 1 mark for the
correct answer with fully correct working]

21 E.g.
$(2x + 4)^2 + x^2 = 5$ *[1 mark]*
$(4x^2 + 16x + 16) + x^2 = 5$ *[1 mark]*
$5x^2 + 16x + 11 = 0$ *[1 mark]*
$(5x + 11)(x + 1) = 0$ *[1 mark]*
So $x = -2.2$ and $x = -1$ *[1 mark]*
Substituting into $y = 2x + 4$:
$y = 2(-2.2) + 4 = -0.4$
$y = 2(-1) + 4 = 2$
So the solutions are $x = -2.2$, $y = -0.4$ and $x = -1$, $y = 2$ *[1 mark]*
[6 marks available in total — as above]

Index

Index

Formula Sheet

Arithmetic series

Sum to n terms, $S_n = \frac{n}{2}[2a + (n-1)d]$

Area of trapezium $= \frac{1}{2}(a + b)h$

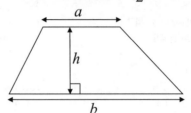

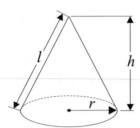

Volume of cone $= \frac{1}{3}\pi r^2 h$

Curved surface area of cone $= \pi r l$

Volume of prism = area of cross section × length

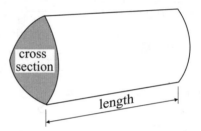

The quadratic equation

The solutions of $ax^2 + bx + c = 0$,
where $a \neq 0$, are given by:

$$x = \frac{-b \pm \sqrt{b^2 - 4ac}}{2a}$$

Volume of sphere $= \frac{4}{3}\pi r^3$

Surface area of sphere $= 4\pi r^2$

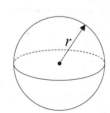

For any triangle ABC:

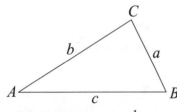

Sine rule: $\dfrac{a}{\sin A} = \dfrac{b}{\sin B} = \dfrac{c}{\sin C}$

Cosine rule: $a^2 = b^2 + c^2 - 2bc \cos A$

Area of triangle $= \frac{1}{2}ab \sin C$

Volume of cylinder $= \pi r^2 h$

Curved surface area of cylinder $= 2\pi r h$

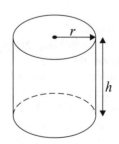